Basic Astronomy

BASIC ASTRONOMY

BY

Peter van de Kamp

Director, Sproul Observatory
Professor of Astronomy, Swarthmore College

 RANDOM HOUSE · NEW YORK

TO **Jan van der Bilt** ASTRONOMER

Seventh Printing

COPYRIGHT, 1952, BY PETER VAN DE KAMP

All rights reserved under International and Pan-American Copyright Conventions. Published in New York by Random House, Inc., and simultaneously in Toronto, Canada, by Random House of Canada, Limited.

LIBRARY OF CONGRESS CATALOG CARD NUMBER: 52—5551

Manufactured in the United States of America

The star maps in this volume are reproduced with the permission of Harper and Brothers.

CONTENTS

PART THREE: The Physical-Chemical Properties of
              Sun and Stars

PART FOUR: The Milky Way System and Beyond

LIST OF ILLUSTRATIONS

Illustrations face page xvi.

COURTESY OF

COURTESY OF

PREFACE

Astronomy is concerned with the organization of the vast physical universe, and the place of the Earth within this universe. In a narrow sense, only objects beyond the Earth and its atmosphere fall within the scope of astronomy, since, astronomically speaking, the crust of the Earth, its composition and its animal and vegetable life are at such close range. It is desirable, however, to include certain surface aspects of the Earth and its atmosphere in astronomical studies.

We are constantly aware of such astronomical objects as Sun and Moon. At night the sky reveals not only numerous stars, but also the planets or "wandering stars," while much of the time the comparative brilliance of the Moon dominates the night sky.

Although the telescope was not invented till 1608, much important astronomical information had already been accumulated by that time. The application of the telescope to astronomical problems has yielded a wealth of additional information and an ever-widening horizon of knowledge. Not only did the telescope permit a more detailed scrutiny of known objects, but it also revealed the existence of many objects too faint to be observed with the unaided eye. The telescope and its various accessories have been of invaluable aid in studying Sun, Moon and planets. They have, moreover, expanded the scope of inquiry toward the numerous faint stars, nebulae and star clusters. The introduction of photography meant another important step forward. Whereas the naked eye can recognize a few thousand stars at most, large telescopes, aided by long exposures on sensitive photographic emulsions, have revealed millions of faint stars, nebulae and star clusters.

More than four hundred years ago (1543) Copernicus developed the heliocentric concept of our solar system. For the study of astronomy an understanding of the Copernican view is essential; its development is reviewed in the first two chapters of Part Two of this book. The Earth is one of several planets, each of which is in a state of rotation and at the same time revolving in an almost circular orbit around the Sun.* With few exceptions, the direction of "spin," both for rotation and revolution, is the same for all planets; the planes of the different orbits are only slightly inclined with respect to each other. As seen from the Sun, the state of motion in the solar system thus becomes extremely simple; as seen from the Earth, however, planetary motions are complex. Other factors such as the rotation of the Earth influence our perception of the stellar world, while the diffusion of sunlight in our atmosphere prevents us from seeing the stars in daytime and causes the twilight transition between night and day.

In the study of large-scale phenomena, extending well beyond the confines of the solar system, we shall prefer to look at the

---

* Revolving refers to the motion of one object about another, rotation to the spinning of an object about a line or axis passing through it.

universe from the comparative stability of the point represented
by the center of the Sun. The daily and annual gyrations of our
Earth—a mere "dust speck"—will then confuse us no longer,
and our subsequent study of the stellar world will be simpler.

The first part of this book, after two preparatory chapters,
gives a brief description of the solar system—the well-known
assembly of Sun, planets, satellites, comets and meteors. The
three subsequent parts deal with the mechanical, physical and
large-scale aspects of the universe. An attempt is made here to
make the reader aware of the methods employed by the astronomer, and of the development of his ideas and knowledge.

Part Two (Chapters 6–14) is concerned with the mechanics
of the motions of stars and planets. The notions of relative
motion and of parallax are introduced, the heliocentric viewpoint is developed, and stellar distances and motions are studied. Insight into the character of cosmic mechanics is obtained
first from the motions of single stars, next from the orbital motions of double stars and from the motions of the planets in the
solar system. This information leads to the universal law of
gravitation which is so clearly revealed in daily life and so significant for understanding the mechanics of the universe, for
deriving the masses of visible stars and planets, and for discovering unseen stars and planets.

In Part Three (Chapters 15–22) the physical-chemical properties of stars and planets are considered. Thus, the laws of
spectroscopy are examined and applied; the brightness, size,
mass and density of the nearer stars are studied; and fundamental notions of atomic structure and radiation are reviewed.
These combined terrestrial and stellar data facilitate an analysis
of the structure and composition of stellar atmospheres and
interiors; the current explanation for the source of stellar and

solar energy is given. Part Three concludes with a study of the distinction between stars and planets and of the place of the Sun among stars.

In Part Four (Chapters 23–32) an attempt is made to obtain a picture of the arrangement and state of motion of the stars in the Milky Way system. The observational limitations and difficulties inherent in such a study are emphasized, and the distance problem of faraway stars is considered, together with the distorting influences caused by the dimming of light by obscuring material. The importance of the globular star clusters in outlining the size and shape of the stellar system is shown. A study is made of patterns of stellar motions, and of the motion of our solar system. The galactocentric viewpoint, based on the rotating Milky Way system, is developed, and a comparison of this system is made with the extragalactic objects, or "galaxies." Finally, the origin of galaxies, stars and planets is discussed.

In a volume as inclusive as this, it is manifestly impossible to do more than survey the general aspects of many important facets of the entire subject of astronomy. For example, the study of variable stars is in itself a highly specialized field which can be examined here only in a limited manner. The comprehensive nature of this undertaking imposes the requirement that detailed study be sacrificed for generous representation and clarity, that this work may provide the fundamentals with which an ever-widening exploration of the cosmos can be carried forward.

I wish to express my sincere thanks to Professor J. C. Duncan for the use of his magnificent star maps; to John Calvin for his meticulous line drawings; to my colleagues and associates who contributed valuable photographs and offered suggestions for the improvement of the contents and appearance of this book;

to the editorial and production departments of Random House
for their faith and co-operation; and to my students whose interest encouraged me to undertake this book for them and for
others.

P. v. d. K.

Swarthmore, Penna.
February, 1952

GUIDE TO THE STAR MAPS

(See Chapters 1 and 6)

These eight star maps cover the entire celestial sphere. The principal constellations are marked, as well as the celestial coordinates. Visibility of the stars depends on three things—geographic latitude, the time of the year and the time of the night. Maps 1 and 8 include stars within 40° of the southern and northern celestial poles, respectively. These stars are always above the horizon, at geographic latitudes below 40° south and above 40° north. Maps 2 to 7 include stars within 60° on either side of the celestial equator. These maps are used to best advantage at the following times:

MAP	6 P.M. to 10 P.M.	8 P.M. to 12 P.M.	10 P.M. to 2 A.M.	12 P.M. to 4 A.M.
2	August	July	June	May
3	June	May	April	March
4	April	March	February	January
5	February	January	December	November
6	December	November	October	September
7	October	September	August	July

MAP 1

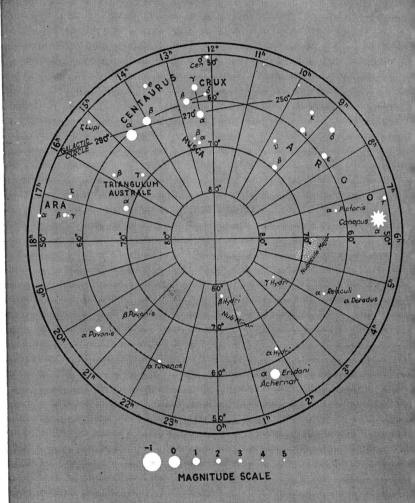

MAGNITUDE SCALE

MAP 2

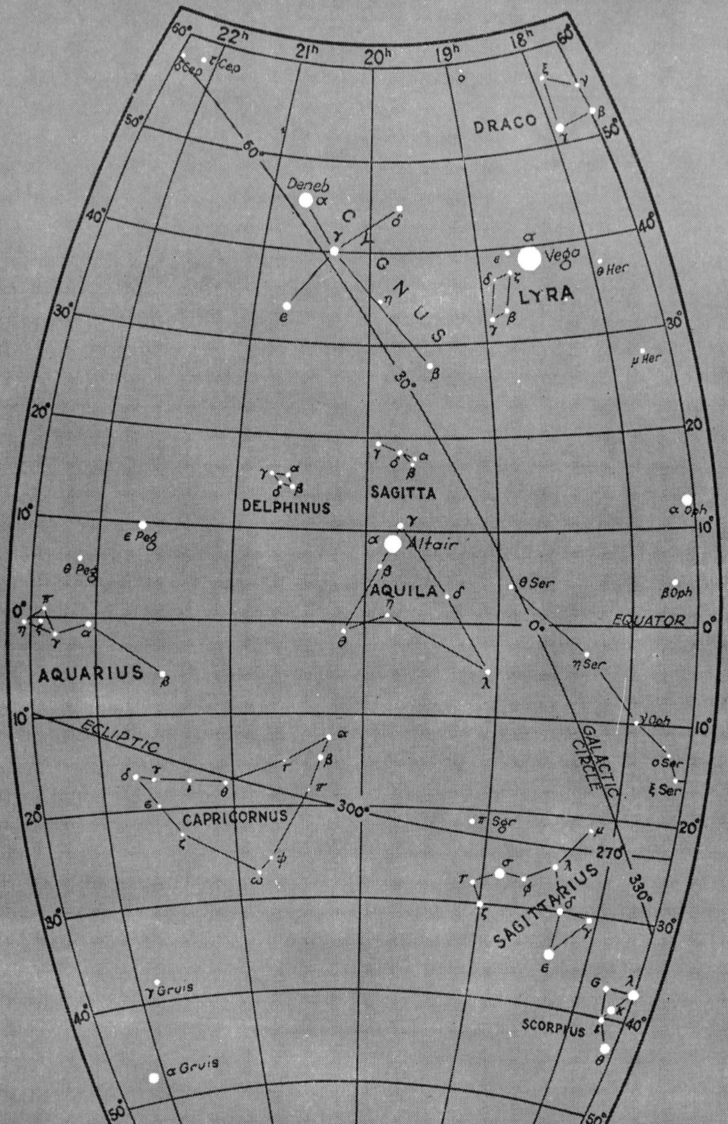

DRACO
CYGNUS
Deneb
LYRA
Vega
SAGITTA
DELPHINUS
AQUILA
Altair
AQUARIUS
EQUATOR
ECLIPTIC
GALACTIC CIRCLE
CAPRICORNUS
SAGITTARIUS
SCORPIUS
α Gruis
γ Gruis
α Pavonis
ε Peg
θ Peg
θ Ser
η Ser
ο Ser
ξ Ser
α Oph
β Oph
γ Oph
θ Her
μ Her
π Sgr
22h
21h
20h
19h
18h

MAP 3

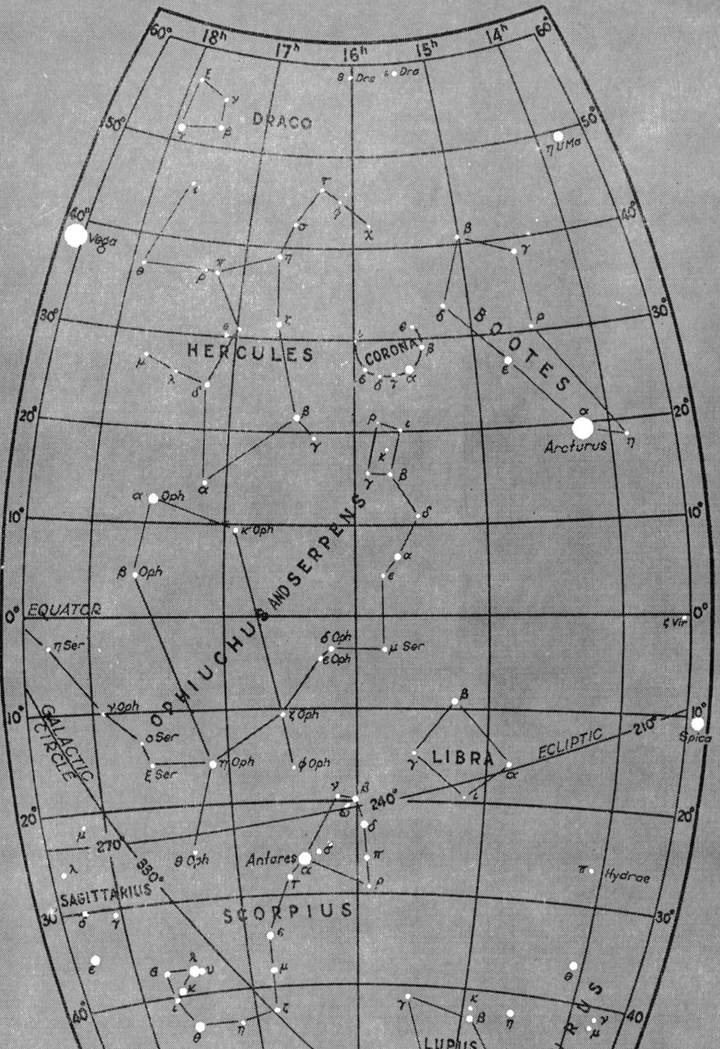

DRACO
HERCULES
CORONA
BOOTES
Vega
Arcturus
η UMa
α Oph
κ Oph
β Oph
OPHIUCHUS AND SERPENS
EQUATOR
η Ser
δ Oph
ε Oph
μ Ser
ζ Vir
γ Oph
ο Ser
ξ Ser
η Oph
ζ Oph
φ Oph
LIBRA
ECLIPTIC
Spica
GALACTIC CIRCLE
240°
270°
330°
300
210°
θ Oph
Antares
π Hydrae
SAGITTARIUS
SCORPIUS
LUPUS
CENTAURUS
ARA
18h
17h
16h
15h
14h

MAP 4

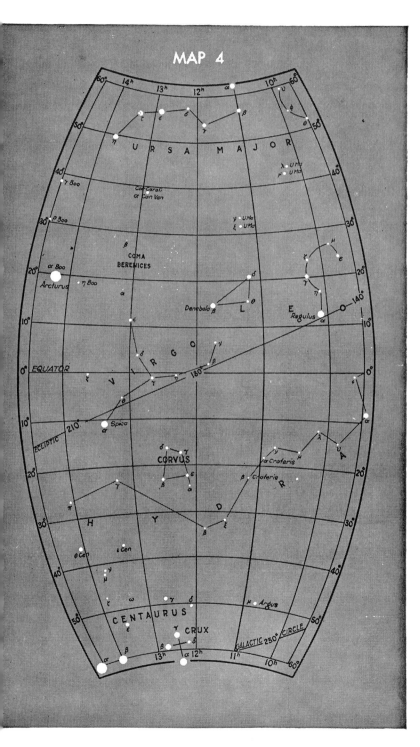

MAP 5

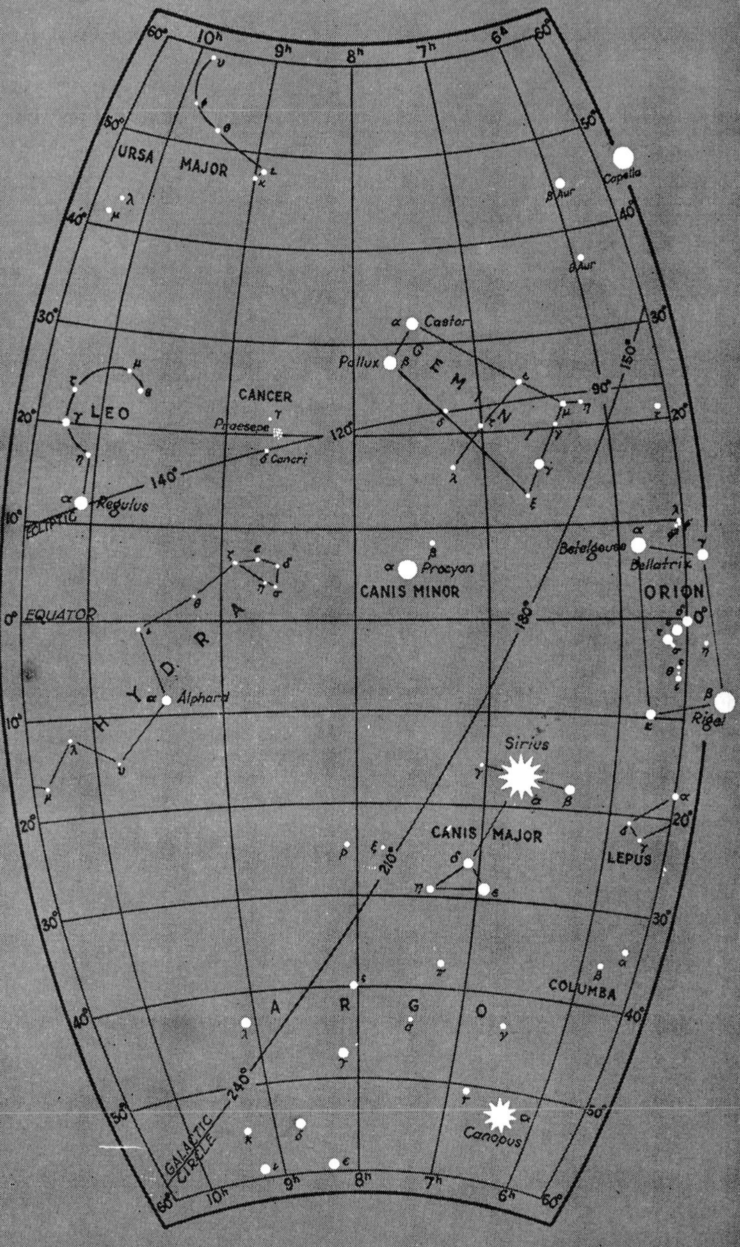

URSA MAJOR
Capella
LEO
Regulus
CANCER
Praesepe
δ Cancri
Castor
Pollux
GEMINI
ECLIPTIC
Betelgeuse
Bellatrix
Procyon
CANIS MINOR
ORION
EQUATOR
HYDRA
Alphard
Rigel
Sirius
CANIS MAJOR
LEPUS
COLUMBA
ARGO
Canopus
GALACTIC CIRCLE

MAP 6

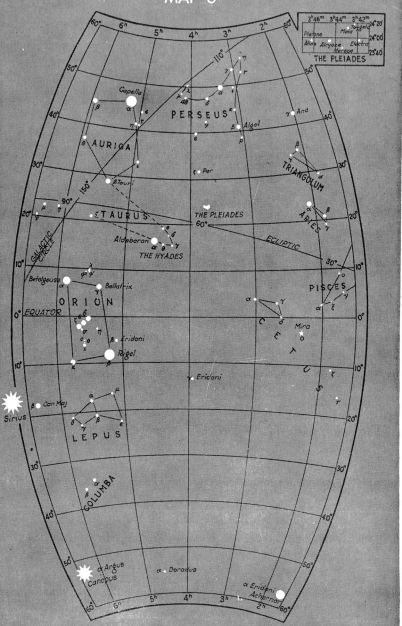

THE PLEIADES

3ʰ46ᵐ	3ʰ44ᵐ	3ʰ42ᵐ	24°20
Pleione		Taygeta Maia	24°00
Atlas	Alcyone	Electra	
	Merope		23°40

MAP 7

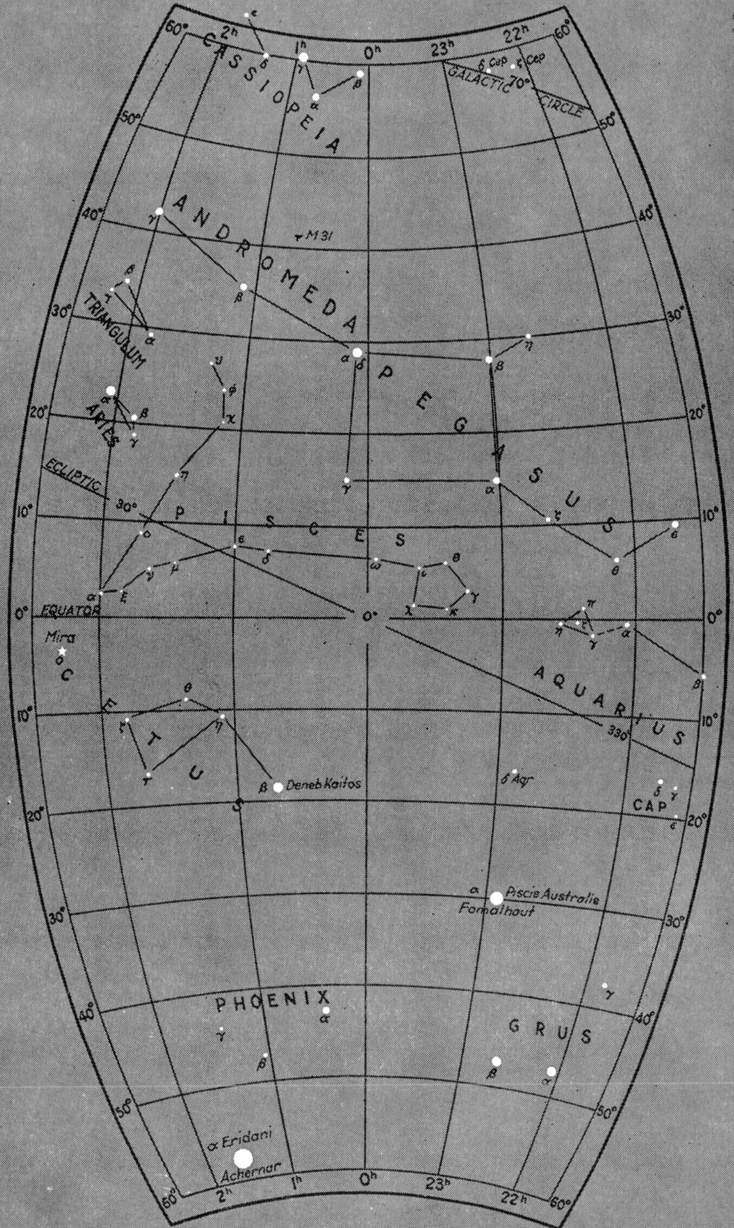

CASSIOPEIA
ANDROMEDA
M31
TRIANGULUM
ARIES
PEGASUS
PISCES
ECLIPTIC
EQUATOR
GALACTIC CIRCLE
δ Cep
ζ Cep
Mira
CETUS
Deneb Kaitos
AQUARIUS
δ Aqr
CAP
α Piscis Australis
Fomalhaut
PHOENIX
GRUS
α Eridani
Achernar
2h
1h
0h
23h
22h
60°
50°
40°
30°
20°
10°
0°
30°
330°
70°

MAP 8

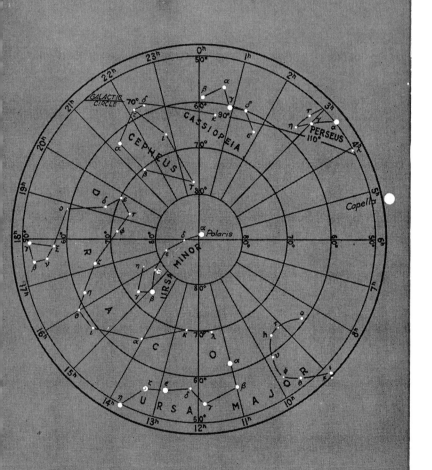

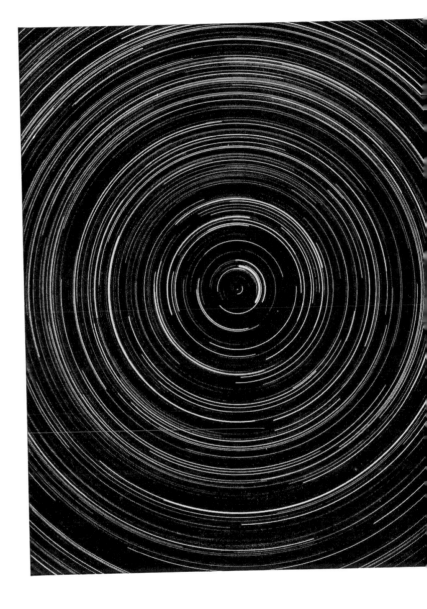

1. NORTH CIRCUMPOLAR STAR TRAILS

An eight-hour exposure showing one-third the diurnal rotation of the celestial sphere. The bright star trails near the center are made by Polaris.

2. Moon at first quarter.

3. Moon at last quarter.

4. The mountain range Apennines and vicinity.

5. The crater Copernicus, 90 kilometers in diameter, and surroundings.

6. Blue-violet part of solar spectrum with comparison spectr[u] of iron on both sides. (In these three illustrations, blue is left, r[ed] is right.)

B [α]
B [s]
A [α]
A [s]
F [α]
F [s]
d [G]
d [G]
c K
g K
d [M]
g [f]

7. Harvard classification of stellar spectra.

8. Star field near P Cygni photographed with prismatic camera. The majority of stars are of the "early" spectral types B, A, and F. Note the Balmer series of hydrogen absorption lines.

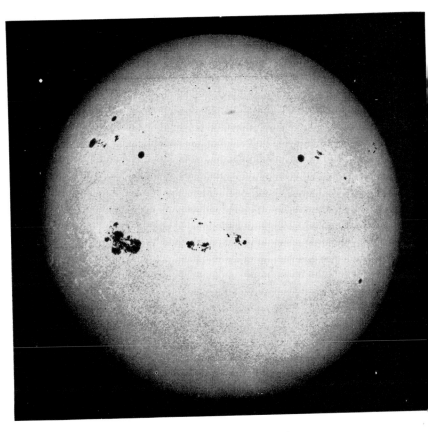

9. Sun with spots, August 12, 1917; disk represents the Earth.

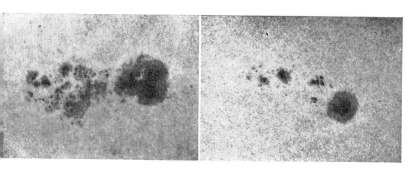

10. Sunspot: June 22, 1885.   11. Sunspot: April 1, 1894.

12. Twenty-four-hour development of sunspot, August 18 and 19, 1917; disk represents the Earth.

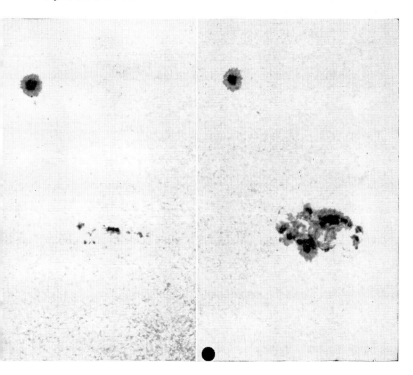

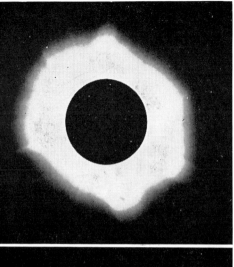

13. 1926 (January 14): outer corona.

14. 1929 (May 9): chromosphere with prominences.

15. 1930 (October 21): inner corona.

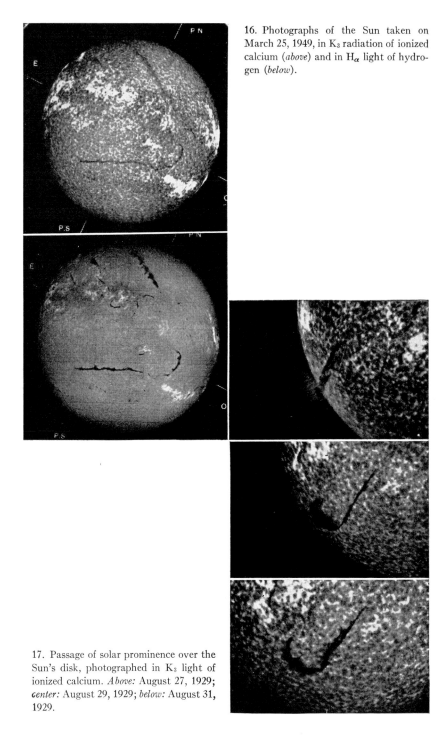

16. Photographs of the Sun taken on March 25, 1949, in K₃ radiation of ionized calcium (*above*) and in H$_\alpha$ light of hydrogen (*below*).

17. Passage of solar prominence over the Sun's disk, photographed in K₃ light of ionized calcium. *Above:* August 27, 1929; *center:* August 29, 1929; *below:* August 31, 1929.

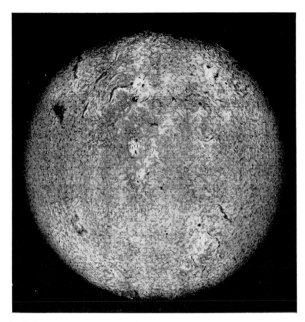

18. Photograph of the Sun taken in H_α light of hydrogen.

19. The great chromospheric eruption of July 25, 1946, photographed in H_α light of hydrogen.

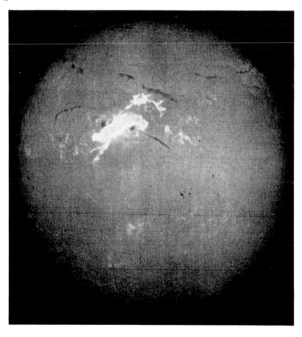

20. *upper left:* Earth-lit portion of "new" crescent Moon.

21. *upper right:* Mars.

22. *center:* Jupiter.

23. *lower right:* Saturn.

24. *lower left:* Venus.

25. Halley's Comet: May 6, 1910.

26. The Wolf Creek Meteor crater in Australia.

27. Parallax and proper motion of Barnard's star. A composite print of three photographs, separated approximately half a year each. The "fixed" background stars in the upper right each give one image, while Barnard's star gives three separate images, showing both proper motion (south-north) and parallax (east-west). See diagram on page 96.

28. Flare-up of Krüger 60 B on July 26, 1939. Four successive exposures of the binary Krüger 60 and its optical companion. The last exposure (*left*) shows a fourfold increase in brightness of the fainter component during the two-and-a-quarter-minute exposure.

29. Change in brightness of Nova Herculis, 1934, from the fourth magnitude, March 10, 1935 (*left*), to the thirteenth magnitude, May 6, 1935 (*right*).

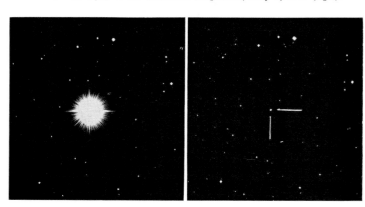

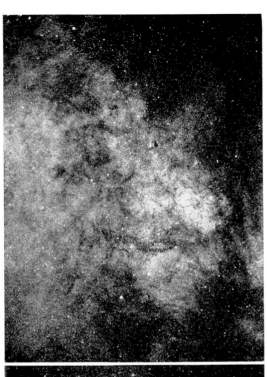

30. Milky Way in Sagittarius; region of galactic center.

31. Milky Way in Orion (Sirius *lower left*).

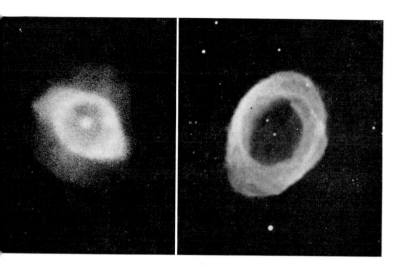

32. *left:* NGC 3242 in Hydra.

33. *right:* NGC 6720 (the Ring Nebula) in Lyra.

34. Comparison of dark (*left*) and bright (*right*) diffuse nebulae.

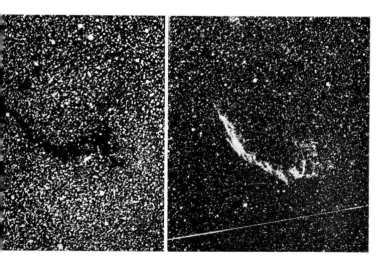

35. The North America (*left*) and Pelican (*right*) diffuse nebulae. The bright
star is Deneb (Alpha Cygni).

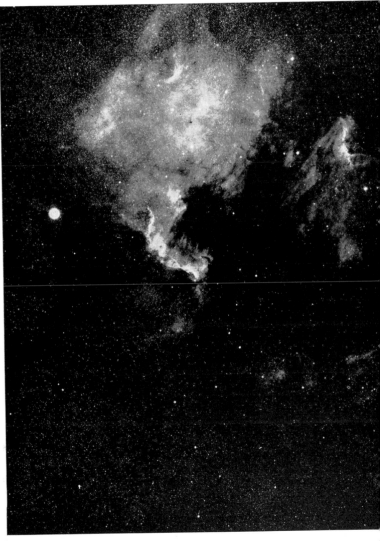

36. Diffuse nebula NGC 6523.

37. Diffuse nebula in Orion (I.C. 434).

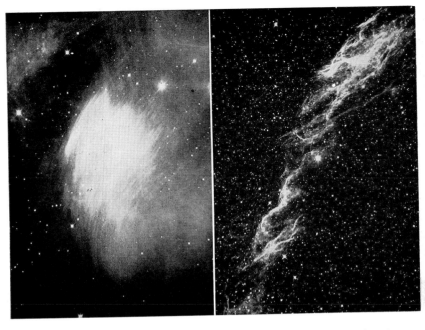

38. Diffuse nebula (NGC 1432) around Merope, one of the stars in the Pleiades.

39. Diffuse "network" nebula (NGC 6992) in Cygnus.

40. Dark diffuse nebula (Barnard 86).

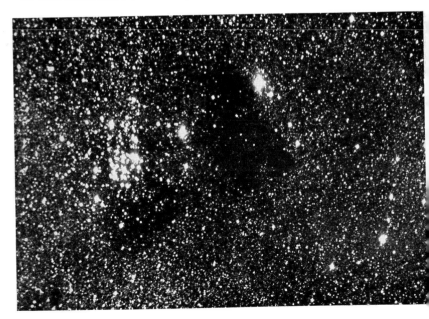

41. The Pleiades—example of an open or galactic cluster.

42. Messier 3—example of a globular cluster.

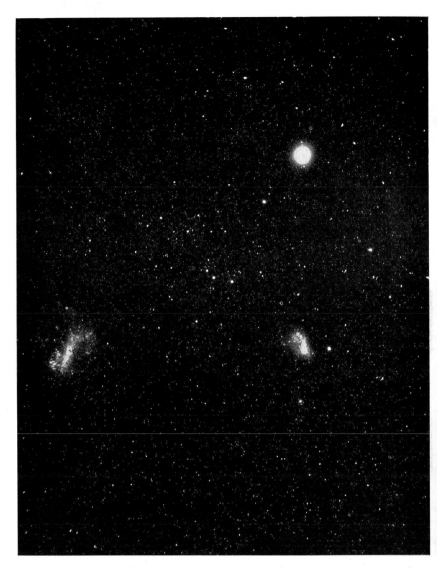

43. The Large and Small Magellanic Clouds. The bright star is Achernar (Alpha Eridani).

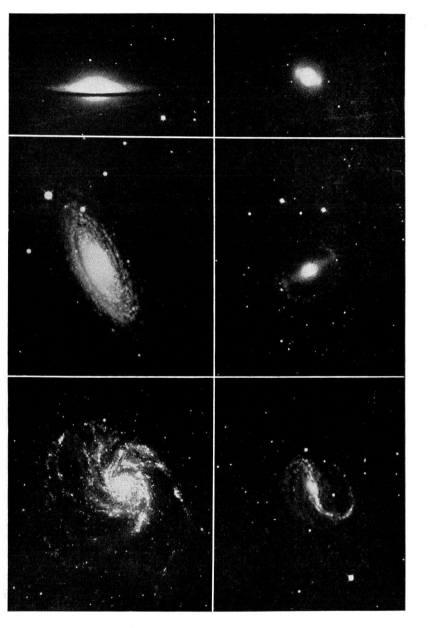

44. Typical spiral galaxies.

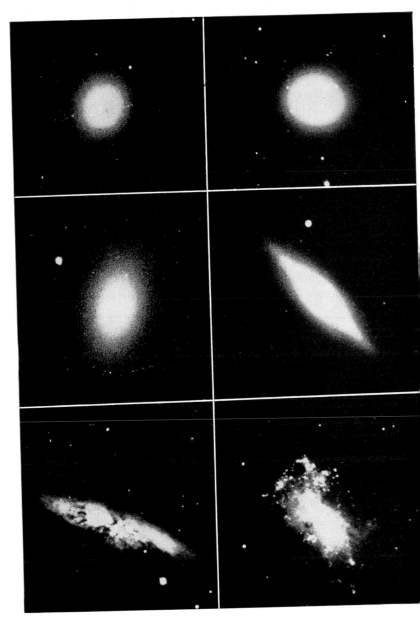

45. Typical elliptical and irregular galaxies.

46. Andromeda nebula (M 31) and its two elliptical companions (M 32 and NGC 205).

47. Enlarged portion of Andromeda nebula, illustrating resolution into stars.

48. *upper left:* Messier 33
49. *upper right:* Messier 51
50. *below:* NGC 4565

51. A group of galaxies.

52. The Corona Borealis cluster of galaxies.

A Survey of the Solar System

⌐1⌐ SKY AND TELESCOPE

THE BEST introduction to the stellar world is obtained in the open on a clear, dark, moonless night, away from disturbing terrestrial light sources and structures. Wherever we are and whenever we look, we are rewarded with one of the most beautiful revelations of nature, the starry sky.

Distribution of stars

The first impression of the unaided eye is that the number of stars is countless. If we proceed to count, however, we find visible at any one time not more than some two to three thousand stars, although the feebly glowing sky background creates an illusion that there are more. Next we notice, at certain times of the night and of the year, a fairly well-defined concentration in this luminous background, the Milky Way. The latter encircles the sky like a luminous belt of varying intensity and width, and it suggests the presence of numerous stars too feeble to be seen individually with the naked eye. This assumption is confirmed

3

through telescopic observations; even a small instrument or a field glass reveals large numbers of stars that are never seen with the unaided eye.

We notice that the stars are distributed unevenly, but that they are not lacking in any large sections of the sky; they appear "everywhere." The abundance of stars is greatest in those parts of the sky that are close to the Milky Way, while the stars are more sparsely spread in portions of the sky further removed from the Milky Way. This contrast becomes more striking as we extend our observations to faint telescopic stars.

The celestial sphere

In trying to understand some of the basic phenomena which influence and complicate our view of the heavens, we notice first the striking general appearance of the starry sky; it gives the illusion of being a hollow shell, resting on the horizon. This illusion is also present in daytime, in the quality of the sky— clear, cloudy, blue, gray, or another color or combination of colors. The sky is not real in the sense that it can be studied as an isolated object possessing physical properties such as size and shape; it is, however, an illusion of such persistence that we accept it and include it in our astronomical vocabulary. Why the illusion exists is of no particular concern to us, though it probably has something to do with our inability to perceive distances beyond a certain depth. As a result, the unaided eye assigns the same distance, be it ever so indefinite, to all celestial objects. The situation is actually more complex, since the sky overhead seems somewhat nearer than the horizon. We shall, however, cease to be concerned about the illusion as such, but make use of it instead by idealizing it in the form of a celestial sphere having all the simple properties of a sphere. The observer is assumed to be in the center; half of the sphere is seen above the horizon, whereas the "lower" half is invisible, being blocked out by the opaque Earth below. In our imagination,

The celestial sphere.

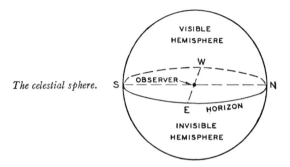

however, we may imagine that the Earth is transparent and observe the lower half of the sphere, or we may shrink the Earth into a single point from which to observe the cosmos (Chapter 7).

Rotation of the celestial sphere

We note after a few hours of observation that the stars move with respect to the horizon. In northern latitudes we notice that the stars above the southern horizon move from east to west, while low above the northern horizon they move from west to east. Over the eastern horizon stars appear to rise, while over the western horizon others set, thus confirming the existence of a complete celestial sphere. At the same time, however, one obvious but none the less very important fact is evident: the relative places of the stars do not change. Man's sense of design, aided by his imagination, has grouped the brighter stars together into constellations, and it is a well-known fact that the constellations remain undisturbed as time goes by, not only within themselves but in relation to one another. Though the brighter stars in the constellations may seem to "belong" to each other, any such connection is completely artificial. This grouping together is based on common direction and apparent brightness only, and does not necessarily involve any physical relation between the stars, which may be at entirely different distances from us. It appears, however, *as if* the stars, and hence the constellations, were attached or fixed to the celestial sphere. This is also an illusion convenient for descriptive purposes.

The star maps facing page xvi are provided to help identify the constellations as outlined by the brighter visible stars, and to aid the observer in general orientation.

The observed state of motion of the starry world may be described as a rotation of the celestial sphere, resulting in the rising and setting of stars on the eastern and western horizons respectively. The period of this so-called diurnal rotation is nearly four minutes shorter than the familiar solar day, whose length depends on the rising and setting of the Sun. Because of the rotation of the celestial sphere, the stars describe diurnal paths, crossing the north-south vertical plane twice in the course of one complete rotation of the celestial sphere. This plane and the circle which it defines on the celestial sphere are called the local meridian; the two crossings or transits are distinguished as upper and lower transits or culminations.

The diurnal rotation does not affect the continued paucity of stars near the horizon; the latter is caused by an increased dimming of starlight in our atmosphere at lower altitudes. If we could eliminate our atmosphere, the stars would appear just as bright near the horizon as higher up in the sky. In this connection we may remind ourselves of the obvious fact that the absence of stars in daytime is not real; the stars are present just the same, but are completely camouflaged by the sky light, which is due to the atmospheric scattering of some of the sun-light in all directions.

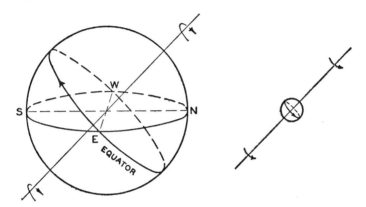

The diurnal rotation of the celestial sphere (left) is ascribed to the Earth's rotation (right).

As we shall see later (Chapter 6), the rotation of the celestial sphere is interpreted as an apparent effect, caused by the Earth's rotation around its axis.

Telescopes

Even for such comparatively nearby objects as Sun and Moon, astronomical information is obtained primarily through the application of astronomical telescopes and their accessories. Particularly during the present century, photography has been of tremendous importance for a wide variety of astronomical studies.

The primary function of an astronomical telescope is to gather a comparatively wide stream or bundle of light and converge it into a focal image of the distant object. There is, in the first place, the refracting type of telescope, or refractor, whose light-gathering and focusing qualities are due to the passage of light through a combination of two or more lenses referred to as the objective. Another prominent type is the reflecting telescope, or reflector; here the image is obtained by reflection from a concave mirror which is usually made of glass and coated with a shiny surface of silver or aluminum. Many recent telescopes are of this type, and can be built up to very large dimensions, since only one accurately reflecting surface is required. The refracting type of telescope requires at least two lenses, i.e., four accurately figured surfaces (Chapter 8), while the glass must be of the highest optical quality, free from stresses, bubbles and other imperfections. These stringent conditions do not permit the construction of refractors with apertures as large as modern reflectors. But refractors have certain optical advantages which make them, for example, suitable for any work in which minute changes in the positions of the stars are involved.

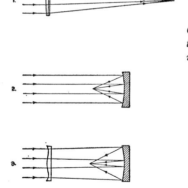

Convergence of light rays from a distant object in three types of astronomical telescopes.

1. *Refractor: compound objective lens.*
2. *Reflector: reflecting parabolic surface.*
3. *Schmidt telescope: correcting plate and reflecting surface.*

Other types of telescopes exist, employing various combinations of lenses and mirrors. One of the most promising recent developments is the Schmidt telescope, a combination of reflecting mirror and so-called correcting plate. The result is a fast camera giving sharper photographs over larger portions of the sky than can be obtained with the usual telescope of the refracting or reflecting type.

The most important purposes of telescopes are increased light-gathering and resolving power. The lens, or mirror, gathers more light than the comparatively small aperture of the eye; and the larger aperture brings about an increased resolution of details, such as the separation of stars that are placed close together. The focal image may be viewed with magnifying eyepieces of different powers. What is often more effective, we may employ the instrument as a camera, by putting a photographic plate in the focal plane and making a permanent record of the object and its surroundings. We may study the color composition of the starlight by letting the light pass through a glass prism (Chapters 15ff). We may also use photocells to analyze the intensity and the color composition of the focused rays. Numerous other accessories are available.

As a rule, telescopes are mounted in such a way that they rotate around an axis, counteracting the Earth's rotation. In other words, the motion of the telescope follows the diurnal motion of the celestial sphere.

Magnitudes

Even to the casual observer the stars exhibit different degrees of brightness as perceived by the eye. Long ago Claudius Ptolemy (*circa* 140 A.D.) introduced a system for grading the apparent brightness of the stars; these grades are referred to as magnitudes. The brightest stars are said to be of the first magnitude, while the faintest stars visible to the unaided eye are of the sixth magnitude. Intermediate magnitudes are assigned

according to a natural grading system, in which it is as easy for
the eye to detect the difference between a first- and a second-
magnitude star as to distinguish between, say, a fourth- and
fifth-magnitude star, and so on. With this principle in mind, the
magnitude scale can be extended even to objects brighter than
the first and fainter than the sixth magnitude; fractional numbers may also be used. Thus, Sirius, the brightest of all stars,
is recognized as a star of magnitude minus 1.6; on the other
hand, faint stars are revealed by the telescope down to somewhat fainter than magnitude 21 on long-exposure photographs
with the largest existing astronomical cameras.

Telescopic stars; light ratio

The stellar-magnitude scale bears a definite relation to the true
brightness or intensity scale established by measurements with
physical instruments. It has been found that equal differences
in magnitudes correspond to equal ratios of intensities. The
relation is such that we receive one hundred times as much light
from a first-magnitude star as from a star of the sixth magnitude. The so-called light ratio, corresponding to a magnitude
difference of one, is therefore $\sqrt[5]{100}$ or 2.512. . .; this ratio has
been adopted in order to extend the magnitude scale to fainter
stars. Since each difference of five magnitudes corresponds to a
brightness ratio of 100, we receive from a star of the twenty-
first magnitude only 1/100,000,000 times as much light as from
a star of the first magnitude. The penetrating power of large
telescopes aided by photographic technique is hence impressively illustrated.

Thus, a large variety of telescopes, having different apertures
and focal lengths, is used in astronomical research, with or without the aid of accessories. Among the more obvious telescopic
contributions is the measuring of the stellar positions and mag-

nitudes of the numerous stars beyond the visibility range of the unaided eye. The photographic study of these problems has been especially fruitful. In particular, it has permitted us to extend our knowledge of stellar magnitudes to the numerous faint stars, the intensity of the extended photographic star image being a direct measure of the stars' apparent brightness.

From apparent sky to depth view

Thousands of years ago maps of the sky were made, showing the relative locations of the "fixed" stars. At present we have accurate knowledge about the location on the celestial sphere of thousands of stars, nebulae and other objects; these locations represent the directions in which we see the various objects. From the beginning it was obvious that distances of objects should be obtained for a more complete understanding of the structure of the physical universe. A knowledge of distances has not only permitted us to study the momentary arrangement and orbital paths of obviously moving objects such as Sun, Moon and planets, but will also make it possible for us to compare the intrinsic brightnesses of different objects such as stars.

Later on we shall see how there has been gradual progress in computing the distances of celestial objects. First, the distances of objects within the comparatively small solar system were found; then, during the past century, the distances to numerous stars were determined; and finally, in the last few decades, considerable information has been accumulated for the distances of such faraway objects as star clusters and certain types of nebulae. Gradually we are making progress, and the apparent two-dimensional view of the universe is changing into a real, spatial depth view.

$\boxed{2}$ MATTER AND LIGHT

A GREAT DEAL of information about the composition of cosmic objects has been obtained with the aid of our terrestrial knowledge of physics and chemistry.

Atoms and molecules

All matter is considered to be built up of a combination of elemental substances. Of these chemical elements, ninety-two are found in nature, while man is able to create a few more, albeit for a limited existence (Table I). Examples of chemical elements are hydrogen (H), helium (He), carbon (C), nitrogen (N), oxygen (O), and iron (Fe). If we take a certain quantity of a chemical element and subdivide it into smaller and smaller portions, the characteristic properties of the material are maintained. This subdivision cannot, however, be carried out beyond a definite limit. Each element has certain smallest particles called atoms which still have the complete properties of the ele-

ment; these atoms can be broken down into still smaller particles, but these no longer have the properties of the element.

Two or more atoms of the same or of different elements may
be bound firmly together. The resulting combination is called a
molecule, the smallest unit of chemical compounds. For example, a molecule of water consists of two hydrogen atoms joined
together with one oxygen atom; the symbol is H_2O.

The chemist is interested in the interaction between atoms
and molecules such as the association of atoms to form molecules, the dissociation of molecules into separate atoms, and the
interchange of atoms between different molecular combinations.
In any chemical reaction the myriads of atoms and molecules
are assumed to be identical for one and the same element or
compound. To the chemist, the atoms are the fundamental
building stones of matter. His concern with the structure of the
atoms is limited primarily to the peripheral properties which
provide the different mutual affinities between atoms of different elements. For the chemist, therefore, the complete list of
elemental particles, or atoms, contains some ninety-odd entries.

Atomic mass

That the actual situation is not quite this simple becomes clear
if we arrange the different elements in a logical sequence. A
sequence which suggests itself is one according to the masses of
the different atoms. The mass of an object is assumed to be an
intrinsic property and depends essentially on the number of
material fundamental particles composing the object. Mass is
also loosely called "quantity of matter." Methods have been
developed for determining with a high degree of precision the
absolute and comparative masses of the atoms of different elements. The lightest atoms are those of hydrogen, which have a

mass of 1.66×10^{-24} grams.* A helium atom is almost four times as massive as a hydrogen atom; an oxygen atom, sixteen times; an iron atom, fifty-six times; and so on. The most massive atom occurring in nature is that of uranium, beyond which there are the still more massive atoms synthesized in the laboratory. The number indicating the mass of an atom in terms of a hydrogen atom is called atomic mass or atomic weight. Thus, the atomic mass is very close to 1 for hydrogen, 4 for helium, 12 for carbon, 14 for nitrogen, 16 for oxygen, 56 for iron, and so on. It looks as though the atomic masses may be considered integers in terms of the mass of hydrogen, and as though hydrogen might be the common building stone of all other atoms. For example, an iron atom might be some sort of cluster of fifty-six hydrogen atoms. The atomic masses of certain elements in terms of hydrogen are not, however, anywhere near integers, but clearly have fractional values. A well-known example is chlorine, which has an atomic mass of 35.5.

Isotopes; atomic number

These fractional atomic masses can, to a great extent, be satisfactorily explained by assuming that the atoms of any one element belong to several groups of slightly different atomic mass. Appropriate experiments have validated this hypothesis; it is common knowledge now that atoms of one and the same chemical element are often distributed over several atomic masses. These masses are still very nearly integers in terms of the mass of hydrogen, but their numbers differ by one from each other. There are atoms which have less and others which have more than the most abundant mass. By physical experi-

* The presentation of very large and very small numbers is simplified by the usual convenient mathematical symbols, namely, by writing numbers like 100, 1000, etc. as 10^2, 10^3, etc., and, on the other hand, 0.1, 0.01, 0.001, etc. as 10^{-1}, 10^{-2}, 10^{-3}, etc.

mentation the different mass groups can be separated, but in their chemical reactions such groups cannot be distinguished from one another. The different forms of the same element are referred to as isotopes; some isotopes play an important role in explaining the life of stars (Chapter 21).

Atoms are considered to be built up of still smaller fundamental particles: protons, neutrons and electrons. Most of the mass of an atom is contained in the minute nucleus which consists of protons and neutrons. Protons carry a small positive electric charge, while neutrons are electrically neutral. Protons and neutrons have the same mass, 1.66×10^{-24} grams. These particles are collectively referred to as nucleons. Surrounding the nucleus are the electrons, units of negative electric charge whose masses are 9×10^{-28} grams, only 1/1837 times that of a proton or neutron. These electrons provide the mechanism for the emission and absorption of radiation. In an electrically neutral atom the number of external electrons equals the number of protons in the nucleus. This number of protons or electrons is called the atomic number and determines the chemical character of the atom. The combined number of protons and neutrons determines the atomic mass. Slight variations in the number of neutrons in the nucleus explain the different isotopes of one and the same element. Returning to the case of chlorine, then, we know that there are two isotopes, represented by the symbols $_{17}Cl^{35}$ and $_{17}Cl^{37}$, the subscript to the left denoting the atomic number and the superscript to the right the atomic mass. In nature these two varieties are mixed in the ratio three to one, resulting in an average particle mass of 35.5.

Atoms may lose one or more of their external electrons and then become ionized. Atoms and radiation will be further discussed in Chapter 18.

Effect of temperature on the state of matter

Matter may exist in three principal "states." In the gaseous or vapor state, which is ordinarily rarefied, the atoms or molecules are comparatively far from each other and enjoy considerable freedom of motion. In the liquid and solid states there is a high degree of cohesion between the atoms or molecules, while in a highly compressed gas there may be little cohesion but considerable crowding.

The significance of temperature should be emphasized. Basically, temperature is nothing but a measure for the state of agitation of matter. Complete stoppage of agitation is reached at a temperature of −273° centigrade; this is the zero point from which the so-called absolute temperatures are counted. This absolute temperature scale is often characterized as the "Kelvin" scale, after William Thomson, Lord Kelvin (1824–1907); the absolute temperatures are followed by the letter K. As a rule, all matter has some degree of temperature; and therefore, matter in any state, whether solid or liquid or gaseous, consists of particles in a state of restlessness. Thermal agitation is required to overcome the internal cohesion of solids and liquids, however. Only if the temperature becomes high enough may cohesion be destroyed and superseded by the gaseous state. For different elements or compounds the transition from the compressed to the rarefied state takes place at different temperatures, depending on the differences in cohesion for their solid or liquid states. At "room" temperature, for example, iron is solid but helium is gaseous. The latter does not liquefy until the temperature is as low as 4.1° K—268.9° below the freezing point of water; on the other hand, iron does not vaporize until a temperature as high as 3000° centigrade is reached. This vaporizing temperature may be appreciably lowered if conditions such as lowered pressure favor evaporation. As we shall see in Chapter 19, the low pressures in stellar atmospheres contribute toward maintaining an advanced state of "loosening-up" and also ionization of atoms.

Specific mass

For different gases in the rarefied state, at the same temperature and pressure, the number of atoms or molecules per cubic centimeter is the same (Chapter 19). This law, first announced in 1811 by Amadeo Avogadro (1776–1856), implies that at the same temperature and pressure, the specific masses of gases (i.e., grams per cubic centimeter) are proportional to their atomic or molecular masses. The situation is different when the element or compound exists in the solid or liquid state. In this case the specific spacing of the atoms obviously determines the mass of one cubic centimeter of the material. For example, solid iodine has a specific mass of 4.9, while solid chromium has a specific mass of 7.1. On the other hand, the atomic masses of these two elements are 127 and 52 respectively. We conclude that in solid iodine the atoms are spaced wider apart than are those in chromium. Nevertheless, there is a general correspondence between the specific and atomic masses, indicating an approximately constant pattern for the spacing of atoms or molecules of different materials in the solid and liquid states. The amount of this spacing is about 10^{-8} centimeters; it is the same for the compressed gaseous state of similar specific density.*

* The accepted system of measurement in all scientific work is the metric system. As a rule, the metric system is used in this book. The English system is related to the metric system as follows:

    1 kilometer = .621 miles or 1 mile = 1.61 kilometers
    1 centimeter = .394 inches or 1 inch = 2.54 centimeters
    1 kilogram   = 2.204 pounds or 1 pound = 454 grams

TABLE I.   *The Chemical Elements*

ATOMIC NUMBER	NAME	SYMBOL	ATOMIC MASS MOST ABUNDANT	RANGE
1	Hydrogen	H	1	1– 3
2	Helium	He	4	3– 6
3	Lithium	Li	7	5– 8
4	Beryllium	Be	9	6– 11
5	Boron	B	11	9– 13
6	Carbon	C	12	10– 15
7	Nitrogen	N	14	12– 17
8	Oxygen	O	16	14– 19
9	Fluorine	F	19	16– 21
10	Neon	Ne	20	18– 23
11	Sodium	Na	23	21– 25
12	Magnesium	Mg	24	22– 27
13	Aluminum	Al	27	25– 30
14	Silicon	Si	28	27– 32
15	Phosphorus	P	31	29– 34
16	Sulphur	S	32	31– 37
17	Chlorine	Cl	35	33– 39
18	Argon	A	40	35– 41
19	Potassium	K	39	37– 43
20	Calcium	Ca	40	39– 49
21	Scandium	Sc	45	41– 49
22	Titanium	Ti	48	45– 51
23	Vanadium	V	51	47– 52
24	Chromium	Cr	52	49– 55
25	Manganese	Mn	55	51– 56

TABLE I. *The Chemical Elements (Continued)*

ATOMIC NUMBER	NAME	SYMBOL	ATOMIC MASS MOST ABUNDANT	RANGE
26	Iron	Fe	56	53– 59
27	Cobalt	Co	59	55– 60
28	Nickel	Ni	58	57– 64
29	Copper	Cu	63	58– 66
30	Zinc	Zn	64	63– 70
31	Gallium	Ga	69	64– 74
32	Germanium	Ge	74	69– 78
33	Arsenic	As	75	72– 78
34	Selenium	Se	80	74– 83
35	Bromine	Br	79	78– 87
36	Krypton	Kr	84	78– 95
37	Rubidium	Rb	85	82– 95
38	Strontium	Sr	88	84– 95
39	Yttrium	Y	89	86– 95
40	Zirconium	Zr	90	89– 97
41	Niobium	Nb	93	90– 97
42	Molybdenum	Mo	98	92–102
43	Technetium	Tc	. . .	96–102
44	Ruthenium	Ru	102	96–107
45	Rhodium	Rh	103	102–107
46	Palladium	Pd	106	102–112
47	Silver	Ag	107	105–112
48	Cadmium	Cd	114	106–118
49	Indium	In	115	110–117
50	Tin	Sn	120	112–128

TABLE 1. *The Chemical Elements* (*Continued*)

ATOMIC NUMBER	NAME	SYMBOL	ATOMIC MASS MOST ABUNDANT	RANGE
51	Antimony	Sb	121	120–136
52	Tellurium	Te	130	120–137
53	Iodine	I	127	124–137
54	Xenon	Xe	132	124–144
55	Caesium	Cs	133	130–143
56	Barium	Ba	138	130–145
57	Lanthanum	La	139	137–145
58	Cerium	Ce	140	136–147
59	Praseodymium	Pr	141	140–147
60	Neodymium	Nd	142	141–150
61	Promethium	Pm	. . .	143–147
62	Samarium	Sm	152	144–154
63	Europium	Eu	153	151–158
64	Gadolinium	Gd	158	152–160
65	Terbium	Tb	159	159–160
66	Dysprosium	Dy	164	158–165
67	Holmium	Ho	165	165–166
68	Erbium	Er	166	162–170
69	Thulium	Tm	169	169–170
70	Ytterbium	Yb	174	168–176
71	Lutecium	Lu	175	175–177
72	Hafnium	Hf	180	174–181
73	Tantalum	Ta	181	180–182
74	Tungsten	W	184	180–187
75	Rhenium	Re	187	184–188

TABLE I. *The Chemical Elements (Continued)*

ATOMIC NUMBER	NAME	SYMBOL	ATOMIC MASS MOST ABUNDANT	RANGE
76	Osmium	Os	192	184–193
77	Iridium	Ir	193	191–194
78	Platinum	Pt	194	192–199
79	Gold	Au	197	196–200
80	Mercury	Hg	202	196–205
81	Thallium	Tl	205	198–210
82	Lead	Pb	208	203–214
83	Bismuth	Bi	209	207–214
84	Polonium	Po	. . .	210–218
85	Astatine	At	211	211
86	Radon	Rn	. . .	219–222
87	Francium	Fa	. . .	223
88	Radium	Ra	. . .	223–228
89	Actinium	Ac	. . .	227–228
90	Thorium	Th	232	227–234
91	Protoactinium	Pa	. . .	231–234
92	Uranium	U	238	233–239
93	Neptunium	Np	. . .	231–239
94	Plutonium	Pu	. . .	238–239
95	Americum	Am	. . .	241
96	Curium	Cm	. . .	240–242
97	Berkelium	Bk	. . .	. . .
98	Californium	Cf	. . .	. . .

Spectroscopy

Important information about the physical and chemical composition of celestial bodies is obtained from an analysis of their light by spectroscopic means. This method is based on the spreading-out of composite light into a "spectrum" of its component colors by means, for example, of a glass prism. Light from a glowing gas reveals primarily a restricted number of different colors usually referred to as "lines." On the other hand, light from an incandescent source of solid or liquid matter contains all colors; the same is true for the accumulated radiation from a sufficiently deep layer of a hot, ionized gas. When "continuous" radiation passes through a comparatively shallow and cooler layer of rarefied gas, it loses to some extent those discrete colors or lines which are characteristic of the gas vapors. The result is an "absorption spectrum." The Sun is a sphere of hot, compressed, ionized gases, whose "surface" may be visualized as a transition layer between the gaseous interior of high density and a solar atmosphere of comparatively lower density. The surface of the Sun sends out a continuous spectrum of radiation. However, in the solar spectrum a large number of discrete colors are weakened and appear as absorption or Fraunhofer lines (see photograph 6). Joseph von Fraunhofer (1787–1826) was the first to describe, in 1814, these most prominent absorption lines in the solar spectrum. The Fraunhofer spectrum points to the existence in the solar atmosphere of definite chemical elements or compounds, whose atoms or molecules are responsible for the appearance of their absorption lines. Considerable knowledge has thus been obtained about the atmospheres of Sun, Moon, stars and planets through spectroscopic analysis (Chapters 15 and 16).

Of additional significance is the fact that the rate at which an object approaches or recedes from us is revealed in the spectrum through a shift of the spectral lines to the violet or the red, the amount of displacement depending on the rate of the motion. This is known as the Doppler effect and it is of tremendous aid in studying the motions of celestial objects toward and away from us. The nature of light and the laws of radiation are discussed in more detail in Chapters 9, 15 and 18.

3 | SUN, EARTH AND MOON

To THE inhabitants of the Earth, the three most conspicuous cosmic objects are Sun, Earth and Moon; the Earth for obvious reasons, the Sun and Moon because of their apparent size, which distinguishes them from the stars and planets. Sun and Moon appear to be of approximately equal size, half a degree in diameter; but the Sun is almost four hundred times as far away as the Moon, and has a correspondingly much larger size. Earth

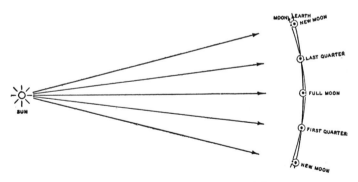

Motion of Earth and Moon during one synodic period.

and Moon are on the average 384,400 kilometers apart, and revolve around each other in a period of 27.32 days. Earth and Moon may be regarded as a double planet; while performing their mutual revolution, the two move in a large orbit around the Sun at an average distance of 149,700,000 kilometers in a period of 365.2564 days. These orbits are slightly elongated, while the plane of the Moon's orbit about the Earth is tilted a little over five degrees on the Earth's orbit around the Sun.

The Sun is an example of a star, i.e., a large sphere of hot glowing vapors, while Earth and Moon are examples of the comparatively smaller, cooler objects similar to the other planets and moons in the solar system. The apparent difference between the latter objects and the more familiar Sun, Earth and Moon is primarily a matter of distance. Because of their great distances from us, the other planets and moons do not appear as disks but look like points or stars to the unaided eye. The stars reach such staggering distances that we still do not know whether even the nearer stars have planets around them.

Sun

The Sun is the nearest of all stars. Our distance from the Sun varies each year between 147,200,000 kilometers in the beginning of January to 152,200,000 kilometers in the beginning of July. The corresponding range in the angular diameter* of the Sun is between 32′ 36″ and 31′ 31″, the average value being close to 32′. The diameter of the Sun is 1,393,000 kilometers, or 109.2 times the diameter of the Earth; hence, its volume is $(109.2)^3$ or 1,300,000 times that of the Earth. The mass of the Sun is 334,000 times that of the Earth, and its average density is 1.41 times that of water, as compared with an average den-

* A right angle contains 90 degrees (°) of arc. One degree of arc equals 60 minutes (′) of arc; one minute of arc equals 60 seconds (″) of arc.

sity of 5.52 for the Earth. The total mass of the Sun is 2×10^{33} grams and that of the Earth nearly 6×10^{27} grams. The pull of gravity at the Sun's surface is 28 times that on the surface of the Earth.

On our Earth one square centimeter held perpendicular to the impact of the Sun's radiation receives 1.94 calories per minute, if we allow for absorption in our atmosphere. This quantity is called the solar constant. (One calorie is the amount of heat needed to raise the temperature of one gram of water by one degree centigrade.) We can now calculate that a square centimeter at the Sun's surface sends out 1500 calories each second. By means of the laws of radiation (Chapter 15), one may deduce that the surface temperature of the Sun is 5750° K. In the interior of the Sun the temperatures are much higher, rising to 16,000,000° in the center.

The visible surface of the Sun is called the photosphere. Its telescopic appearance is characterized by a fine granular structure, and by conspicuous dark areas, the sunspots (see photograph 9). Irregular bright clouds, faculae, are found near the sunspots. The granulations vary at all times, having a short individual lifetime of about three minutes. They may be explained as rising and falling masses of gases. Sunspots usually appear in groups. A spot consists of a darker central area called the umbra, surrounded by a comparatively brighter penumbra. Sunspots ordinarily have lifetimes of a few months from the period of their gradual appearance to their complete disappearance; occasional large spots have lasted over one year. Great sunspots cover areas larger than the Earth's diameter, and are visible to the naked eye (see photographs 10, 11, 12).

The Sun rotates about an axis which makes an angle of 83° with the orbital plane of the Earth's motion around the Sun. Sunspots never appear within about five degrees on either side of, nor rarely further than forty degrees from the Sun's equator. The period of rotation increases between five and forty degrees; outside these limits the Doppler principle is used to establish the period of rotation, which is found to range from about twenty-five days at the equator to about thirty-three days at the Sun's poles.

Sunspots are cooler portions of the Sun—the temperature of the umbra is something like 4500° K—and therefore appear as relatively dark areas. They are seats of comparatively strong magnetic fields. Sunspots represent areas of expanding and hence cooled vapors, while their magnetic character may be ascribed to electric currents caused by electrons as they whirl upward. Sunspots show a clearly pronounced periodic behavior; the Sun's spottiness goes through cycles with an average period of 11.1 years, individual cycles varying in length from 9.0 to 13.6 years.

The photosphere is surrounded by the solar atmosphere, which for descriptive purposes is usually divided into several parts. First there is the reversing layer, only a few hundred kilometers thick, with a temperature of about 4400° K. The vapors in this layer are primarily responsible for the weakening of the colors in the solar spectrum, i.e., for the absorption lines. The reversing layer is the lowest and densest part of the chromosphere, which extends some ten thousand kilometers above the photosphere. The name is derived from its appearance during a total eclipse, when the photosphere is completely covered by the Moon and the chromosphere appears as a reddish ring whose color is due primarily to radiation from hydrogen vapors. Ionized calcium and helium are the other elements abundant in the chromosphere. The reddish clouds observed in the chromosphere are named prominences or protuberances. Chromosphere and prominences are not static, but are in a continuous state of motion resulting from material ejected from and falling back to the photosphere. Surrounding the chromosphere is the corona, an extremely rarefied and hot gaseous atmosphere containing vapors of highly ionized iron, nickel and calcium. Although to some extent observable on any clear day by a special technique of observation, the full glory of the corona is best observed during a total eclipse of the Sun. This occurs from time to time when the spacing and alignment of Sun, Earth and Moon result in the Moon's covering the Sun's surface completely for anywhere from a fraction of a second to as long as seven and a half minutes (see photographs 13, 14, 15). As the Moon's disk crosses the Sun we observe a sharp transition—within a matter of a few hundred kilometers—between the Sun's photosphere and atmosphere.

By means of filters and similar equipment, photographs of the Sun (limited to a very narrow range of color) have been obtained. These photographs are of great interest. For example, photographs taken in the particular red color sent out by hydrogen give us a picture of the distribution of hydrogen on the Sun (see photographs 16, 18). Similarly, photographs taken in a certain violet color emitted by calcium vapors give a picture of the distribution of calcium on the Sun (see photographs, 16, 17). The prominences are particularly apparent on such photographs, both as protuberances from the Sun's edge and as thin dark filaments projected on the Sun's surface. The hydrogen photographs also clearly reveal the sunspots as whirlpools. In the neighborhood of sunspots are indicated bright clouds called flocculi which may be related to the above-mentioned faculae. From time to time bright flocculi near a sunspot may suddenly become very much brighter for several minutes. These chromospheric eruptions or flares (see photograph 19) are always accom-panied by fade-outs in short-wave radio.

Earth

The planet Earth is not quite a sphere, but is slightly flattened, the polar diameter (12,714 kilometers) being 1/297 shorter than the equatorial diameter (12,756 kilometers). The Earth rotates around the polar axis once in 23 hours, 56 minutes and 4.09 seconds.

The Earth has a solid crust, which is generously covered with water and surrounded by a gaseous atmosphere. The "Earth light" observed on the Moon a few days before and after new Moon proves that the Earth is a good reflector of sunlight; this is what one may expect from a planet covered with an atmosphere (see photograph 20). The axis of rotation of the Earth is tilted 23.5° from the perpendicular to the orbital plane around the Sun. This affects the noon height of the Sun at different times of the year. The resulting annual seasonal variations in the lengths of day and night and the total daily impact of sunlight increase with the geographic latitude and reach the well-known extremes in the polar regions. An observer far away from the Earth would notice the seasonal changes in the polar ice and snow caps, and also the color changes resulting from vegetation.

Apart from organic matter in the form of soil, the outer shells of the solid crust of the Earth consist mostly of minerals, inorganic materials in the form of rocks. The latter appear in two principal forms, the igneous rocks, which were solidified from liquid states, and the sedimentary rocks, which were deposited as more or less stratified beds, either on the floors of rivers, lakes or seas, or on land. The most abundant materials in the Earth's crust are silica (SiO_2) and silicates, compounds of silica and metallic oxides. Silica appears in the form of sand and sandy rocks; in the very pure state as quartz; and, when colored, as gem stones.

Apart from our knowledge of the outer crust, what we know of the interior of the Earth is derived mostly from the Earth's reaction to earthquakes, or seismic waves. The central temperature of the Earth is more than 1000° centigrade, and is most likely the residue from an original molten state of the Earth. A central core about half the diameter of the Earth is probably still partly molten, consisting of iron and nickel compressed into a high density of 10 or more. Around this we visualize an intermediate shell of average density (the average density of the Earth is 5.52), consisting of a mixture of iron and stone under high pressure. Surrounding this shell there is an outer shell of approximate density 4.3, which may be visualized as an outside layer of heavy rock about 50 kilometers thick, floating on a sticky, partly molten layer of rocky material.

The average surface temperature of the Earth is about four degrees above the freezing point of water, i.e., 277° K. Life on Earth is related to a comparatively narrow temperature range, considering existing temperatures in the universe, which range all the way from absolute zero (−273° centigrade) to millions of degrees in the interiors of Sun and stars.

The Earth's atmosphere is essential to life. In the first place, the atmosphere transmits a great deal of sunlight which is used for heating the Earth; the Earth in turn radiates the accumulated energy mostly in the form of infra-red heat radiation which is effectively absorbed by the Earth's atmosphere. This is the well-known greenhouse effect, the atmosphere acting as a blanket which keeps the Earth warm at night.

Apart from water vapor, whose abundance varies with the location and the time, the atmosphere, by volume, includes 78.1 per cent nitrogen, 20.9 per cent oxygen, .9 per cent argon, .03 per cent carbon dioxide, and so on. Water is necessary for both animal and plant life, while the oxygen, nitrogen and carbon dioxide play a fundamental role in the balance between animal and plant life. Plants contain the green substance, chlorophyll, which feeds the plants by converting carbon dioxide from the atmosphere into organic matter. Plants draw nitrogen and carbon dioxide from the atmosphere and release oxygen, which in turn is needed for animal life.

The density of our atmosphere decreases rapidly with height. Half of all the air in our atmosphere is below a height of 6 kilometers; all but one-millionth is below 100 kilometers. In the lower part of the atmosphere, the so-called troposphere, the temperature drops with increasing height down to a constant temperature of about $-55°$ centigrade in the stratosphere. Higher up in the atmosphere temperature fluctuations occur again. The ionosphere consists of different high atmospheric layers ionized by ultraviolet radiation from the Sun. The transmission of radio waves over great distances depends on reflection from the ionospheric layers. The transmission is subject to daily and seasonal variations, but is also affected by sunspots and by the chromospheric eruptions which cause fade-outs in short-wave radio. Best known of the ionospheric layers are the so-called D-layer at about 60 kilometers, the E-layer between 80 and 150 kilometers, and the F-layer between 210 and 300 kilometers. Radio echoes indicate an upper limit of about 500 kilometers for the height of the atmosphere.

Much of the radiation from the Sun is absorbed by the atmosphere before it reaches the Earth's surface. We are protected against deep ultraviolet radiation through its absorption in the upper atmosphere by molecules of ozone (O_3), oxygen (O_2) and nitrogen (N_2). The infra-red heat radiation is absorbed by the carbon dioxide (CO_2) and water vapor (H_2O) in the atmosphere, and the low-frequency, long radio waves are reflected by the ionospheric layers. The Earth's atmosphere is, however,

transparent for short radio waves, at frequencies of the order of
10^7 to 10^9 vibrations per second (10 to 1000 megacycles).

At all times the atmosphere protects us to some extent from
the impact of cosmic particles which manage to penetrate the
upper atmosphere. These include meteors which are mostly
vaporized, and the cosmic ray particles, consisting of hydrogen
and helium atoms plus a small admixture of certain heavier
atoms.

Earth and Moon

The Moon describes a somewhat elongated orbit around the
Earth in a period of 27.32 days. Since during this interval the
Earth and Moon have moved in their orbits around the Sun, it
takes an average of 29.53 days for Earth, Moon and Sun to
reach approximately the same geometrical arrangement in space.
This period of 29.53 days, known as the synodic period, represents the recurrence of the same phases of the Moon.

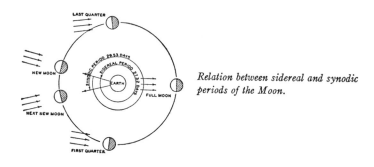

*Relation between sidereal and synodic
periods of the Moon.*

Because of its comparative nearness the Moon's gravitational
effect is noticeably larger on the part of the Earth turned toward the Moon than on the Earth's center, while it is still less
on the part of the Earth turned away from the Moon. The re-

sult is a tidal bulge for the body of water covering the Earth—both toward and away from the Moon. To a lesser extent the Sun has a similar effect. The tide-raising force of the Moon affects not only the water on the Earth's surface, but also the Earth's crust itself. The fact that the yielding of the Earth's crust represents 30 per cent of the tidal action proves that the Earth as a whole is more rigid than steel.

Moon

The Moon's diameter is 3840 kilometers. The Moon's mass is 1.23 per cent of the Earth's, its density 3.33 times that of water. At the surface of the Moon gravity is only one-sixth of that on Earth.

Objects more than 100 meters across on the Moon's surface can be recognized in the telescope. No certain change has ever been observed on the Moon. It has no atmosphere, a fact that must be attributed to insufficient gravitational force resulting in the gradual dispersion in space of any atmosphere which may have existed in the past. Because of the absence of an atmosphere, temperature changes on the Moon are quite violent; a contributing factor is the Moon's slow rotation. When the Sun is overhead, the Moon's surface reaches a temperature of $+100°$ centigrade, while at lunar midnight the temperature drops to $-150°$ centigrade. During a Moon eclipse a drop in temperature at the rate of $150°$ centigrade per hour has been observed.

The dark areas on the Moon bear the historical name, seas, an inappropriate designation since the Moon has no water. The dark areas are merely flat, dry plains. The mountain ranges on the Moon contain some very high peaks, their height being calculated from the length of their shadows cast on the lunar surface by the Sun. The rills or ditches are cracks often over 1 kilometer deep; some are over 100 kilometers long. Several straight markings on the Moon obviously represent boundaries (rock faults) between different levels (see photographs 2, 3).

The most conspicuous surface features of the Moon are its craters, which range from over 200 kilometers in diameter to very much smaller sizes; the smallest craters visible on photographs are some 3 kilometers in diameter (see photographs 4, 5). The craters may have been created by the impact of meteors, or by volcanic action, which would have been aided by the low gravity on the Moon. (A variation of volcanic action would be the formation of craters by the bursting of gas bubbles created from the interior.) Near full Moon the rays emanating from several of the larger craters are striking. They are material of a lighter color which may have been ejected from the craters as a result of the meteoric impact or volcanic explosion in the formation of these craters. In either case we must assume that the Moon is covered with dust, ashes or some porous material. Undoubtedly the Moon is still continually bombarded by small meteors which must create still more craters and more dust. The change in the reflection of sunlight at different phases of the Moon supports the idea that it has a dusty surface. The Moon is a very poor reflector of sunlight. As the astronomer puts it, it has a low albedo; only 7 per cent of the incident light is reflected. This suggests that the dust is not very fine, but coarse like gravel, and yellowish in color.

That the Moon keeps the same side turned toward the Earth is attributed to a tidal bulge some 300 meters high, which has frozen the Moon, so to speak, in its rotation. This rotation has exactly the same period (27.32 days) as does the Moon's revolution about the Earth. Since the orbit of the Moon is elongated and the speed in the orbit not quite constant, and since the equatorial plane of the Moon makes an angle of 7° with the Moon's orbit, we are permitted a partial view of the "other side" of the

Moon. Thus we have altogether observational knowledge of 59 per cent of the Moon's surface. Direct knowledge of the remaining 41 per cent must probably await a successful rocket trip around the Moon.

It is of interest to compare the distance to the Moon with the size of the Sun. If the Earth were placed at the center of the Sun, the Moon's orbit would be well below the Sun's surface, since the diameter of the Moon's orbit is less than three-fifths the diameter of the Sun.

4 | THE PLANETARY SYSTEM

Historical review

The solar or planetary system derives its name from the well-known assembly of the Sun and the planets, of which the Earth is one. Five planets—Mercury, Venus, Mars, Jupiter and Saturn —can be seen with the naked eye. These objects move back and forth on the background of the so-called fixed stars. It was not until the sixteenth and seventeenth centuries, however, that the character of these motions became clearly understood.

Nicolaus Copernicus (1473-1543) pointed out that the yearly back-and-forth motions of these planets are simply explained by the fact that the Earth is a planet, too, and that all the planets, including the Earth, describe orbital paths around the Sun. These orbital paths are not far from one and the same plane and are slightly elongated. Johannes Kepler (1571–1630) gave an exact description of the motions, which take place in elliptical paths. Isaac Newton (1642–1727) later synthesized Kepler's discoveries into the law of universal gravitation. The more recent discoveries of Uranus, Neptune and Pluto increased the number of known planetary dependents of the solar family.

The Earth's orbit is located between those of Venus and Mars. Mercury and Venus, having their orbits inside the Earth's orbit with respect to the Sun, are referred to as the inner planets. They can never be observed far away from the Sun; and even

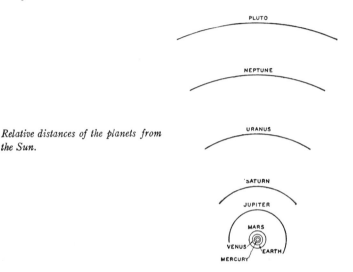

Relative distances of the planets from the Sun.

at their greatest "elongations" from the Sun they are best seen at dawn or dusk. In contrast, the outer planets, Mars, Jupiter, etc., are visible at different times of the night (see photographs 21–24).

The law of gravitation implies that the speeds of the orbital velocities gradually diminish as we go outward in the system. The dimensions of the planetary orbits are in a more or less regular (geometric) progression, if we include the "average" asteroid (minor planet). As the accompanying diagram shows, each planet is somewhat less than twice as distant from the Sun as its predecessor. We have already noted that the planetary orbits are more or less in the same plane. The direction of the orbital motions is the same for all planets; as seen from a point far above the north pole of the Earth, the motions would appear counterclockwise, or, as the astronomer says, direct. This direct motion holds for the rotation of the planets (with the exception of Uranus) and for the orbital motions of the numerous satellites, although a few move in a clockwise or "retrograde" direction. We note the tremendous spaciousness of the celestial mechanism in which the Sun, and even more so, the planets, appear as comparatively minute concentrations of matter.

Terrestrial and major planets

Physically, the planets fall into two groups. The terrestrial planets—Mercury, Venus, Mars, the Earth and Pluto—are comparable in size and mass. They are rather dense, as if they contained a large proportion of iron or stone. These planets are sparingly or not at all provided with satellites. Quite distinct from the terrestrial planets are the large or major planets— Jupiter, Saturn, Uranus and Neptune. These objects have an average density not very different from that of water. Due to their greater distance from the Sun, they are very cold. The major planets are accompanied by a large number of satellites.

Other solar dependents

Besides the nine planets, the population of the solar system includes the minor planets or asteroids; these are small objects whose orbits are mostly between those of Mars and Jupiter. In addition, there are the comets and meteors, dust particles and atoms, and, of course, the continual flow of energy radiating from the Sun.

General study of the planets

While the Sun is self-luminous, the planets shine by reflected sunlight. The very motions of the planets on the celestial sphere, together with their periodic variation in brightness, indicate that these objects are relatively near to the Earth, and that their distances vary. Stars, even under the highest magnification, never show disks; this is due to their tremendous distances. Even in small telescopes the planets look like extended, almost spherical objects. The observed disks of the planets Uranus, Neptune and Pluto are comparatively small. A good knowledge of the planetary markings requires an ideal atmosphere, a well-trained eye and a good telescope which need not necessarily be large. The best seeing conditions are usually obtained with a telescope which has an aperture not over 50 centimeters in diameter; under the best circumstances objects $0''.1$ (one-tenth of a second of arc) apart can be separately seen. Photography, especially in different colors of light, plays a role in studying surface features; but for fine detail, visual observations remain unsurpassed.

The reflectivity or albedo of a planet gives indications of its atmosphere, since a dense atmosphere is a better reflector of sunlight than the surface of the planet itself. Planetary atmospheres are further studied by means of spectral analysis. The sunlight reflected from the surface of a planet reveals a weakening of certain colors, i.e., absorption lines caused by the back-and-forth trip of the light through the planetary atmosphere. The situation is complicated, of course, since the light has also traveled through both the Sun's and the Earth's atmospheres. If we take advantage of the Doppler principle, however, these various effects may be disentangled.

The terrestrial planets

MERCURY is difficult to observe because its maximum elongation from the Sun amounts to only 28°. The planet seems to have permanent surface markings. The same side of the planet is always turned toward the Sun; in other words, its period of rotation equals its period of revolution around the Sun, which is 88 days. The mass of Mercury is about 5 per cent of the mass of the Earth. Mercury is somewhat bigger than our Moon, having a diameter of 5150 kilometers; like the Moon, it has a poor albedo—only 6 per cent—which indicates that it has a very thin atmosphere. The part of Mercury turned toward the Sun heats up to over 400° centigrade; on the other hand, the dark side of Mercury has a temperature not far above absolute zero. There is a strong similarity between Mercury and our Moon.

Mercury has no known satellite.

VENUS is easier to observe than Mercury, since its maximum elongation amounts to nearly 50°. It has impermanent surface markings, and there is evidence of clouds moving over the surface. The albedo is high (60 per cent); and the planet appears to have a thick atmosphere regulating the surface temperature, which ranges from about 80° centigrade on the sunlit side to −20° centigrade on the dark side. While Venus' period of revolution is 225 days, its period of rotation is probably not more than a month. In contrast with Mercury, therefore, no part of Venus is continually turned toward or away from the Sun; this is one more reason why the ranges in temperature keep within bounds.

The color of Venus is white. Spectroscopic observations show that there is no measurable amount of oxygen or water vapor on the planet. There is evidence, however, for the presence of atmospheric carbon dioxide, which is transparent to both the visual and ultraviolet sunlight. These rays heat the surface of Venus; the resulting heat radiation does not, however, penetrate the carbon dioxide. As a result of this greenhouse effect, the surface of Venus may become quite hot, perhaps over 100° centigrade.

As far as size and mass are concerned, Venus and the Earth are very much alike, Venus being only very slightly smaller (diameter 12,630 kilometers; mass 85 per cent of that of the Earth). While on the Earth oxygen combined with hydrogen to become water, on Venus hydrogen may have been less abundant, resulting in the combination of oxygen with carbon instead.

Venus has no known satellite.

MARS   The most conspicuous surface features of Mars are its polar ice caps, which change with the Martian seasons. The general appearance of the planet is that of an orange-colored disk, showing blue-green surface markings. These markings are permanent, and have led to an accurate determination of Mars' period of rotation, which amounts to 24^h 37^m $22^s.58$, a little more than our day. Mars is rather smaller than the Earth, having a diameter of only 6850 kilometers, and only 11 per cent of the mass of the Earth. Its albedo is low, only 15 per cent.

Sometimes clouds are observed on Mars. Photographs taken in different colors show the clouds to be bright in violet light and invisible in infra-red light. This would indicate that they are thin clouds of water or ice crystals, reflecting violet, but transmitting infra-red light. The polar caps appear in both colors, although they are brighter in violet light; they must be surface deposits covered by clouds. Photographs of Mars taken in violet include the Martian atmosphere; those taken in red light represent the surface. The former are larger than the latter, suggesting the existence of an appreciable atmosphere, some 60 kilometers high.

Spectroscopic evidence gives rather negative information about the existence of water vapor and oxygen on Mars; all we can say is that the Martian atmosphere contains less than 5 per cent of the water vapor in our atmosphere, while the comparable figure for oxygen is less than 0.1 per cent. However, carbon dioxide is found in the atmosphere of Mars. The spectrum of the general orange background color on Mars suggests the presence of igneous rocks similar to felsite, while the green areas, which change in color with the Martian seasons, indicate some sort of vegetation, probably hardy plants like lichens and dry mosses. The temperature at Martian noon may go up to almost 50° centigrade; the twilight temperature is something like $-10°$ centigrade, while at Martian midnight the temperature probably drops to $-20°$ centigrade, or below.

Several observers have noticed sharp lines running across the Martian surface which are often called canals, an erroneous translation of the original designation "canali" (channels) by the Italian astronomer Giovanni Schiaparelli (1835–1910). These lines often radiate from large spots referred to as oases. Recent observations have not confirmed the general sharpness of these features which the earlier observers saw. The Martian surface is probably covered with a wealth of details which the eye cannot resolve. As a result, the eye or the photographic plate may record lines which really are nothing but a summation of features too small to be observed separately. If some of the canals prove to be real, it is very likely that they will not prove to be sharp straight lines, but rather extended areas. It has been suggested that the oases are eroded craters caused by the impact of falling minor planets and that the canals are cracks in the Martian surface.

Mars has two small satellites.

PLUTO Little is known about the terrestrial planet Pluto which was discovered in 1930. In the large Hale telescope at Palomar, the planet shows a small disk. Pluto's diameter is estimated at about 6000 kilometers, its mass at about one-tenth that of the Earth. Hence Pluto is of the size of Mars, possibly

		RELATIVE MASS (EARTH=1)	NO. OF MOONS
MERCURY	•	0.05	—
VENUS	o	0.85	—
EARTH	o	1.00	1
MARS	o	0.11	2
(ASTEROIDS)			
JUPITER		319	12
SATURN		95	9 + RINGS
URANUS		15	5
NEPTUNE		17	2
PLUTO	o	0.1	—

Comparative sizes of Sun and planets.

larger; its albedo is low, about 17 per cent. The surface temperature is below −200° centigrade.

The only other known terrestrial planet, the Earth—and its
satellite, our Moon—were discussed in Chapter 2.

The major planets

The major planets—Jupiter, Saturn, Uranus, and Neptune—
differ from the terrestrial planets in that their dimensions and
masses are much larger. At the same time, their densities are
much lower, similar to the density of water. They are all in a
state of rapid rotation, which has resulted in a noticeable flattening. From this it can be deduced that the densities of these
planets must increase appreciably from the surface to the interior; i.e., that they have dense cores. The major planets are
very cold, due to their great distance from the Sun. They are
good reflectors of sunlight, with albedos of about 40 to 50 per
cent. They have very thick atmospheres, in which the vapors
of ammonia (NH_3) and methane (CH_4) are conspicuous. The
major planets are well endowed with satellites, whose masses,
however, are very small compared with the parent bodies.

JUPITER   has an equatorial diameter of 143,800 kilometers and
a polar diameter of 135,000 kilometers. Its mass is 319 times
that of the Earth. The flattening of the planet, about one part
in seventeen, is conspicuous even in a small telescope, which
also reveals semipermanent surface markings in the form of
bands of clouds. These clouds reveal the rapid rotation of
Jupiter around its axis in about $9^h 55^m$. The equatorial arrangement of the clouds is undoubtedly due to atmospheric currents
running parallel to the equator. Some of the clouds compare in
size with the Earth and are probably very deep, which may

explain why they sometimes have an existence drawn out over several decades.

Since the average density of Jupiter is 1.3 times that of water, it follows that the outer layers must consist of very light material or gases. A spectroscopic analysis of the sunlight reflected from Jupiter reveals the presence of ammonia and methane vapors. The high abundance of hydrogen in these gases indicates that free hydrogen may be present and, perhaps, hydrogen tied up in the form of ice.

There is a hypothesis that Jupiter consists of a rocky and metallic core of average density 6.0, surrounded by a layer of highly compressed ice of density 1.5, and there is a shell of hydrogen, so cool that it cannot be detected spectroscopically. Above it there are the clouds of ammonia and methane. Since the observed surface temperature of Jupiter is $-140°$ centigrade the ammonia must exist primarily in crystals, which form the clouds we observe. Some ammonia would evaporate, and this together with the gaseous methane is what we observe spectroscopically.

Twelve satellites of Jupiter are known, forming a miniature planetary system. The brighter four satellites were discovered by Galileo Galilei (1564–1642). Three of these are very much like our Moon, the fourth one being somewhat smaller. The four Galilean satellites have high albedos, and it is likely that they are covered with a frozen atmosphere. The other, fainter satellites are very small, some of them being only a few kilometers in diameter. Three of the fainter satellites have retrograde motions.

SATURN has an equatorial diameter of 121,000 kilometers and a polar diameter of 109,000 kilometers. Its mass is 95 times that of the Earth. Saturn shows equatorial cloud formations, in less detail, however, than those of Jupiter. The period of rotation is slightly over ten hours. The average density of Saturn amounts to 0.7. Spectroscopic observations reveal relatively more methane and less ammonia than for Jupiter. Since the surface temperature of Saturn is below −150° centigrade, more ammonia would be frozen, and the atmosphere would be relatively richer in methane—assuming that the chemical abundance of these two materials is the same on Jupiter and Saturn.

Saturn has nine known satellites, of which one has retrograde motion. The most striking and unique feature about Saturn is its system of concentric rings separated by narrow empty spaces. The rings are situated exactly in the planet's equatorial plane, which is tilted 28° to the Earth's orbit around the Sun. It takes Saturn thirty years to complete its revolution around the Sun; and, as a result, our view of the rings changes in the course of each thirty years. For fifteen years we see the rings from one side; for another fifteen years from the other side. In between, twice every thirty years, we see the rings on edge; and at those times they vanish completely from sight for a few days and are not visible even in large telescopes. This indicates that the rings are very thin, probably less than ten kilometers. Theoretical considerations show that the rings can be neither solid nor liquid, but consist of large numbers of small particles pursuing their individual orbits around Saturn. All the particles revolve in the same plane and in the same direction; their orbital speeds depend only on their distance from the center of Saturn and decrease outward. Spectroscopic observations making use of the Doppler principle (Chapter 9) confirm this conclusion.

The rings are excellent reflectors of sunlight, which indicates that the material is highly pulverized, consisting probably of rocks, pebbles, dust and ice. The total mass of the rings must be less than one-millionth that of Saturn. The empty spaces in the system of rings correspond to periods of revolution which are simple fractions ($\frac{1}{2}$, $\frac{1}{3}$, $\frac{1}{4}$, $\frac{2}{5}$ . . . and the like) of the periods of some of the inner satellites. The corresponding orbits would be "resonant," which means that the gravitational effects caused by some of the moons of Saturn would gradually distort and destroy the original orbital paths.

URANUS AND NEPTUNE   The planets Uranus and Neptune are very much alike, both having diameters about four times the diameter of the Earth (Uranus: 53,500 kilometers; Neptune: 50,000 kilometers). Their masses are respectively 15 and 17 times that of the Earth. Spectroscopic observations reveal that these planets rotate rapidly—in less than 11 and 16 hours respectively. Uranus shows faint cloud belts; no surface markings have been observed on Neptune. Both planets have high albedos, indicating that they have atmospheres. Spectroscopic observations show only a trace of ammonia, which is easily explained by the low surface temperatures of these planets—amounting to less than $-180°$ centigrade and $-200°$ centigrade for Uranus and Neptune respectively; at these temperatures comparatively little ammonia exists as vapor. The atmospheres are relatively strong in methane, which absorbs sufficient yellow and red radiations to explain the green color of these planets.

Both the rotation of Uranus and the orbital motions of its five satellites are almost perpendicular to the plane of orbital motion of the planet around the Sun; careful observations show that these motions are actually slightly retrograde. Neptune has two known satellites; the larger one is probably bigger and heavier than our Moon. Its motion around Neptune is retrograde.

5 | ASTEROIDS, COMETS AND METEORS

Minor planets or asteroids

The minor planets, also called asteroids, appear as faint, starlike objects. The first, Ceres, was found in 1801. Since then over two thousand asteroids have been discovered; they are all very small and their orbits lie mostly between those of Mars and Jupiter. Their periods of revolution range between three and twelve years. Their orbits are as a rule elongated and not too highly inclined with respect to the general plane of the planetary system. The orbital motions are all direct. The arrangement of the orbits appears to be governed by Jupiter, the heaviest planet in the solar system. No asteroid is known, for example, whose period of revolution is one-half or one-third that of Jupiter; such orbits would be resonant and could not be maintained. A dozen asteroids are known to move around the Sun in the same orbit and with the same period as Jupiter, but about one-sixth of a revolution ahead or behind that planet. These objects are an interesting case of gravitational equilibrium under the combined influence of two bodies, namely, the Sun and Jupiter.

It is believed that tens of thousands of asteroids remain to be discovered. The total mass of all asteroids is estimated to be less than one-tenth the mass of the Earth.

The brightest four asteroids appear as minute disks. The largest is Ceres, which has a diameter of about 770 kilometers, less than one-quarter the diameter of the Moon. The smallest asteroids known are probably about one kilometer in diameter. Asteroids are undoubtedly solid bodies shining by reflected light. We recall that our Moon's brightness varies rapidly with its phases; the full Moon is very much brighter than either the first or last quarter. On the other hand, there is less change in the intensity of the reflected sunlight with phase in the case of the planets Venus and the Earth. For the Earth this has been discovered by studying the reflected "Earth light" which can be observed on the Moon just after and before new Moon. For the asteroids, the change of illumination with phase is quite appreciable, and we therefore conclude that, like the Moon and Mercury, but in contrast to the Earth and Venus, the asteroids have no atmosphere. The colors of the asteroids are gray or brown, which suggests that they have a rocky structure.

The brightnesses of several asteroids vary; an example is the asteroid Eros. Since no variation in color is observed, the variation in brightness is probably due to irregular shape rather than spottiness. Eros is assumed to be an irregular, elongated object, some 20 kilometers long and 6 kilometers wide, and in a state of rapid rotation. The light of the asteroid Vesta is polarized; that is, the reflected sunlight shows preference for vibrations in a particular plane. The same has been observed for the surfaces of the Moon and of Mercury. This polarization points to a surface composition of ashes, perhaps due to the impact of meteors

As illustrated by Eros, the asteroids may just be irregular fragments. It is hard to see how they could be caused by some gradually solidifying process. It is more likely that the asteroids had a catastrophic origin. Perhaps a planet not larger than the Earth at some time in the past approached so close to Jupiter that the difference in gravitational pull, or tidal action, on the close and far sides led to its disruption into numerous small parts. Some of these parts may have been lost to the solar system, while others have remained as asteroids.

In their orbits around the Sun, certain asteroids get very close to the Earth. Hermes, for example, which is only a few kilometers across, has approached the Earth to about one million kilometers. Due to their faintness and rapid motion, objects of this sort are extremely difficult to discover and observe. Each year thousands of them may get to within one million kilometers of the Earth. The chances for collision are remote, however—of the order of less than one collision in every hundred thousand years.

A striking example of an asteroid with a very eccentric orbit is Icarus which can approach the Sun to within 33 million kilometers.

Comets

Comets are not solid bodies, but clouds of loose material which are vulnerable to a variety of dispersive actions; comets have occasionally been lost, split or disrupted. The basic structure of a comet is its head, which may be as large as the planet Jupiter. The head consists of a highly dispersed cluster of small particles embedded in an extremely tenuous gaseous atmosphere; this material is often concentrated, giving the appearance of a nucleus. Telescopic observations of comets show that no solid bodies over half a kilometer exist in comets. This was illustrated in 1910. As Halley's Comet crossed the Sun it could not be seen (see photograph 25).

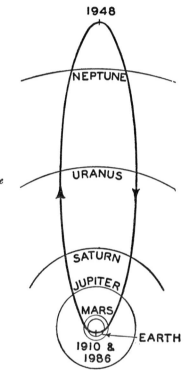

Orbit of Halley's Comet as seen on the general plane of the solar system.

Comets are members of the solar system. Numerous comets have been observed whose orbits are definitely periodic; that is, they move in elliptical orbits around the Sun. Comets with periods as short as 3.3 years are known. There are many others, however, whose orbits are so elongated that it is difficult to establish their periods. Although these orbits are ellipses their far ends are so distantly removed from the Sun that the designation "parabolic orbit" becomes proper. The comets with nearly parabolic orbits show no organization in the arrangement of their orbits; they may be regarded as forming a huge cloud filling the solar system in all directions. The elliptical orbits of, say, less than a hundred years' period are more organized. They are generally neither very elongated nor highly inclined toward

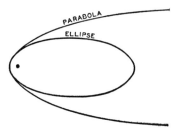

A parabola (an extreme case of an ellipse, the far end being at infinity).

the plane of the solar system, while their motions are direct. These comets are dominated by the strong gravitational influence of Jupiter; the greatest separation from the Sun of a large number of them occurs near the orbit of Jupiter. There can be no doubt that Jupiter has molded—or if one wishes, captured—the orbits of these objects. Although there must be hundreds of thousands of comets, their total mass is probably much less than 1/10,000 of the Earth's mass.

When a comet gets close to the Sun, inside the orbit of Mars, for example, a tail generally appears, pointing away from the Sun. Tails may develop tremendous lengths, even exceeding the distance of the Earth from the Sun. The tail is caused by the pressure of the Sun's radiation on the minute dust particles, molecules or atoms in the comet's head. The tail thus represents a streaming away of matter which is forever lost to the comet. This explains why the short periodic comets grow no more tails, having gone through the process too often. Since comets lose material through tail formation, and perhaps through meteoric collisions and other dispersive forces, their nuclei may eventually become very feeble. In this way a comet may be disrupted into a cloud of meteors.

Spectroscopic observations reveal that a comet shines partly because of sunlight reflected by small particles of dust. As the comet approaches the Sun, the strong ultraviolet radiation from the latter stimulates the gases in the comet's head, which are now revealed as glowing molecules, some chemically complete, others incomplete, such as carbon (C_2), cyanogen (CN), methyne (CH), carbon monoxide (CO), nitrogen (N_2), nitrogenhydride (NH), and hydroxide (OH). When comets get still closer to the Sun other radiations appear which may be attributed to atoms of sodium (Na), iron (Fe), nickel (Ni), and chromium (Cr). The carbon monoxide and nitrogen molecules appear mostly in the tail.

Meteors

Meteors, or "shooting stars," are now recognized as cosmic objects subject to the gravitational attraction of the Sun, though the attraction of the Earth plays an important role by the time we see them. A meteor is generally a small particle of matter sweeping through and colliding with the atoms and molecules in the upper atmosphere. As a result, atoms are broken off the surface of the meteor, are heated up to some 2000° centigrade and radiate light. A very bright meteor may not burn up completely, however; if a remnant reaches the Earth and is located, we have a meteorite.

Up to the end of the eighteenth century, meteors were believed to be atmospheric phenomena. We know now, by the simple process of surveying from two different locations, that meteors appear at a great height, usually about 100 kilometers, have velocities up to 40 kilometers per second, and come from parts of space well beyond the Moon. Further progress in understanding meteors was made in 1833, when a so-called shower of meteors was observed. The meteors appear to diverge from one point, which can be explained as a perspective effect of an extended group of meteors moving in more or less parallel paths as they approach and pass by the observer.

Bright meteors have been observed to leave luminous meteor trains; this occurs at the critical height of 80 kilometers, where our atmosphere reaches the low temperature of $-100°$ centigrade.

The brightest of all meteors are called fireballs; it is estimated that several thousands of these must occur daily. They are known to penetrate to an altitude of about 20 kilometers or lower, and may even reach the Earth's surface as meteorites. The ordinary, or sporadic, meteors usually make their first appearance at a height of about one hundred kilometers, while the meteors which are organized in showers appear somewhat higher. The orbits of the sporadic meteors are nearly parabolic; most of them originate outside the solar system. Certain sporadic meteors have been found moving in periodic orbits similar to those followed by asteroids and short-period comets.

On a moonless night—at any time of the year—a careful observer may note as many as ten sporadic meteors in one hour. It is estimated that the Earth sweeps up millions of meteors daily. These are meteors which at night would be visible to the naked eye. Adding those that could be observed with the telescope, some eight thousand million meteors are estimated to fall daily. The total addition to the Earth's weight due to meteors and meteorites is estimated to be over one thousand kilograms daily. Even over the interval of three thousand million years representing the age of the Earth, the accumulation due to meteoric falls would be only something like a one-centimeter-thick accretion of sand and gravel.

One of the richest meteor showers takes place annually in November. Since the meteors appear to radiate from a location (radiant) in the constellation Leo, these meteors are called Leonids. The Leonid meteors are scattered along an orbit and complete their respective orbital paths in thirty-three years. Within the scattered band there is a condensation, with the result that every thirty-three years the Leonid shower has appeared particularly strong. (There are indications that the condensation has weakened considerably in historic times.) On the other hand, the Perseid meteors in August are rather evenly spread along their orbital band; there is no evidence of a concentration.

Several cases are known of a comet and meteor swarm moving in the same orbit. This is particularly true of short-period comets; it is believed that gravitational perturbations have in several cases led to the disruption of comets into meteor swarms.

While the average separation between sporadic meteors is something like 500 kilometers, the spacing of the small particles in showers is much closer, the lowest observed value being about 30 kilometers.

A spectroscopic analysis of meteors reveals the presence of iron (Fe) and calcium (Ca); the latter is more abundant in meteors belonging to showers. Magnesium (Mg), silicon (Si) and sodium (Na) are also observed.

Meteorites

These are meteors that reach the Earth. Meteorites therefore provide the only direct material link with the cosmos outside the Earth's atmosphere. Some fourteen hundred meteorites are on record. There are two principal types of meteorites; the metallic, nickel-iron meteorites which are easily recognized, and the stony ones. Occasionally meteorites are found to contain both metal and stone. With few exceptions, meteorites are shattered in their fall, although sometimes it has been possible to fit pieces of a fallen meteorite together. The present discovery rate of meteorites is about twenty-five per year. The largest known meteorite has a volume of about eight cubic meters.

When large meteors enter the atmosphere, the air is compressed to an intense heat which melts the surface material. Liquid droplets are seen as sparks and produce loud detonations; the meteor appears as a fireball. As its speed slows down, the "fire" ceases and the liquid surface is frozen into a dark crust. If the meteor reaches the Earth, and thus becomes a meteorite, a detailed study becomes possible of what only a short time ago was a cosmic object. The surface crust of the metallic meteorites consists of iron and nickel oxides; that of the stony meteorites is glass, i.e., compounds of silica (SiO_2) and metallic oxides. The high pressure of the compressed air shatters the meteorites, the metallic to a lesser extent than the stony ones. As mentioned before, an intact meteorite is seldom found; the larger meteorites usually bury themselves on impact. Before entering the Earth's atmosphere, these meteorites were heated by sunlight to a temperature slightly above the freezing point of water. During their short trip through the Earth's atmosphere their outer crust becomes very hot, but is cooled quickly after the meteorite has fallen.

A very large meteorite, hundreds of meters across, would create a terrific impact. The concussion of meteor and Earth would result in the vaporizing of much material and an explosion which might destroy the whole meteorite, although a portion might penetrate the Earth. The hot air would destroy vegetation and life in the neighborhood. A huge crater with an upturned rim would be created. There are several craterlike formations on our Earth which may be ascribed to volcanic action, steam "bubbles," or sinking processes; but there are some ten craters known at present which must be of meteoric origin (see photograph 26). They range in diameter from 50 meters up to 4 kilometers—the diameter of the recently discovered meteoric crater in northern Quebec. A huge meteorite fell in Siberia in 1908 and caused a terrific explosion and devastation. In all these cases fragments of the meteorite were found in the vicinity below the surface of the crater. These craters are nearly circular in shape. The appearance of groups of craters indicates that a swarm of bodies has hit the Earth. It is estimated that once a century the Earth is hit by a meteor large enough to make a crater of over ten meters in diameter.

Erosion may have erased many old craters on Earth. There is some evidence of very large, eroded craters, several kilometers across, which may have been caused by the collision of an asteroid with the Earth. Compare this with the Moon's surface, where the same thing may have happened unhindered by a protective atmosphere, and where the craters would be preserved because of the absence of erosion and wind.

The chemical analysis of metallic meteorites yields 90.8 per cent iron and 8.5 per cent nickel on the average. The most abundant chemical elements in the stony meteorites are found to average about 36 per cent oxygen, 26 per cent iron, 19 per cent silicon and 14 per cent magnesium. It is of interest to compare this with the high abundance of oxygen, 48 per cent, and silicon, 26 per cent, in the Earth's crust.

Heated meteorite powder yields vapors of hydrogen (H_2), carbon monoxide (CO), carbon dioxide (CO_2), nitrogen (N_2) and methane (CH_4). These same gases are observed in comets.

The analogy is interesting and suggestive, but so far no missing link has been found in the form of a meteorite from a meteor shower. It is believed that stony and metallic meteorites may both be the fragments of a large solid body somewhat like the Earth. We must remember that the composition of meteorites is very much like the inner core of the Earth. If, therefore, they are fragments of a planetlike object, that object must have been like the Earth or Venus.

Possibly meteorites and asteroids have the same origin; in this connection it is worth noticing that certain small asteroids have orbits similar to those of large meteorites.

Zodiacal light

This is a faint band of light following the zodiac, the sequence of constellations circling the Sun's annual path (ecliptic) along the celestial sphere. The light is widest and most intense near the Sun—it may, in fact, form its outer corona—and is believed to be caused by the reflection from numerous small meteoric particles in their orbits around the Sun.

Space travel

A few words may be said about the possibility of interplanetary rocket travel and navigation. The law of gravitation (Chapter 12) permits the calculations for this problem, which is particularly intricate for the close approach to or landing on any celestial object. The amount of energy required for the control of motion makes the use of atomic energy (Chapter 21) mandatory, since no chemical source of energy would be sufficient. The effect of persistent changes in gravity on the human body are to a great extent still an unknown factor. The possibility of damage by meteors is very real because of the large velocities of these bodies.

PART 2

The Mechanics of Stars and Planets

6 THE EARTH AS OBSERVATIONAL CENTER OF THE UNIVERSE

Choice between rotation of celestial sphere and Earth's rotation

As was explained before, the observed rotation of the celestial sphere need not be considered as real, but may be interpreted as an apparent effect caused by the Earth's rotation in a direction from west to east. The direction of any star changes uniformly, completing one full sweep of 360° in the period of diurnal motion. This observed state of affairs can be explained equally well by a uniform rotation of the Earth.

In our limited space-time existence on this Earth we attach explicit significance to such contrasting concepts as rest and motion, or rest and rotation. For example, the train moves (with respect to the tracks), the merry-go-round rotates (with respect to the surrounding landscape). In common parlance, the qualifications given in parentheses are left out, since no possible misunderstanding can arise. Ambiguity may exist, however, in the case of phenomena which occur beyond the grasp of immediate daily experience or experiments. In such cases it is important to remain open-minded toward any interpretation; a distinction should be made between the strict context of the data observed and any possible interpretation. Any choice of convenient or conventional interpretations may thus be superseded by new interpretations after a wider range of facts has become available.

In this light we must consider the observed rotation of the celestial sphere. The impression of the "whirling-by" of the landscape that a person on a rotating merry-go-round experiences will serve as an excellent analogy for our purposes. No one on a merry-go-round would be tempted to think that the landscape is rotating, while he is at rest; previous experience, plus the reactions of the senses, prevent him from adopting this interpretation. We must keep in mind that the most natural property of any motion is its inertia, i.e., its constancy of motion both in speed and direction (Chapter 9); a change can be brought about only by external action. The matter of a rotating solid body is held together by cohesion; without this, each particle would pursue a uniform straight motion determined by the initial impulse of rotation; i.e., the body would fly apart. If we find ourselves involved in the rotation of this merry-go-round, of which we are not integrally a part, we have to exert muscular effort to hold on. Thus we are able to counteract the so-called centrifugal effect, which is simply an expression of the natural law of inertia. The latter does not affect the merry-go-round itself because it has sufficient internal cohesion to oppose the centrifugal action.

Identical nature of centrifugal and falling acceleration

The centrifugal "flying-away" effect is comparable in nature to the effect of gravity, which manifests itself in falling bodies. Like falling, it is an accelerated motion, i.e., a motion subject to a continuous change in velocity. In the case of gravity, the direction of the falling motion does not change, and the rate of change in speed is virtually constant; i.e., the velocity of falling increases proportionally to the time. In the case of centrifugal motion, the rate of flying-away also remains the same (for a uniform rotation). The direction of the centrifugal acceleration does change, however; it remains pointed away from the center of rotation. Using the word falling in a general sense, we may say that a "falling-outward" is added to the normal vertical gravity effect. The result is a modified gravity effect, turned slightly outward. Another illustration is a train's motion relative to railroad tracks along curves, which are tilted to maintain a normal, perpendicular pressure of the moving train on the rails. An observer from the train witnesses an opposite tilt of the stationary landscape, since his organs of equilibrium are conditioned to feel the tilted effect as normal, downward gravity.

The rotating Earth

Previous experience and physiological structure fail us when we consider the possible alternative between the rotating celestial sphere and the rotating Earth. Compared with the rapidly turning merry-go-round, or the train going around the curve, the centrifugal effect of the Earth's rotation is so gentle that our unaided sense organs do not feel it. The choice between the two interpretations can be made only on the basis of further evidence not provided by the original observations. Through certain delicate experiments the Earth's rotation can be demonstrated, or "felt," so that the interpretation of a rotating Earth is acceptable; a simple astronomical proof will be given in Chapter 7.

Regarding again the starry sky, we are aware now of being on the surface of the Earth-ball which is floating in space. The Earth gently spins without destroying our illusion of standing on top of it. The illusion is determined by the effect of gravity, which is directed toward the center of the Earth. This impression, and nothing else, defines the conventional notions of up and down, which result from the reaction of our sense organs to gravity. Once this is clearly understood, it becomes unnecessary for us to be concerned for the safety of our antipodal neighbors. Beyond their conventional, local use, the terms up and down have no meaning in the geometrical structure of the universe.

Orientation of the celestial sphere

It is convenient to introduce the notion of an axis of rotation of the Earth, i.e., that imaginary line located at the geometrical center of the Earth's rotational motion. The northern end of

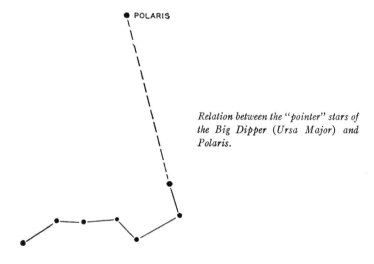

Relation between the "pointer" stars of the Big Dipper (Ursa Major) and Polaris.

this axis points to the celestial north pole, which is close to the bright star Alpha Ursae Minoris, or Polaris (see photograph 1). Being close to the north pole of the celestial sphere, Polaris is a useful skymark for navigation in the northern hemisphere.

After a century or so, the present pole star will gradually lose its significance, due to the gradual long-term change of direction in the Earth's axis. Apart from its diurnal rotation the Earth's axis describes a conical motion, completing one cycle each 25,800 years, while preserving its inclination of 66.5° to its orbital plane. This effect, called precession, will be explained in Chapter 12.

The plane of the Earth's equator, when extended, defines a great circle on the celestial sphere which is named the celestial equator; the plane of this circle is, of course, at right angles to the axis of rotation of the celestial sphere. The orientation of the rotating celestial sphere with respect to the horizon appears to depend on the geographic latitude. The elevation of the north pole of rotation above the horizon, its altitude, is equal to the latitude of the place of observation. This is the result of the

The latitude (φ) of the place of obser-
vation equals the altitude (h) of the
pole of the celestial sphere.

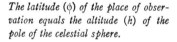

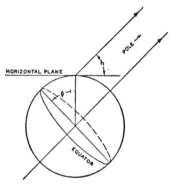

curvature of the Earth's surface, combined with our insistence on preserving such local notions as horizon, up and down. Hence the added significance of the pole star for the northern hemisphere; not only does its stationary position indicate approximately the north point, but its altitude equals the observed latitude as well.

For observers located on one and the same geographic longitude the meridians coincide and the meridian transits of stars occur at the same time. For observers at the north and south poles the stars do not rise and set, but describe diurnal paths parallel to the horizon; at the equator these paths are perpendicular to the horizon, while at all other latitudes their orientation is inclined.

Sun, Moon and planets

Upon the background of stars other cosmic objects appear to be projected; most important of these are Sun, Moon, and the planets, of which Mercury, Venus, Mars, Jupiter and Saturn are visible to the unaided eye. All these objects participate in the diurnal rotation; but, in addition, they slowly change their locations with respect to the stars. This is easily observed for the Moon and the planets, while observations of the Sun's path across the starry sky are complicated by the presence of daylight. However, appropriate studies indicate a circling of the

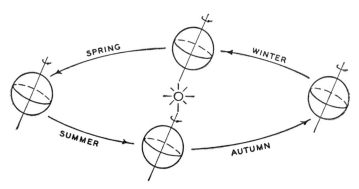

Cause of the seasons.

Sun around the celestial sphere in a period of one year; this motion takes place in a direction approximately opposite to that of the diurnal rotation. The Sun's yearly motion is explained as an apparent reflex motion due to the Earth's orbital movement around the Sun (Chapter 7). The 23°.5 tilt of the Earth's equator on the orbital plane is the cause of the seasons.

All celestial objects—stars, planets, Moon, Sun—appear to rise and set on the eastern and western horizons respectively. Because of the gradual eastward crawl of the Sun, the time between successive sunrises or sunsets is larger than the corre-

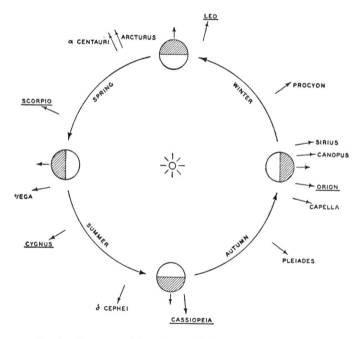

The changing aspect of the stellar world in the course of the year as indicated by some of the conspicuous constellations and stars as they cross the meridian at midnight.

sponding period for stars. The Sun determines our civil calendar day, which proves to be nearly four minutes longer than the period of the diurnal rotation of the celestial sphere. The annual eastward circuit of the Sun along the celestial sphere corresponds to a gradual westward motion of the celestial sphere if we observe the latter at the same time on successive civil days.

Path of Sun; the year; vernal equinox

The plane of the Sun's path is called the ecliptic; it is inclined 66°.5 to the axis of rotation of the Earth, and hence 23°.5 to the celestial equator. The point at which the Sun's path passes from below to above the celestial equator is called the vernal equinox; this point is reached about March 22 and marks the

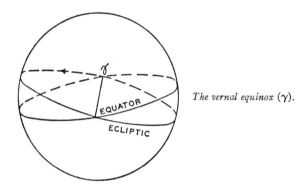

The vernal equinox (γ).

beginning of spring. The opposite direction is called the autumnal equinox. The time interval between successive passages of the Sun through the vernal equinox is 365.2422 days. This period determines the year of the seasons, or tropical year, by which we regulate our yearly calendar. Because of the precessional motion of the equator the vernal equinox moves along the ecliptic in a westward direction, completing one circuit in 25,800 years. Hence, the actual period of revolution, as observed on the background of fixed stars, is slightly longer than the tropical year. It takes 365.2564 days for the Sun to complete one turn of 360° in space; this interval is called the sidereal year.

Orbits of Sun and Moon

Attention is drawn to a simple fact which is related to the "depth" structure, i.e., the spatial orbits, of Sun and Moon. We recall that the apparent diameter of the Sun ranges in the course of a year from 32′ 36″ on about January 1, to 31′ 31″ on about July 1. Similarly, the apparent diameter of the Moon ranges from 33′.5 to 28′.8 in the course of one period of revolution. These changes in the apparent size of Sun and Moon are due to slight variations in distance; we conclude that the Earth could not be in the geometrical center of these orbits. We also note that the rates of motion are not uniform but vary slightly in the course of one complete circuit.

The Moon's orbital plane is inclined about five degrees to the Sun's orbital plane, while the shape of the Moon's orbital path differs more from a circle than does the Sun's. The Moon is a relatively small object maintaining an average distance of only 384,400 kilometers; it is a close companion of the Earth, in comparison to its relation with the Sun which is so much further away (Chapter 7).

In this summary we do not take account of the many changes to which the orbits of both Sun and Moon are subject; for the purposes of most of our subsequent studies these various complications are not relevant. The general properties of the orbital motion of celestial objects will be discussed in Chapters 10 and 11.

Equatorial co-ordinates; sidereal time; solar time

The vernal equinox is employed as a useful skymark and plays an important role in various astronomical problems such as measuring celestial co-ordinates and measuring time. A system of "fixed" co-ordinates analogous to the system of fixed geographical co-ordinates—longitude and latitude—on the terrestrial globe, has been introduced on the celestial sphere. The celestial equator is the fundamental line, the vernal equinox (γ) the fundamental point, or origin, of this "equatorial" co-ordinate system. One co-ordinate is declination (corresponding to geographic latitude), which is the angular distance PP' from an object P to the celestial equator (positive if north, negative if south), counted along the hour circle, which is the equivalent of the terrestrial meridian. The other co-ordinate is right ascension $\gamma P'$, which is counted along the celestial equator from the vernal equinox eastward to the projection of the star on the equator through its hour circle; it is usually expressed in hours (24^h = $360°$). By appropriate methods of observation the right ascension and declination of different objects can be compared and referred to the equator and equinox. The angular distance MP' of the hour

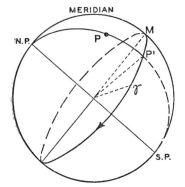

The equatorial co-ordinate system.

circle to the observer's meridian is called the hour angle; it is counted westward and expressed in hours. Hour angle is of course not a fixed co-ordinate, but a quantity which changes as the celestial sphere turns.

The equatorial mounting permits the pointing and clamping of the telescope in any particular right ascension and declination. A clockwork rotates the telescope around the polar axis, which is parallel to the Earth axis. Ideally the rate of this clockwork equals that of sidereal time; in practice minute adjustments and corrections have to be made by the observer.

The position of the vernal equinox defines the time of the sidereal day, which begins when the vernal equinox passes the meridian at upper culmination. The length of the sidereal day is thus the time elapsing between two successive upper transits of the vernal equinox; because of the precessional motion of the equator the sidereal day is about $1/120$ second shorter than the period of rotation referred to a fixed point among the stars. Sidereal time is defined by the fraction of the rotation of the celestial sphere since the last transit of the vernal equinox, i.e., the hour angle $M\gamma$ of the vernal equinox. Sidereal time is measured by observing the transit of a star past the meridian, at which moment the sidereal time equals the right ascension of the star.

These sidereal-time measures are the stellar analogies of the solar day and of solar time based on the Sun. The civil or mean time actually used, however, is an adjusted solar time. Due to the slight lack of uniformity in the Sun's motion with respect to the celestial sphere, and due also to the inclination of the ecliptic on the equator, a fictitious, "mean" sun is introduced. The mean sun follows a uniform motion along the equator, thus, as it were, providing an ideal timepiece for measuring civil time. At the vernal equinox, the mean sun and the true Sun coincide;

both complete their seasonal circuit in one tropical year. The constant interval between successive transits of the mean sun is called the mean solar day; the hour angle of the mean sun determines the mean solar time of our civil timepieces. The hour angle of the true Sun determines what is called apparent solar time, as shown by a sundial, for example. The accumulated difference—mean solar time minus apparent solar time—is referred to as the equation of time; its value depends on the time of the year. The equation of time reaches an extreme positive value of nearly 16.5 minutes about November 3 and an extreme negative value of nearly 14.5 minutes about February 12. Obviously the intervals between successive upper culminations of the Sun, i.e., the true solar days, are not uniform in length, but may exceed the mean solar day—by as much as 28 seconds. On the other hand, they may be as much as 20 seconds shorter than the mean solar day.

The Earth clock

The rotating Earth is the master-clock of all terrestrial timepieces. By noting the passage of stars through the meridian, the astronomer compares his star or sidereal clocks with the rate of the rotating Earth, after making proper allowance for certain effects such as aberration (Chapter 7), precession and periodic variations in precession (nutation). Modern astronomical clocks rely for their rate not on a pendulum, but on the constant period of vibration of a quartz crystal; these quartz clocks are accurate to one-hundredth of a second. Another type of clock makes use of vibrating atoms in molecules consisting of three or more atoms. The Earth clock is very accurate, but it has slight imperfections. Long-range astronomical observations have revealed a reliable cosmic clock in the orbital motion of the planets around the Sun, operating according to the universal law of gravitation

(Chapter 12). There is a gradual slowing-down of the Earth's rotation, amounting to an increase in the length of the sidereal day of about one-thousandth of a second per century. This is due to the friction of the tides, caused by the gravitational effects of the Moon and, to a lesser extent, of the Sun on the body of water covering the Earth's surface (Chapter 12). In addition, there are irregular variations in the Earth's rotation, which, for example, slowed down somewhat between 1785 and 1899, with an accumulated loss of about one minute of time. Occasional changes of this sort are ascribed to very slight changes in the internal structure and the size of the Earth.

The Earth wobbles slightly in a period of twelve months around its axis of rotation, due, probably, to meteorological causes. There is also a wobble due to the fact that the Earth's axis of rotation does not coincide exactly with its short axis of symmetry. These wanderings of the Earth about the poles of rotation are limited to an area about twenty meters across. If the Earth were perfectly rigid, the period of the motion would have to be ten months. The observed period, however, is fourteen months, from which it is concluded that, although the Earth is not perfectly rigid, it is nevertheless twice as rigid as steel.

7 MOTIONS OF THE PLANETS AS VIEWED FROM EARTH AND SUN

The background of fixed stars

As we remarked in the first chapter, the constellations seem at first sight to remain unchanged through the centuries, and the same holds for their positions relative to one another. Continued observation and an increase in observational accuracy, however, have revealed small displacements of the stars, implying a gradual, slow distortion of the constellations. These motions have nothing to do with the diurnal rotation of the whole starry sky, which we ascribe to the diurnal rotation of the Earth. At this point we are facing real motions of the stars themselves. We conclude that stars move, and that the resulting displacements will lead eventually to a thorough distortion of the familiar constellations as we now know them. Similarly, of course, in the distant past these constellations have looked quite different. Gradually the illusion of the celestial sphere of "fixed" stars has yielded to the view of a universe of stars in motion (Chapter 9 *et al.*).

The motions of the "fixed" stars were not discovered before the beginning of the eighteenth century, while the first measurement of a stellar distance was not made until 1838. Long before this, however, a correct interpretation had been made of the arrangement and state of motion of Sun and planets;

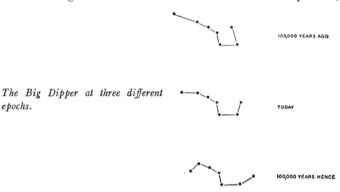

The Big Dipper at three different epochs.

interestingly enough, complete understanding on this score was achieved before the invention of the telescope. We can understand why this should have been so. The changes in location of the Sun and planets are so conspicuous that a clear picture of the character of these motions could be obtained. The very motions of Sun and planets suggest that they are much nearer than the stars. Nevertheless, it looks as if these objects are moving "on" the illusory celestial sphere. This is explained by the tremendous distances from the Sun and planets to the Earth.

In the next chapter we shall learn that the stars are farther away, ever so much farther away than the Sun, planets and other objects collectively referred to as the planetary or solar system. Any stellar motions are comparatively minute, and therefore the stars provide an ideal, virtually fixed background on which the projected complex of motions of the Sun, Moon and planets may be studied. For analogy we note that the flight of a bird may be conveniently described if it is projected against distant reference marks such as trees or mountains.

Paths of the planets; parallax; geocentric viewpoint

The motions of the planets or "wandering stars" along the celestial sphere are more complicated than those of the Sun and Moon (Chapter 6). The general behavior is again a west-to-east motion, but part of the time the planets appear to move from east to west. In the present chapter, in accordance with historical pre-telescopic methods, the planets will be considered small, pointlike objects.

The nearness of the planets is demonstrated by the fact that an observer notes slight discrepancies in their direction at different times of the night. These shifts are easily observed with the telescope; their total maximum range is some three seconds of arc for Jupiter, and as much as one minute of arc for Mars. While observations of these fluctuations prove the relative nearness of the planets, they provide at the same time a simple proof for the Earth's rotation; for the apparent displacement of the planets is due to the actual change of the Earth's orientation. The astronomer calls this stereoscopic effect parallax. It is customary to refer the motions of the planets to the center of the Earth, i.e., make it appear as if our observations were made from the Earth's center. It is convenient to introduce this simplification because it unifies the different terrestrial observational locations, which after all are so little apart, cosmically speaking. Thus, by "shrinking" the Earth into a point, we can refer our observations to what is called the geocentric viewpoint.

Spatial motions of the planets

The location of the planets in space at any one time can be ascertained through the application of the methods of survey ing, with the Earth's orbit as a base of operations. The interpretation of the results of this planetary surveying has been the subject of centuries of work; no satisfactory picture of the distribution and state of motion of the planets was obtained before the middle of the sixteenth century. Progress was delayed mainly because the observer is part of the experiment he is observing, and is at all times traveling along his baseline. Moreover, the motions of the planets (including the Earth) do not permit a bird's-eye view of the situation; they all take place in more or less the same plane—which confuses the analysis. It required the imagination, persistence and courage of Copernicus to overcome these difficulties.

In 1543 Copernicus demonstrated that the distribution and state of motion of the planets can be simply described if the observer imagines himself to be viewing the planets from the standpoint of the Sun. In other words, if we transfer the observer in our imagination to the Sun, the apparent complexity of planetary motions, as seen from the Earth, disappears entirely.

Relativity of motion

As in the case of the rotating celestial sphere, we can describe the observed paths of Sun and planets in different ways. The only thing that any observation of the position of an object can establish is the relative location of observer and object. Any sequence of locations observed at different times involves a change in the relative alignment of two points; thus, the same principle of the relative nature of motion holds in the case of a path. Consider, for example, two objects A and B. Observations of directions cannot distinguish between a motion $A_1 A_2$ of A and an equal but opposite motion $B_1 B_2$ of B unless observations of other objects are made also. This principle of the relative

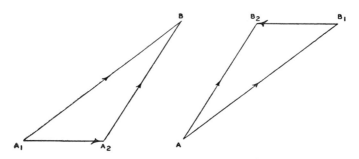

Relative motion of two objects A and B.

nature of locations and motions is inherent in our outlook on the universe. A choice of possible interpretations can be made only with appropriate additional evidence.

Heliocentric viewpoint

Consider the Sun, which appears to describe a yearly orbit around the Earth. Even if we accept the alternate description—that the Earth revolves around the Sun—the apparent path of the Sun remains exactly the same. The annual revolution

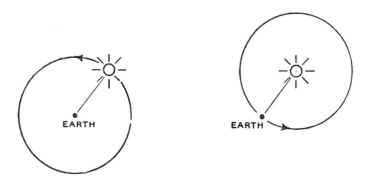

From the geocentric to the heliocentric viewpoint.

around the Sun cannot possibly be felt by us, since its centrifugal effect is even gentler than that caused by the Earth's diurnal rotation, which amounts to one-third of one per cent of gravity. Now if, with Copernicus, we choose the heliocentric viewpoint, i.e., the Sun as center, the orbits of the planets are much less complicated. Sun and planetary attendants are found to form a simple cosmic mechanism in which all planets including the Earth follow a single pattern of motion. The orbits are nearly circular and differ in size. The general sense of direction of travel is the same for all planets, and the orbital planes differ little; in other words, the planetary system can at all times be fitted into a flattened space pocket. Since our observations are made from the Earth, our view of the planets shifts periodically with the yearly seasons. Part of the time there is an increased rate in the general eastward or direct motion, part of the time the planets move in a westward or retrograde direction. The observed retrograde motions of the

Relation between the orbital motions of Jupiter and the Earth in the year 1951.

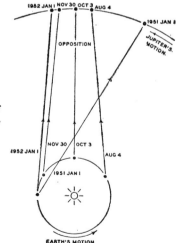

outer planets—those beyond the Earth's orbit—occur around the epoch of closest approach; their duration ranges from less than three months for the nearest outer planet, Mars, to almost half a year for the most distant planet, Pluto. Closest approach occurs near opposition, that is, the moment that planet and Sun are in nearly opposite directions as seen from the Earth.

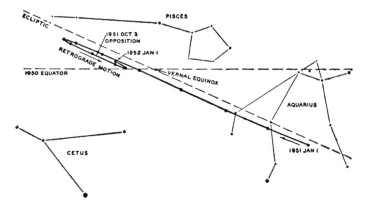

Path of Jupiter on the celestial sphere during the year 1951.

The angular sweep of the retrograde motions is different for each planet; the amplitude of the retrograde motions decreases as we observe planets at greater distances from the Sun. Apart from the direct, forward orbital motion of a planet, the amplitude of the retrograde motion is found to vary with the inverse distance to the planet. The retrograde motion is an apparent reflex imposed on the planet's motion as a result of the fact that we are viewing the planet from the moving Earth rather than from the "stationary" Sun. Naturally these reflex motions must be smaller for the more distant planets, and their presence and size are a beautiful revelation of the motion of the Earth in its orbit and the general spatial arrangement of the planetary orbits. For the inner planets, Mercury and Venus, a corresponding situation exists, though it is more difficult to analyze because of the rapid orbital motions of these objects.

The above outline is very much idealized. Our picture of the back-and-forth motions of the planets is complicated principally by the fact that the planetary orbits are not quite in the same plane. Such complications do not, however, change the essential outcome of the Copernican picture.

Scale of planetary system; distance to Sun; astronomical unit

We now have a map of the planetary orbits. The linear scale of the map, in kilometers, is obtained by making use of the extended size of the Earth, which provides a convenient base for deriving distances within the solar system. The distances of the planets are determined through observations of their parallactic shifts from different locations on the Earth, or, via the Earth's rotation, from the same surface location at different times. As we shall see later (Chapter 11), the relative sizes of the planetary orbits may be accurately obtained from their periods of revolution. The measurement of any planetary distance at any time serves therefore to determine the *scale* of the planetary system. In particular, it furnishes a value for the distance of the Sun, or in other words, the length of the so-called astronomical unit of distance.

The last accurate determination for the scale of the solar system resulted from observations of the asteroid Eros, which approached the Earth to within 25,000,000 kilometers in the year 1931. Thirty different telescopes at twenty-four observatories in fourteen countries were used in this international campaign of scientific co-operation. The discussion of the observations by Harold Spencer Jones (1895–   ) may be summarized as follows: There is a difference (angle) of 8″.790 between the position of the Sun S as seen from the center C and from the equator O of the Earth, or, in other words, the positions of the center and the equator of the Earth, as seen from the Sun. This angle is called the geocentric parallax p of the Sun. The equa-

Geocentric parallax.

torial radius of the Earth being 6378 kilometers, a simple computation yields 149,700,000 kilometers for the astronomical unit, i.e., the distance from the (center of the) Earth to the (center of the) Sun. To be exact, this value is the mean distance, i.e., the average between the maximum and minimum distances (Chapter 11).

Crucial test of heliocentric parallax

Although the heliocentric viewpoint is of such overwhelming simplicity and beauty that from a purely descriptive standpoint its acceptance could hardly be challenged, the question arose whether or not additional evidence exists. If it is not the Sun which revolves around the Earth, but rather the Earth which revolves around the Sun, then the effect of the Earth's orbital motion should be revealed in the stars—just as it is in the case of the other planets—in the form of parallactic shifts in direction in the course of a year. If the Earth and stars are at rest with respect to each other, no effect should be found; if, however, the Sun and stars are at rest with respect to each other, the effect of the Earth's orbital motion should be noted in the stars. This argument was an old one and was considered crucial by many of the earlier astronomers. The Earth's orbit has a diameter of nearly 300,000,000 kilometers. So huge a baseline would seem to hold some promise of revealing annual changes in the positions of fixed stars due to heliocentric parallactic

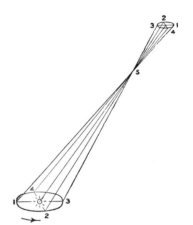

Parallactic orbit of a star.

effects. But these shifts were not observed for three centuries after Copernicus; and in the meantime the heliocentric viewpoint was not acceptable to many astronomers, Tycho Brahe (1546–1601), for instance.

We now know that the early failure on the part of astronomers to notice any heliocentric parallactic shifts was due to the tremendous distances of the fixed stars. As mentioned before, it was not until 1838 that reliable observations of such a shift were made for one of the nearer stars; and only comparatively recently, after 1900, has a technique been developed which is adequate for an all-round attack on this problem. We recall that the Copernican view (1543) of the solar system was proposed long before the invention of the telescope (1608). While the older astronomers were able to measure directions and angles with an accuracy of one minute of arc at best (the angle subtended by one yard at a distance of two miles), the use of the telescope made possible a much higher accuracy. Several early attempts were made to detect the heliocentric parallactic effect for fixed stars, but all without success.

Aberration of starlight

However, one of these historical investigations in 1727 proved to be of great interest. The astronomer James Bradley (1693–1762) had a suitable telescope at his disposal at the Greenwich Observatory, and made another attempt to look for the annual parallactic effect. To create the most favorable conditions he observed a star which was located in a direction almost perpendicular to the plane of the ecliptic. Assuming that the star has no motion of its own, and that the Earth describes an orbit around the Sun, a telescope would in the course of the year have to be tilted ever so slightly inward, i.e., toward the direction of the star as seen from the Sun. To his surprise, Bradley did not find any such effect, but discovered instead another type of tilt. In the course of one year his telescope had to be tilted slightly forward, i.e., toward the direction of the Earth's path at any particular moment. Bradley correctly ascribed this effect to the finite velocity of light, which had been discovered in 1675 by Olaus Römer (1644–1710).

The position of a star as observed with a telescope is defined by the axis of the cone of light which converges from the objective toward the focal image of the star; this position may be rigorously measured by pointing the telescope so that the focal image of the star is bisected by a set of cross wires in the focal plane. Since the light rays have a finite velocity, it takes time for the light to travel from the objective toward the focus. Imagine now the telescope moving at an angle with the incoming light rays. The telescope will have to be tilted slightly forward toward the direction of motion in order that the star image may still be observed on the cross wires. The direction in which the

Aberration of starlight.

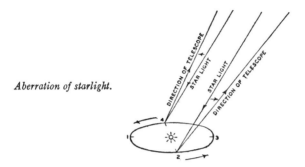

telescope is pointed thus reveals a corresponding shift. Obviously the distance of the star does not enter into these considerations; what counts is the position of the star and the velocity of light.

For analogy imagine a person walking in a downpour holding his umbrella in such a way as to provide maximum protection against the falling rain. The umbrella has to be tilted forward slightly in the direction of motion in order to anticipate the raindrops which are falling with a finite velocity. The amount of tilt varies directly with the speed of the observer's motion and inversely with the speed of the drops; the faster the drops come down, the smaller the tilt need be. While the tilt of the umbrella against the rain may have to be considerable, the analagous tilt observed for fast moving "light drops," the so-called aberration of light, is quite small, 20″.5 at most; however. such a quantity could be easily measured even in Bradley's time. Although Bradley's discovery thus unexpectedly confirmed the heliocentric viewpoint, his observations failed to indicate any stellar parallactic effect, which therefore still had to be judged as very small indeed.

Finite speed of light

A few words should be said about Römer's discovery of the finite velocity of light. Römer was observing the four bright satellites of Jupiter, which form a sort of miniature planetary system. Jupiter and its family of moons describe an orbit around the Sun every 11.9 years; their distance from the Sun is about 5.2 astronomical units. The four bright moons of Jupiter describe orbits around Jupiter in periods ranging from a little less than two to somewhat over sixteen days. Since their orbital planes coincide fairly closely with that of Jupiter and that of the Earth, eclipses of Jupiter's moons in the planet's shadow or occultations behind the planet's disk are common occurrences. The Jupiter satellite system is a beautiful example of the many cosmic mechanisms that find their analogy in our timepieces, the only difference being that these celestial timepieces need no winding up, and run with extraordinary accuracy. It is of interest, therefore, to compare the clock whose hands are represented by the motions of the satellites with that embodied in the motion of a man-made timepiece or the master cosmic timepiece nearest at hand, the rotating Earth.

The timing of the Jupiter satellites is facilitated by the frequent occurrence of the aforementioned eclipses and occultations. Römer found that his terrestrial clock and the Jupiter "clock" did not agree, but that there was a periodic, annual change in rate which can be described as follows. During half of the year the Earth approaches Jupiter, while during the other half of the year the Earth and Jupiter get farther away from each other. Römer's observations showed that compared with his clock, the Jupiter "clock" ran fast while the Earth was approaching Jupiter, but had a slow rate when the Earth was retreating; the accumulated effect amounted to about a quarter of an hour either way. Now it was impossible to accept such a large irregularity in the Jupiter satellite clockwork or in any existing terrestrial precision clockworks. Römer concluded that another effect, overlooked till then, was responsible. It takes time for us to see what has happened in the Jupiter system; i.e., it takes time for cosmic events to be revealed on Earth. This explains the respective "fast" and "slow" rates in the Jupiter satellite mechanism. In other words, the light messages are not received instantaneously, but only after some time—the time it takes for light to travel from Jupiter to the Earth.

Velocity of light

Quantitatively the situation can be described as follows: The light from the Jupiter system moves at such a rate that it takes almost a thousand seconds to traverse the diameter of the Earth's orbit, or nearly 300,000,000 kilometers. Hence the speed of light would be about 300,000 kilometers per second. By terrestrial standards the speed of light is tremendous, but in the vast cosmic spaces it is a mere crawl.

Römer's determination of the velocity of light was not accurate by modern standards, but it represents the first quantitative revelation of the finite speed of light, and, of course, a proof, too, of the Earth's revolution about the Sun! This important finding found further confirmation in Bradley's discovery of aberration. At present it is no longer necessary to derive the speed of light from observations of Jupiter's satellites. Laboratory experiments have yielded the accurate value of 299,776 kilometers per second; however, for many problems it is adequate and convenient to employ the round figure 300,000 kilometers per second.

From a combined knowledge of the velocity of light and the observed aberration of starlight, the Earth's orbital speed can be accurately derived; this in turn has yielded an accurate determination for the size of the Earth's orbit, i.e., the length of the astronomical unit.

8 | THE DISTANCES OF THE STARS

Stellar parallax

In 1838 Friedrich Wilhelm Bessel (1784–1846) made the first successful observations of the heliocentric parallax of a star. Bessel chose a star which offered some promise of being relatively near. How do we know that a star is near to us? The best criterion for nearness is the star's motion on the celestial sphere, its so-called proper motion. Bessel had noted that a faint star in the constellation Cygnus, referred to as 61 Cygni, had an unusually large proper motion, amounting to as much as $5''.2$ per year; at this rate the star traverses an angle represented by the Moon's diameter in about 360 years. This large motion is a sign of comparative proximity in the same way that the rate of motion of a bird or an airplane across the sky provides a clue to its nearness. True, the star or bird may be moving close to the line of sight; it has been found, however, that generally the size of the cross motion of a star is a useful criterion for its nearness.

Bessel's studies were rewarded with success; a measurable parallactic displacement was found. Technically speaking, a value of 0″.3 was derived for the heliocentric or annual parallax. This is the angle p under which an observer, located at the star, sees the unforeshortened radius OE_1 of the Earth's orbit. In other words, the annual parallax is the major axis of the small

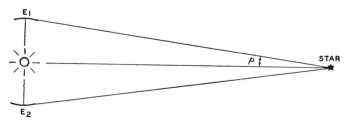

Heliocentric or annual parallax.

ellipse which the star seems to describe on the celestial sphere in the course of a year.

Since Bessel's first attempt, the parallactic shifts of thousands of stars have been observed, particularly during the present century. These shifts confirm the Copernican viewpoint; they would, in fact, have pointed to it even if the Sun and other planets had been too faint to be seen.

The parallactic shifts prove to be of the utmost significance for our studies of the stellar world, since they enable us to determine stellar distances. The Earth's orbit furnishes the fundamental baseline for determining stellar distances, just as the extended size of the Earth furnished the base for determining the distances of Moon, Sun and planets. As a result of the revolution of the Earth around the Sun, a nearby star, seen from the Earth, is displaced on the virtually stationary background of distant stars; the amount of this displacement is a measure of the nearness of the star.

The problem of studying the parallactic shifts of stars may be illustrated by the following analogy. Suppose a bird is seen projected against a distant background of trees or mountains. Let us first assume that the bird is "standing still," just as a hummingbird does. If the observer is located on a merry-go-round, his change of position at different times will result in his seeing the stationary bird projected on different parts of the stationary background. The observed back-and-forth motion of the bird is fully ascribed to the observer's motion; in fact, the observer's motion is thus "made visible." We also see that the angular back-and-forth shift provides a measure for the distance of the bird, the amount of shift varying with the inverse of the distance; if one bird is twice as far away as another, the former will reveal only half the "parallactic" shift of the latter. The problem is not changed essentially if the bird is not stationary but moves along with a uniform speed in a certain direction. In this case the back-and-forth motion is simply superimposed upon the forward shift of the bird and a little arithmetical calculation permits a distinction between this continued forward shift and the back-and-forth parallactic shift.

For a moment it may seem that the now shattered illusion of "fixed stars" has deprived us of any "background" on which to observe these small parallactic shifts. The ancient astronomers found these "fixed" stars an ideal background for studying the paths of the planets, and we still do. Relatively few stars, however, show appreciable proper motions, and even fewer exhibit measurable parallactic shifts. There is therefore an overwhelming majority of faint distant stars which are virtually "fixed," and for all practical purposes these form an adequate background for studying the behavior of the nearer stars; the effect of possible small shifts on the part of these background stars can be kept within bounds, and allowances can be made for such fluctuations. The proper motions and parallactic shifts of the nearer stars are revealed as small but measurable changes in direction on the background of the readily available "fixed" stars; these small displacements are expressed in the usual angular measure. In the present problem the most adequate unit of measurement is the second of arc, which may be described as the angle subtended by one inch at a distance of about three miles. There are several methods for measuring angular displacements of such a small order. The observational approach to these quantities relies to a great extent on modern photographic methods; the technical details were worked out in the beginning of the present century. The method of determining stellar distances by the heliocentric-parallax method will now be studied in some detail.

Photographic astrometry

The ideal instrument for measuring the small parallactic displacements is a camera of long focal length and commonly of large aperture. The possibilities of this approach were first demonstrated by photographs made with the largest existing visual refractor—at the Yerkes Observatory—in the beginning of the century. The necessary techniques of accurate positional measurement, the methods of photographic astrometry, were developed by Frank Schlesinger (1871–1943), who succeeded in measuring stellar distances with an accuracy not achieved before.

The astronomical refractor

As mentioned before, both the light-gathering and focusing qualities of a refractor are provided by the refraction of light through a lens or system of lenses. By using a combination of two lenses one may obtain partial correction for the difference in refraction of light of different colors (Chapter 15). Such a visually corrected achromatic objective provides the best compromise method for the focusing of light in the yellow-green color range, to which the eye is most sensitive. Other refractors have been corrected for the conventional photographic color range, the blue. Panchromatic plates used in conjunction with the visual refractor, however, have proved particularly useful for positional work. Besides using such a telescope visually, one may place a photographic plate in the focus of the objective; and sharply defined photographs may thus be made, if a yellow or rather "minus-blue" filter is used to eliminate the out-of-focus blue rays. This photovisual technique yields results which have certain advantages over conventional photographs taken in blue light. The reasons are partly atmospheric, blue light being more subject to scattering, and partly cosmic, because of the predominantly red color of our stellar neighbors (Chapter 17).

The power of a large refractor lies, in the first place, in its great focal length, which reproduces any configuration of stars on a large scale. For example, with the Sproul refractor of a focal length of 36 feet (1093 centimeters), the scale value in the focal plane amounts to $1'' = 0.053$ millimeters. Thus the image of the Moon in the focus is nearly four inches across and fills the greater part of the useful optical field. Secondly, the generally large aperture permits the photographing of faint stars. Last, but not least, there is the remarkable precision of photographically recorded positions; small variations in the positions of star images on photographs taken at different times are readily measured with considerable accuracy.

Let us first recognize that the angular diameters of even the nearest and largest stars are so small (less than $0''.1$) that no photographed star image can reveal any information about the star's diameter. Any star seen through the telescope appears as a minute disk because of the very nature of light. The star image on a focal-plane photograph appears as a considerably larger disk due primarily to the photographic spreading effect of the emulsion. Both visual and photographic star images are, of course, affected by turbulence in the atmosphere. The sizes of photographic images are of no interest other than to provide a measure for the brightness of the star. The images are simply diluted representations of the locations of the pointlike stars; the centers of these images represent the positions of the stars.

Accuracy of photographic positions

The location of one star image with respect to another may be determined on a measuring machine. In such a machine the photographic plate is mounted on a carriage which can be moved in a plane at an angle of, say, 60° with the horizontal. The plate is viewed with a low-power microscope attached to a nut which fits a horizontal long-precision screw with a pitch of one millimeter. By turning the latter and moving the carriage up and down, one can examine all portions of the plate. The microscope contains a vertical thread (and a horizontal one to indicate the center of the field), for bisecting the star images. At one end the screw is provided with a dial, so that the amount of turning, and hence the distance moved, can be read and recorded.

Thus the location of any star image may be obtained, but precautions of all sorts are necessary to achieve high positional accuracy. Although the diameters of star images range from about 0.05 millimeters to 0.20 millimeters, experience has shown that the relative location of two stars can be found from the measured centers of their images with an average accuracy that is only a small fraction of the image size. From a plate taken with the Sproul telescope we may obtain the photographic location of a star on an appropriate background of three or four stars with an average uncertainty of only .002 millimeters (two microns), which is about 0ʺ03 in terms of direction. This is the angle subtended by an inch at a distance of one hundred miles, which gives us an idea of the power of the long-focus photographic method in measuring small shifts in direction. Accuracy may be increased by taking several exposures on several plates, and uncertainty may thus be decreased to as little as 0ʺ01 for certain problems. This small amount represents the limit of attainable accuracy in photographic positions with present equipment and methods. The heliocentric parallax is slightly over 0ʺ03 at a distance of 100 lightyears, the approximate limit of distance penetration by the photographic method.

Stellar distances

The photographic method has yielded measurable parallaxes for thousands of stars. The nearest star, Alpha Centauri, has a heliocentric parallax of 0ʺ78, which is therefore the maximum angle at which the distance from Earth to Sun, or astronomical unit, would appear from this star. By a simple computation the distance of Alpha Centauri is found to be about 270,000 times that of the Sun, or 270,000 astronomical units. Numbers as large as these are more easily handled through the introduction of a new, large unit of distance such as the lightyear—the distance traveled by light in one year. The velocity of light being nearly 300,000 kilometers per second, it takes $8\frac{1}{3}$ minutes of time for the light of the Sun to reach us; hence one lightyear is 63,300 times the distance to the Sun, or nearly nine and a half million million kilometers. The corresponding light time for Alpha Centauri is 4.3 years and the distance is thus conveniently expressed as 4.3 lightyears. The more technical distance unit commonly used is the parsec—the distance corresponding to a heliocentric parallax of one second of arc. One parsec equals 3.26 lightyears.

The second nearest star is Barnard's star, the star of largest known proper motion, discovered in 1916 by Edward Emerson Barnard (1857–1923). This tenth-magnitude star has a yearly proper motion of $10''.3$ in a direction almost due north. At this rate its displacement equals the size of the Moon's diameter in about 180 years. It is one of the most interesting stars from the vantage point of our solar system. The star has an annual parallax of $0''.53$ and is only 6.1 lightyears away.

Barnard's star affords an ideal opportunity to demonstrate annual parallax by direct visual inspection (see photograph 27). The star was photographed with the Sproul refractor at three successive epochs of extreme parallactic displacement separated by approximately half a year each. In the composite print the three photographs have been superimposed. The "fixed" background stars each give one image, whereas Barnard's star gives three separate images, each corresponding to one of the three positions marked on the diagram. (The orientation is inverted,

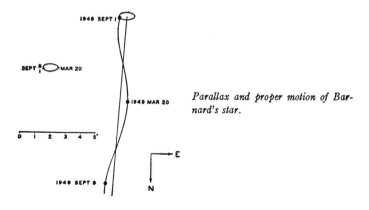

Parallax and proper motion of Barnard's star.

corresponding to that ordinarily presented by the astronomical telescope.)

The scale in the diagram may be used to check the more than ten-second, almost south-north displacement of Barnard's star caused by the proper motion. The displacement east-west, slightly over one second, is due to annual parallax, but is twice the normally expressed value of the parallax, which is based on one astronomical unit. In other words, the photographs show the apparent displacement caused by the Earth's motion from one end to the other of a diameter of its nearly circular orbit, whereas parallax is always stated as based on the radius of the orbit.

Actually, as shown in the diagram, the annual parallax causes a star to appear to trace a small ellipse on the sky. The combination of the stars' parallactic ellipse and its proper motion with respect to the Sun yields the sinuous geocentric path across the sky on which the three observed positions are marked.

The stars are far away, long ago, and widely spaced

Stellar parallaxes reveal the tremendous structure of the universe. Contemplation of the starry sky cannot fail to impress us with the grandeur and continuity of the distant cosmic past. There we see Sirius, nine lightyears away and nine lightyears ago. There is Vega, twenty-seven lightyears away and twenty-seven lightyears ago. There, too, that faint hazy object in the constellation Andromeda which is the so-called Andromeda nebula, eight hundred thousand lightyears away and eight hundred thousand lightyears ago!

In Chapter 17 we will study in some detail the different properties of the stars in our immediate neighborhood. For the present we can anticipate two findings. First there is the very wide spacing between stars. On the average the stars are separated by several lightyears from one another, while stellar diameters rarely run as high as half a light hour. Our own Sun, for example, has a diameter of 1,393,000 kilometers, a distance which would be traveled by light in only 4.6 seconds. Most stars are smaller than the Sun, and it becomes clear that the sizes of stars are exceedingly minute compared with the huge distances separating one star from another.

Luminosities of the stars

Secondly, we are prepared now to distinguish between the apparent brightness of a star and its intrinsic brightness of which we become aware as soon as the distance of the star is known. The apparent brightness of a star depends on two things, its true luminosity or candle power and its distance from us. Two stars which appear equally bright to us may of course have quite different luminosities, the apparent equality being caused simply by difference in distance. A knowledge of the distances of these stars enables us now to compare their intrinsic brightnesses by placing them, so to speak, at the same distance. Or, to put it more rigorously: the apparent brightness of a star can be translated into intrinsic luminosity whenever the star's distance is known. Our knowledge about stellar distances leaves no doubt that the tremendous discrepancy between the apparent luminosity of the Sun and that of the stars must be attributed to the great remoteness of the stars as compared with the relative nearness of the Sun.

Take the bright star Vega; the light that we receive from Vega is exceedingly weak compared with the Sun's illumination. It is possible to arrange photometric experiments which will give us the actual ratio of the illumination provided by the Sun and by Vega. It has thus been found that 46,500,000,000

stars like Vega would be needed to equal the apparent brightness of the Sun, while parallax measurements have revealed
that the distance to Vega is twenty-seven lightyears.

Now we are ready to compare the intrinsic luminosity of Vega
with that of the Sun. The distance to the Sun is 149,700,000 kilometers; expressed in light time this distance is only 8⅓ light
minutes or 1/63,300 of a lightyear. Hence Vega is 27 × 63,300
or about 1,710,000 times as far away as the Sun. The dilution
in the intensity of light from a source small in size compared
with the distance covered by the light rays is inversely proportional to the square of the distance. As the light "front" reaches
distances whose ratios are 1, 2, 3, etc., the light is spread, or
diluted, over a surface whose ratios are 1, 4, 9, etc. If, therefore,
Vega were placed at the distance of the Sun, its brilliance would
increase $(1,710,000)^2$-fold, and it would be evident that Vega
actually emits $(1,710,000)^2$ divided by 46,500,000,000, or 63
times as much light as the Sun. We say, therefore, that Vega
has a luminosity of 63 (times that of the Sun). Astronomers
generally use absolute magnitudes; the absolute magnitude of
a star is the magnitude it would appear to have if placed at a
distance of 10 parsecs (32.6 lightyears). The absolute magnitude of the Sun is close to 5, i.e., at a distance of 10 parsecs the
Sun would appear as a star of the fifth magnitude. The absolute magnitude of Vega is 0.5.

The stars are suns; the Sun is a star

The distances of several thousand stars have been measured
with sufficient accuracy to permit a computation of their intrinsic luminosities. A tremendous range in stellar luminosities
is found extending from less than 1/500,000 to more than
100,000 times the Sun's luminosity. We shall study these results

in more detail in Chapter 17; for the moment we note that they have an essential bearing on the physical nature of stars. Stars appear to be very luminous, apparently self-luminous objects like our Sun. The stars are not unlike that huge sphere of incandescent matter which we call the Sun; conversely, it looks as if our Sun is just another star.

9 | THE MOTIONS OF THE STARS

Proper motions

It was not until 1718 that the illusion of "fixed" stars was destroyed. In that year Edmund Halley (1656–1742) showed that the bright stars Sirius, Betelgeuse, Aldebaran and Arcturus had moved appreciably from the positions recorded by Ptolemy in the second century A.D. The rates of these proper motions are now known with high accuracy; the annual displacements of Sirius and Arcturus are quite large, amounting to $1''.32$ for the former and $2''.29$ for the latter. The accumulated displacements over the fifteen centuries between Ptolemy and Halley are therefore $33'$ for Sirius, and as much as $37'$ for Arcturus; and there could be no doubt about the reality of these observed displacements, since they exceeded the apparent diameter of the Moon. Gradually more and more stars were found to be moving; the rate of motion of each star remains the same as time goes by. At present proper motions are known for more than one hundred thousand stars. While the majority of stars prove to have small motions, large proper motions are sufficiently frequent to give the stellar world an aspect of restlessness. The number of known stars of large proper motion includes a large proportion of faint stars.

The cumulative effect of time plays an important role in the accurate determination of stellar motions. Telescopic observations of the locations of thousands of stars have been carried on for more than two centuries. These long-range studies are made with so-called transit circles, which are telescopic instruments equipped with vertical, finely graduated dials or circles. The instrument is usually mounted in such a way that the transit of a star may be observed when the diurnal rotation of the celestial sphere carries the star past the meridian. The altitude of the star can be accurately observed and the time of meridian transit noted on a sidereal clock. Observations of this type permit an accurate mapping of the stars on the celestial sphere down to about the tenth magnitude. From a comparison of the right ascensions and declinations obtained at different times, the proper motions of the stars may be derived. The photographic approach has also proved useful in conjunction with visual observations. The positions and proper motions of fainter stars may be derived photographically by comparing photographs taken at different epochs. The photographic method has resulted in the rapid discovery of large numbers of faint stars of large proper motion; these objects have proven of great interest, since they generally turn out to be relatively near to us. For an example we recall Barnard's star, the star of largest known proper motion (Chapter 8).

The measured values for the cross motions of many stars are supplemented through observations of that part of the stellar motion which takes place in the line of sight, away from or toward us. Before these so-called radial velocities can be discussed, however, it will first be necessary to review some fundamental notions pertaining to the nature of light.

Nature of light

All information about celestial objects is conveyed to us through beams of light. It is often convenient to idealize these beams as consisting of very narrow rays representing a continuous flow of light with a constant speed of 299,776 kilometers per second. The transport of light is referred to as radiation. The straight paths of light rays suggested to Newton that light consists of minute particles or corpuscles ejected from the light source. This corpuscular theory of light was generally accepted up to the end of the eighteenth century. Later it was observed that light bends around corners, as demonstrated by the inherent vagueness of shadows even in the case of light radiating from minute, almost pointlike sources. The effect is also shown by a mosquito screen, through which additional feeble companion images of a light source are seen. Newton's theory did not account for this diffraction of light. The phenomenon was explained in 1680 by Christian Huygens (1629–1695), who ascribed to light an undulating nature like that of water waves or sound waves. The wave theory was not seriously considered up to about 1800, when it did explain certain phenomena of interference. By 1900 the wave theory of light was widely accepted; difficulties arose about 1903, however, when studies of the photoelectric effect suggested again the particle nature of light. These matters will be taken up again in Chapter 18.

We are thus confronted with a phenomenon in nature which cannot be described exclusively in terms of either particles or waves. We do justice to both our knowledge and ignorance if we abandon any specific description, but simply say that light has both particle and undulatory properties. It is difficult to visualize a mechanism of light radiation in this frame of knowledge, particularly since the "waves," unlike water or sound waves, have no medium of vibration. We shall not go into this matter any further, but limit ourselves to stating that a new branch of mathematical physics—wave mechanics—has been developed, in which the observed phenomena are properly described. That is all an objective student of nature can do when it comes to "explaining" nature.

Vibratory character of light; wave length and frequency

We must therefore imagine a light ray as a continuous flow of light particles or photons (Chapters 15 and 18), each of which must be considered as a concentrated portion of a "vibrating structure" extending along the light ray. The "light" is supposed to be everywhere along the ray; the vibrating structures and their concentrated centers, the "particles," are transported with the "velocity of light."

The vibrating aspect of light presents an interesting comparison with sound waves. Whereas light waves, like wave motion in water, are transverse, sound waves are longitudinal. Their transport is provided by periodic back-and-forth motions of the air particles along the direction of the beam of sound. The velocity of sound in air is about 330 meters per second. A tone of a certain pitch has a definite wave length, as exemplified by the varying sizes of organ pipes and the structure of musical instruments. Instead of describing the musical pitch of a sound by its wave length, we may speak instead of its frequency, i.e., the number of vibrations per second. This number is simply the velocity of the wave motion divided by the wave length. For example, the "international A" has a wave length of 75 centimeters and a frequency of 440 cycles per second. Obviously, then, the number of vibrations per second received by our ears determines the pitch of a note; and the quality of a note is determined by the detailed behavior of this vibration. The ear cannot dissect a disorganized mixture of sounds any better than the eye can dissect a mixture of light of all frequencies, but it may very well distinguish the separate, musically related parts of the complex, organized musical score of a symphony. Yet, while the ear can thus analyze a musical, discrete and changing pattern of sound, the unaided eye fails almost completely to analyze the equivalent phenomenon of mixed colors.

Fortunately, however, we have the instrument needed to solve the difficulty. By means of a glass prism, for example, the component colors of a mixture of light may be arranged according to their frequencies. Such an array, of which the rainbow pattern is an example, is called a spectrum. The appearance and properties of spectra will be studied in more detail in Chapter 15. For the moment it is sufficient to know that by means of certain physical experiments, the wave lengths or frequencies of the vibrations in the different colors can be accurately measured. The naturally human curiosity for definition and understanding of the medium through which these different light colors are created and transported with incredible velocity cannot be satisfied. The medium simply isn't there, but that does not stifle our mathematical imagination, which can accept and describe the observed phenomena. The extreme visible red light has a frequency or "pitch" of about 4×10^{14} vibrations per second; the frequency of the extreme violet light is twice this value. The corresponding values for the wave lengths are about .0008 millimeters and .0004 millimeters, or, in the conventional spectroscopic units, 8000 Å and 4000 Å. One Å or Ångstrom unit equals 10^{-8} centimeters.

While the ear is receptive to some eight to ten octaves of sound waves, the visible spectrum of light "tones" covers barely one "octave," i.e., a range confined between two vibrations whose frequencies are in a ratio of one to two. There are, however, many additional octaves on the radiation "keyboard" which are not visible; examples of higher frequency are the ultraviolet and X-rays, while the heat and radio waves represent radiations of lower frequency. There is no doubt that all these radiations are of the same kind and differ in degree only; different "receiving sets," however, are required to detect them. Thus we become aware of our limited "vision" of the physical world from the fact that only one octave of radiation is visible to us.

Doppler effect

There is a most important dependence of the frequency on the approach or recession of the light source. In the case of sound this effect, discernible as a rise or lowering in pitch, is well known. The whistle of a locomotive racing by manifests a drop as the velocity of approach abruptly changes to a velocity of recession. The explanation for this phenomenon lies in the fact that the number of vibrations received by the ear per second is increased or lowered. As a sound source approaches us, the vibrations come in at a higher rate than usual and this effect is recognized by the ear as an increase in pitch. Conversely, the rate of arrival of the vibrations of a receding source is reduced with a result intelligible to the ear as a lowering of pitch. The rate of the rise or drop in pitch depends on the velocity, and in terms of frequency it equals the ratio of the velocity of the source of sound to the velocity of sound. The latter is 330 meters per second in air; a change from a velocity of approach of 33 meters per second to a velocity of recession of 33 meters per second will reduce the observed frequency in the ratio 5 to 4. The result is a drop in pitch amounting to a major third (for example, E to C). In the case of a pattern of tones, or chord, the frequencies of all tones are reduced in the same ratio, which in musical terms means that the heard chord is transposed from one key to another, the amount depending on the velocity of approach or recession.

Light rays exhibit the analogous phenomenon commonly known as the Doppler effect, after its discoverer Christian Doppler (1803–1853). Imagine a source of light approaching us with a velocity of 300 kilometers per second. The arrival of the successive vibrations is speeded up in such a way that the number of light vibrations emitted in one second reaches us in 999/1000 of a second. Hence the vibrations received per second are raised in the ratio 1000/999 by the approach, and the observed frequency or "pitch" of any color in the spectrum is consequently raised in the ratio 1000/999. In case of a recession the opposite takes place. The change in frequency equals the ratio of the velocity of approach or recession to the velocity of light; the increased or lowered frequency corresponds to a very small general color shift, or transposition, toward the blue or red directions of any color pattern or spectrum.

Radial velocities

The Doppler effect enables us to measure that part of a motion which is in the line of sight; this component of a star's motion is called its radial velocity. In complete color arrays the effect would not be noticeable, except possibly in the case of tremendous velocities of approach or recession. It can be studied, however, with great accuracy for discrete color radiations whenever these stand revealed in the spectrum as a definite pattern, either as bright emission lines on a darker background or dark absorption lines in an otherwise continuous color array (Chapter 16). In practice, the small shifts in color are measured by photographing the moving source of light simultaneously with a comparison spectrum of terrestrial, i.e., "fixed" origin. The latter light source may be a spark of iron, or a discharge tube with glowing hydrogen and helium. In many cases a spectrographic study can in this way reveal velocities in the line of sight with a precision of better than one kilometer per second.

Again: the heliocentric viewpoint

Before going further, we should realize that the observed stellar displacements, both transverse and radial, are not quite as straightforward as we have assumed so far. While for a star of large proper motion there is a steady trend of displacement in a certain direction, there is also the aforementioned parallactic effect resulting from the star's finite distance and from the orbital motion of the Earth around the Sun. There appears to be a close correspondence between the sizes of the proper motion and the parallactic displacement; generally, large proper motions go together with large parallactic displacements, and vice versa. Reference to this was made in the preceding chapter when it was noted that as a rule the amount of the proper motion proved to be a good criterion for the size of the parallax, i.e., the degree of nearness of a star. For a study of proper motions pure and simple the parallactic effect need not be considered and we may exclude it from our considerations. This means that the center of description of planetary motions, the Sun, also proves to be the ideal vantage point from which to view stellar paths. We thus "reduce" our observations to the Sun, i.e., to the heliocentric viewpoint.

The parallactic effect is not limited to the position of the star on the celestial sphere, but is also revealed, of course, in periodic parallactic fluctuations in the radial velocity of the star. This quantity may also be "reduced" to the Sun, by making allowance for the orbital effect of the Earth and the radial velocity considered as if it were observed from the Sun, i.e., from the heliocentric viewpoint. Incidentally, accurate observations of this parallactic component of the radial velocities of stars have furnished accurate values for the Earth's orbital velocity, which in turn have yielded a very accurate determination for the size of the Earth's orbit, i.e., the length of the astronomical unit. It is of interest to compare this approach with the aberration method mentioned at the end of Chapter 7.

Space motions

When a star's distance is known, its proper motion can be expressed in astronomical units per year or in kilometers per second. The quantity thus obtained represents the transverse or tangential velocity at right angles to the line of sight. The other component of a star's space motion with respect to the

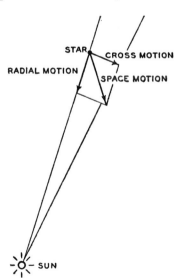

The space motion of a star.

Sun is its radial velocity. For example, Barnard's star has a tangential velocity of nearly 20 astronomical units per year, which may also be expressed as about 92 kilometers per second. Spectroscopic observations establish that Barnard's star has a motion of approach of 110 kilometers per second. The resultant of the cross motion and the radial velocity, computed as the hypotenuse of a right triangle, is about 143 kilometers per second—a comparatively high space velocity for a star. Barnard's star is one of the few stars for which a slow, gradual perspective change in the proper motion can be observed. The proper motion increases each year by "0013; in about ten thousand years the star will be nearest to us. At that time its distance will be slightly under four lightyears, and it will appear one magnitude brighter than it is now.

A great deal of interesting information on stellar motions has been acquired. We find stars that move slowly, others that move fast, the average speed being something like 30 kilometers per second. We find, too, that different stars move in different directions. Some of the general properties of stellar motions will be studied in Chapter 27; for the present we shall limit ourselves to establishing the basic facts of cosmic mechanics.

Again: relativity of motion

We repeat that the context of our observations involves the motions of the stars with respect to the Sun. There is no sense in discussing a possible state of "real" rest of the Sun, or of any other point. We have developed convenient and conventional notions of rest. The rotation and revolution of the Earth have already given us a certain perspective on the relativity of rest and motion. All we can observe is relative locations, relative paths of different bodies with respect to each other; the relativity of these observations alone is "real." Any concept of rest is simply an arbitrary notion, and we have now transferred it from our observation point on the Earth to the Sun. This new vantage point has been chosen for convenience and simplification in grasping the mechanics underlying planetary and stellar motions. Only toward the end of this book, in connection with problems of a higher space-time order, shall we consider still another change of viewpoint.

Law of inertia

One result of the study of stellar motions is outstanding in simplicity and importance. The space motions of the vast majority of stars as observed from the Sun take place in straight lines and with uniform speed. The validity of this statement depends, of course, on the margin of accuracy of the observations. However, it appears, tentatively at least, that stars obey the simplest form of motion imaginable.

The observed constancy in speed and direction of the motions of different stars is not dependent on any notion of rest or, in other words, on the relativity of motion. In our everyday experience we have an analogy in the case of two cars passing each other with different speeds, each constant in amount and direction. From either car, or from any "stationary" location in the landscape, the observed motions are nonaccelerated, i.e., exhibit no change in speed or direction. The law of stellar motions implies, therefore, the virtual absence of any observable acceleration between Sun and stars. This property of stellar motions is the equivalent of the law of inertia first inferred from terrestrial experiments. This law, already recognized by Galileo and later formulated by Newton, may be expressed as follows: a body which is sufficiently far away from other bodies undergoes no acceleration.

This important universal law of motion is beautifully exhibited by the stars. Its illustration in terrestrial experiments is always complicated by the disturbing effects of friction and of gravity, i.e., by the Earth. A smooth billiard ball rolling on a smooth horizontal table provides about the best synthetic experiment for demonstrating the law of inertia. However, proper support against gravity must be provided, while friction can be only partly eliminated. In the stellar world the qualifying condition—sufficiently far away from other bodies—generally seems to be sufficiently satisfied to permit the operation of the law of inertia for a free body, unsupported and obviously not subject to any measurable friction. We thus witness in the stars the cosmic equivalent of billiard balls rolling along in frictionless space and time, each with a uniform speed in a constant direction.

There are other qualifying conditions for the law of inertia, namely, a reasonably limited interval of time and an appropriate choice of background. As a rule these conditions are satisfied in astronomical observations and we need not consider them any further at this time.

Our view of the universe is severely handicapped by our location. We live at the bottom of our atmosphere, which dims the light messages from the cosmos; moreover, any motion in our immediate experience is strongly affected by the gravitational prison which confines us to the surface of the Earth. Biologically, both atmosphere and gravity are necessities; but they do complicate and interfere with our understanding of the inanimate world of astronomy.

10 | THE MECHANICS OF DOUBLE STARS

To THE naked eye all stars appear single except for a few isolated cases in which, with some effort, two stars seem to be so close together that the observer wonders whether they are physically connected. With the application of the telescope, numerous stars, single to the naked eye, resolve into two or sometimes more component stars. We know now that at least one out of every three stars is in reality a double star. Also, hundreds of stars, or more, frequently appear grouped together in relatively small portions of space, in the form of star clusters (Chapters 25 and 26). The property of gregariousness among stars is widespread. At this point we note that the companionable character of our own star, the Sun, is conspicuous in its family of planetary and other dependents.

Double stars

In this chapter we will restrict ourselves to the most common examples of gregariousness, the double stars. Tens of thousands of double stars have been catalogued and are studied by various observational means. Observations of the closer systems are made visually with a large telescope; the relative location of the components of the double star is measured by means of a filar micrometer. This is an attachment to the eye-end of the telescope, containing both fixed and movable spider threads mounted in the focal plane. A simultaneous bisection of both components of the double star by the threads is accomplished by means of a micrometer screw, which thus permits a measurement of the separation of the two stars. The photographic method is unsurpassed for giving accurate information about the relative locations of the components of the more widely separated pairs. The two components of a double-star system generally differ in brightness; but for the moment we are interested only in the locations of the stars. In other words, we can regard the stars as points.

The true physical double star or binary consists of two component stars which are packed into a close unit, very compact compared with the average spacing between these units. There are cases, however, in which two stars are seen in nearly the same direction, while actually they may be at different depths of space. In such a case we are dealing merely with an optical illusion, specifically, an optical double, which is of little interest.

Orbital motion of double stars

After the passage of sufficient time it is always found that the two components of a binary describe a curved path or orbit around each other, of the same general nature as, say, the motion of the Moon around the Earth. This fact was first established in 1803 by William Herschel (1738–1822), and the discovery had far-reaching consequences. The orbital motion always appears to be of a cyclic or periodic character, and for many objects several revolutions have already been observed. As the two component stars move around each other, they also participate in a joint motion which is revealed when they are viewed on a background of distant fixed stars. For an analogy imagine two birds circling around each other but at the same time being carried along by the wind or by some common intention. Both motions can be distinguished if we observe the birds against a distant landscape.

Inertial point

Between the two components of a binary star there is always a point around which the two stars seem to hover in their paths. For reasons which will become clear in a moment, this point may be called the inertial point. Although there may be an appreciable variation in the separation between the two components as time goes by, the distances of the two stars to the inertial point preserve a fixed ratio; generally, the brighter star of the pair stays closer to the inertial point than does the fainter component. In a way, the inertial point may be considered the balancing point of an imaginary lever, with one star at each end. This imaginary lever, pivoting about the inertial point, may vary in length, but the distance ratio of the two portions of the lever on opposite sides of the inertial point remains the same. At the same time the inertial point is found to move in a straight line with uniform speed. In the preceding chapter we noted this law of inertia for stars; and at the time we tacitly referred to single stars. Now we see that the inertial point of the compact binary stars has this same property.

That the two components, conventionally distinguished as primary and companion, maintain a constant distance ratio to the inertial point implies that they have similar orbital motions. Their orbits have the same shape, but differ in size; they are 180°

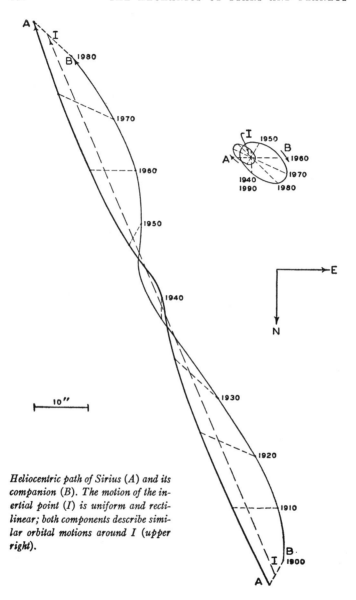

Heliocentric path of Sirius (A) and its companion (B). The motion of the inertial point (I) is uniform and rectilinear; both components describe similar orbital motions around I (upper right).

out of phase with each other, which implies that at any time the two stars are on opposite sides of the inertial point. It is not difficult to see that the motion of the companion, when referred to the primary, describes an orbit similar to the latter's. The

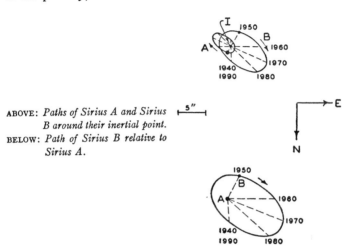

ABOVE: *Paths of Sirius A and Sirius B around their inertial point.*
BELOW: *Path of Sirius B relative to Sirius A.*

scale of this so-called relative orbit equals the sum of the scales of the separate absolute orbits of primary and companion, since at any time, obviously, the total separation of the components equals the sum of their distances from the inertial point.

Parallactic effect

Apart from the binary's orbital motion, there is also, of course, a parallactic shift due to the Earth's revolution around the Sun. We have an analogy in the case of our distant birds as seen from a revolving merry-go-round. The motion of the merry-go-round does not affect the motion of one bird with respect to the other, but it affects the motions of the birds as we see them against a background of trees or mountains. Similarly the parallactic effect of a binary is visible if we choose to project the motion on a background of distant stars. Frequently observations are deliberately arranged in this way in order to determine the distance of the binary as well as the location of the inertial point. However, the relative path of the two components is not affected by any motion of the observer; hence a study of this path is of particular significance.

Character of orbital motion

The continual veering of the double-star components around each other points to some influence which prevents the two bodies from eventually separating. It is as if the two components had first been placed in close proximity and each endowed with some slight motion; according to the law of inertia (Chapter 9) they should now pursue independent paths each with uniform velocity and direction, entailing a gradual separation of the two stars. However, nature does not operate this way; some property prevents the two bodies from ever getting very far apart. What is the nature of this property? We may not be able to fathom its "real" quality, but we can observe what happens and are rewarded with some interesting information. The fact that there is a turning or veering motion of the stars about each other implies a continuous change in both direction and speed. This is expressed in other words by stating that the orbital motion is subject to acceleration.

Acceleration is defined as an instantaneous rate of change of speed. The idea of acceleration (see Chapter 6) is familiar from daily experience. An automobile may be accelerated by increasing the action of the engine. Thus the speed may be increased while the direction of motion is kept the same. By additional action the driver at the steering wheel may also change the direction of motion. This happens, for example, when the road is curved; the continued action of the driver results in a continued veering of the car's motion toward the inside of the curve. Such a continued change of motion may be described as a continued acceleration toward the inside of the curve. This is illustrated by the fact that the driver is continually being pulled in the opposite direction, since he is not rigidly a part of the car and is simply obeying the law of inertia.

Veering motion implies acceleration

The same situation holds for any case of curved motion. A continually veering motion involves continued acceleration directed inward at an angle with the instantaneous direction of motion. In the particular case of a uniform circular motion, the inward acceleration takes place at the same rate throughout, but is pointed at all times to the center of the circle. The cause of the acceleration is another question, but the fact remains that the acceleration must be continual for any continually veering motion, since in its absence the motion would change neither in amount nor in direction. In the case of an automobile, the cause of the acceleration can be traced to the combined efforts of driver, engine and steering wheel. In the case of veering motion observed in the universe, the real cause of the acceleration may not be clear at first, nor may it ever become clear. But the acceleration is none the less very real and must be accepted as an important revelation of nature which we must try to describe accurately and relate to other phenomena. It is as if there exists a continual pull, as might be caused, for example, by an invisible elastic string. The inescapable, inexorable, continual character of the acceleration to which the double-star components appear to be subject is very impressive.

When speaking of curved motions we ordinarily assume that the resulting curved path is flat, i.e., in one plane. Although general considerations are not restricted to such a special occurrence, it is virtually true that in our studies of stellar motions any one path can ordinarily be considered as flat; this assumption simplifies our problems very much. The same situation exists with a high degree of approximation for the various orbital motions in the solar system (Chapter 11).

The apparent orbital paths are ellipses

The orbital characteristics of the so-called visual double stars have been studied for well over a century. Of the many observers of binaries, we mention here Robert Grant Aitken (1864–1951), who discovered about 3000 double stars with the large refractor of the Lick Observatory between 1895 and 1935. Particularly high accuracy has been reached during the past thirty years through the long-focus photographic observations started in 1914 by Ejnar Hertzsprung (1873–   ).

With minor qualifications, the orbital motion of the components of a double star each about the other always appears as an ellipse. An ellipse is a flat symmetrical oval curve; on the longest or major axis of the ellipse are two so-called focal points placed symmetrically on each side of the center. The shape and size of an ellipse are fixed in such a way that the sum of the distances from any point (P) to the two focal points (F and F′)

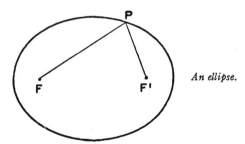

An ellipse.

has a constant value. The eccentricity of the ellipse is defined as the ratio of the distance center-focus to half the major axis.

Spectroscopic binaries

What we see is the motion projected on the background of the sky; however, by means of the Doppler effect (Chapter 9), the motion in the to-and-fro direction can also be studied. We recall that the component of a star's velocity in the line of sight may be determined from the observed Doppler shift in the star's spectrum. The spectra of numerous stars have been found to make minute periodic shifts along the "keyboard" of colors, thereby indicating periodic changes in the radial velocity. Frequently photographed spectra are found to consist of two superimposed spectra which have periodic motions in opposite directions. All these observations disclose the presence of double stars in which the component stars are so close together that direct telescopic observation fails to separate them; their very proximity, however, implies that they have short periods and high orbital velocities, which the spectroscopic method is peculiarly well fitted to reveal. The examination of these important spectroscopic binaries is a welcome and natural supplement to the study of the visual binaries. The latter, of course, can in any case be studied spectroscopically; these studies yield additional information about the double-star orbit, such as which part of the orbit is nearest and which is farthest from us.

The true orbital paths are ellipses

The plane of the relative orbit of the components of a double star may be oriented at any angle. With appropriate geometric and algebraic aids the orientation of the plane of orbital motion can be determined and the true character of the orbital motion unraveled. In this way it is found that the true, untilted path is also elliptical. In other words, if we study the mutual path of the two components in their plane of motion, we will again find that it is always an ellipse. Moreover, the true orbital motion of the two stars takes place in such a fashion that the

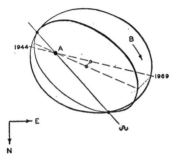

Relation between apparent (foreshortened) and true (unforeshortened) orbits of Sirius B around Sirius A, obtained by tilting the apparent orbit about the line AΩ.

primary is placed in the focus of the companion's orbital motion about it. Recalling the similarity of the orbits concerned, we find also that the orbits of primary and companion about the inertial point are ellipses, with the inertial point in the focus.

Law of areas

Of further significance is the variation in speed throughout the orbit. It is found that the sweep of motion depends on the separation of the two components. By sweep we refer to the angle through which the "hand" joining the two stars turns during a given time. This angular sweep is greater when the stars are moving toward close approach and is smaller when they draw apart. The rate of sweep varies with the inverse of the square of the momentary distance; if, for example, at closest approach (periastron) the stars are three times as near each other as at greatest separation (apastron), the angular sweep at periastron is found to be nine times as large as at apastron. This striking effect can also be very precisely expressed by stating that the line joining the two stars "sweeps over" equal areas of the ellipse in equal times. This revelation of nature is therefore commonly referred to as the law of areas. In the next chapter

The true orbits of Sirius A and Sirius B are ellipses. If Sirius A is considered fixed, it is at the focus of the orbit of the companion B. The orbital motion follows the law of areas.

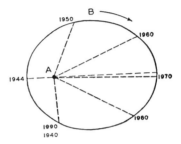

we shall see that for several centuries the planetary orbits have been known to possess the same properties; this knowledge played a role in anticipating the analogous properties in binary stars.

Mutual acceleration

The law of areas and the law of ellipses permit further inquiry into the nature of orbital motion. Geometrical considerations show that the law of areas involves a continual acceleration along the line joining the two stars. Nature reveals, therefore, a mutual attraction between the two stars, which is accurately described as a continuous acceleration toward their inertial point and hence toward each other.

Analogy with falling

The veering motion of double-star components around each other thus indicates a continuous attraction between the two bodies. As we did in Chapter 6, we may call this attraction "falling," using the word as a generalization of the terrestrial falling motion encountered in daily experience. Either falling motion is accelerated; i.e., it is a motion subject to a continuous change in speed. For the conventional vertical falling motion acceleration is virtually constant, i.e., the velocity of falling increases uniformly with time. The same is true in the case of a body thrown with an initial velocity; although the amount and direction of motion vary, the body "falls" at the same rate as before. In the case of the generalized cosmic falling revealed in double stars, a continuous change takes place in both the amount and direction of speed, resulting in a maintenance of "spin" or orbital motion. We may say that the two bodies fall "around" each other. Were it not for this falling, the inherent motion of the two components would eventually lead to their separation; a "double" star would be nothing but an optical illusion caused by the temporary close approach of two stars.

Inverse-square law

The fact that the orbit has an elliptical shape implies that the mutual acceleration (q) varies proportionally with the inverse square of the distance (r). In formula, this reads $q(:) 1/r^2$. For example, if two stars were placed sufficiently close to each other they would start moving toward each other; the falling acceleration would increase with the inverse square of the distance at any specific moment. After a while the two stars would collide; our double star would have been short-lived. As mentioned before, nature has avoided or eliminated such trivial experiments; the observed double stars have sufficient spin around each other to maintain a continued mutual orbital motion of indefinite duration.

For double stars we have thus found an important property of motion, namely, the inverse-square "falling" law. The question arises whether still further insight can be gained. We have already noticed that single stars spaced far enough apart do not at first sight appear to "fall" toward each other; the falling attraction obviously becomes conspicuous when two stars are comparatively close. Is it possible to put the inverse-square behavior on a more comprehensive basis, so that we may compare the orbital characteristics of different binaries? And what is the significance of the inertial point? These questions are best answered by studying a unique cosmic mechanism, perhaps not unique per se, but certainly unique because it is so near at hand. This mechanism is, of course, the solar system, in which, in a certain sense, each planet is the companion of a binary whose primary component is the Sun. In double stars the motion of each primary component can be studied only in relation to its one secondary component; no possibility exists, generally, of finding out how the same primary would react if another secondary component were substituted. In the solar system, however, this possibility does exist, since the same primary—the Sun—has several secondary components—the planets.

11 | KEPLER'S LAWS OF PLANETARY MOTION

Kepler's laws of planetary motion

As already mentioned, planetary motions are restricted to a rather thin layer of space, and hence do not permit a bird's-eye view. The fact that we are situated on one of the moving planets prevents us from grasping the actual state of planetary motions at a glance. The case is very different for double stars; we do obtain a bird's-eye view of hundreds of these objects, mostly because of the very distances which separate us from these systems. Moreover, the situation is simple if we limit ourselves to a study of the mutual orbit of the two components of a binary; the effect of parallax does not enter the picture, since it is the same for both components.

Our knowledge of the state of motion of the planets was obtained by a slow surveying process. By carefully noting the directions of the planets at different times, astronomers plotted the locations of the different planets relative to each other, to the Earth and to the Sun at different epochs. When sufficient data had been accumulated in this way, the pattern of motion gradually became apparent. In principle, the problem is not too difficult; in practice, patience and accurate observations were needed to permit an improvement in our knowledge beyond the Copernican assumption that the motions of the celestial objects are circular.

A long time elapsed before the character of planetary motion was accurately and completely described. During the second half of the sixteenth century the observations of Tycho Brahe furnished the material from which Kepler derived the accurate space-time description of the planetary orbits contained in his three laws. (The first two were published in 1609, the third in 1619.)

1. The orbit of each planet is an ellipse with the Sun at the focus.

2. The line joining planet and Sun sweeps over equal areas in equal intervals of time.

3. The ratio of the cube of the mean distance from the Sun to the square of the period is the same for all planets.

Kepler's three laws contain a clear and complete statement of the actual state of motion of the planets. Nothing is missing in these three laws and nothing need be subtracted. We must not forget that Kepler's laws were derived after an exhaustive analysis of material obtained without telescopes; none of the early instruments used for measuring directions to objects was equipped with lenses. Kepler was unaware of the existence of double stars; and, as a matter of fact, their elliptical state of motion was unknown until the nineteenth century. The unraveling of the observations and the recognition of the surveyed oval orbits of the planets as ellipses ranks as one of the greatest discoveries ever made. The significance of Kepler's laws cannot be overestimated; they are the clue to the universal law of gravitation.

Kepler's first two laws

The orbital characteristics of double stars discussed in the previous chapter are identical with the orbital characteristics of planetary motions first described in Kepler's two initial laws. We recall that the elliptical shape of the orbits and the law of areas imply an attraction whose momentary rate varies with the inverse square of the distance. That there is this mutual attraction between the components of double stars proves that the attraction exists beyond the confines of the planetary system, in which the falling of the planets around the Sun has been known for over three centuries.

Kepler's third law

The orbital properties described in Kepler's first two laws— elliptical motion around the focus, subject to the law of areas— are referred to as Keplerian motion. A further law may be deduced from the planetary motions, linking the space-and-time dimensions of the planetary orbits. Kepler expended a tremendous amount of work and effort on the derivation of his famous third law, the essence of which is contained in Table II.

In this table the unit of distance is the astronomical unit (A.U.), which amounts to 149,700,000 kilometers (Chapter 7). The mean distance in an elliptical orbit is defined as the average between the extreme distances; i.e., it is half the major axis of the ellipse. The points of smallest and greatest distance from the Sun are referred to as perihelion and aphelion; the eccentricity of the Earth's orbit is very small, amounting to only 1/60. It should be realized that the last three planets in this table were unknown to Kepler; Uranus was not discovered till

TABLE II.   *Orbital Data for the Planets*

PLANET	MEAN DISTANCE TO SUN IN A.U.	PERIOD IN YEARS	MEAN ORBITAL VELOCITY IN KM/SEC	ECCENTRICITY
Mercury	0.387	0.24	47.90	0.206
Venus	0.723	0.62	35.05	.007
Earth	1.000	1.00	29.80	.017
Mars	1.524	1.88	24.14	.093
Jupiter	5.203	11.86	13.06	.048
Saturn	9.539	29.46	9.65	.056
Uranus	19.191	84.01	6.80	.047
Neptune	30.071	164.78	5.43	.009
Pluto	39.518	248.42	4.74	.249

1781, Neptune was found in 1846 and Pluto in 1930 (Chapter 14). Nor were the orbital data as accurately known in Kepler's day as they are now.

A comparison of the mean distance of each planet to the Sun with their respective periods of revolution shows the obvious fact that the period increases with the distance. Kepler deduced from the data available to him that this relation can be put in a remarkably simple form, namely, that the squares of the periods of revolution vary proportionally with the cubes of the distances to the Sun. The reader may check this from the data in Table II; it is very easily done for the planets nearest and farthest away from the Sun, Mercury and Pluto. Here the distance ratio is about 100, the ratio of the periods about 1000; obviously $100 \times 100 \times 100 = 1000 \times 1000$.

Any law based on such simple powers is worth treasuring, and it is no wonder that Kepler was so elated with the discovery of this simple relation that he referred to it as the harmonic law. This law reveals the harmony of celestial motion, as further study will show. Technically speaking, it provides the link between different binary systems, if we consider each planet to form a binary, with the Sun as the principal component.

Significance of Kepler's third law

The significance of Kepler's laws was fully understood and analyzed by Newton. As in the case of binaries (Chapter 10), a planet is held in its curved orbit because its instantaneous motion is kept veering inward through the continuous attraction between itself and the Sun. The fact that the curved motion is an ellipse rather than some other oval curve implies that the rate of the falling acceleration varies with the inverse of the square, $1/r^2$, of the momentary distance between planet and Sun. Kepler's third law enabled Newton to obtain a deeper insight into the character of the attraction between celestial objects. We cannot discuss Newton's analysis for the general case of elliptic orbits, since advanced mathematics would be required. Because of the importance of this matter we shall, however, give the deduction based on the assumption that the planetary orbits are circular. Compared with the average double star, the orbits of the planets generally have low eccentricities and the simplified procedure corresponds therefore very closely to the actual state of affairs.

Alternate form of Kepler's third law for circular orbits

The analysis of circular orbits is more easily understood if we rewrite the harmonic law. In the case of circular motion the orbital speed V of any one planet is constant; it is proportional to the radius a of the orbit and inversely proportional to the period of revolution P. Speed is defined as the rate at which distance is covered in a definite unit of time, for example, the second. Since $V(:)\,a/P$ we see that $V^2(:)\,a^2/P^2$, and since Kepler's third law states that a^3/P^2 is constant for all orbits, it follows that $V^2(:)\,1/a$. In other words, the alternate form of Kepler's third law for circular orbits states that the square of the orbital velocity of different planets varies with the inverse of the radius of their orbits.

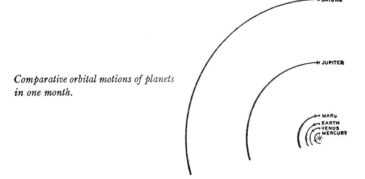

Comparative orbital motions of planets in one month.

In Table II the (average) orbital speeds of the different planets are given. A simple calculation confirms the alternative form of the harmonic law, which holds fairly accurately even though the orbits are not quite circular. The existence of the relation is again easily illustrated by comparing the extreme orbits of Mercury and Pluto. The ratio of the sizes of the two orbits is very close to 100, while the corresponding ratio for the orbital speeds is very close to $1/10$; obviously $(1/10)^2 = 1/100$.

This relation $V^2(:)\,1/a$ enables us to describe simply the mechanism of planetary motions, if such a crude expression may be used in reference to the planetary paths. We notice that the curvature of the larger orbits is gentler than that of the smaller ones. In other words, for an equal distance traveled along the orbit, the veering effect or deflection decreases with the size of the orbit.

Central acceleration in a circular orbit

In the case of a uniform circular motion the amount of the velocity is constant, but its direction is changing all the time. The motion is subject to a continuous change or acceleration pointed to the center of the circular motion; its rate varies with the square of the velocity and with the reciprocal of the orbital radius, i.e., is proportional to V^2/a. This relation may be derived by considering the circular motion as built up of a succession of constant forward motions which are being bent at every instant by an acceleration perpendicular to the forward motion. One can look at it this way: In t seconds, the forward motion carries the planet over a straight path of length Vt. After t seconds, the planet is deflected toward the Sun by an accelerated motion amounting to $1/2\ qt^2$, where q is the rate of acceleration. If t gets smaller and smaller, the two successive operations gradually merge; geometrical considerations show that q must equal V^2/a if t is infinitely small.

Interpretation of Kepler's third law; general inverse-square law

For a uniform circular motion, therefore, the central acceleration depends on the value of V^2/a. Thus, in the case of the circular orbits of the planets, the central acceleration q for different planets varies with the square V^2 of its velocity and the inverse $1/a$ of the radius of its orbit. At any time these accelerations are directed toward the Sun.

The actual amount of these accelerations is revealed by Kepler's third law; for the case of circular orbits the squares V^2 of the velocities of different planets vary with the inverse values $1/a$ of their orbital radii. Hence, the quantity V^2/a, i.e., the central acceleration, varies with the inverse square $1/a^2$ of the orbital radius.

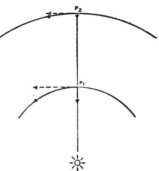

Central acceleration of two objects P_1 and P_2, whose distances from the Sun are in the ratio 1 to 2. The corresponding ratio of the velocities is 1 to $1/\sqrt{2}$, that of the central accelerations is 1 to 1/4.

An analysis of elliptical orbits would have yielded the complete finding that the instantaneous rate of falling motion for any planet at any time is solely determined by the inverse of the square of the instantaneous distance r of the planet to the Sun. The inverse-square property was first found to hold within any one elliptical orbit; it is now seen to have a much wider significance. The simple, important, overwhelming fact has been found that throughout the planetary system the orbital paths are maintained through a continued attraction or acceleration directed to the Sun and depending only on the inverse square $1/r^2$ of the distance. The Sun seems to be the source of this acceleration, the amount of which is "diluted" with increasing distance, just as the intensity of illumination from a source of light is "diluted" with increasing distance.

Mutual character of the inverse-square law

Kepler's laws of planetary motions were formulated with the Sun as the center of description. This formulation facilitated the discovery of the acceleration directed toward the Sun. It looks, therefore, as if the Sun were responsible for this general state of attraction. If, however, we abandon the "as if," the make-believe description, and actually ascribe the attraction to the real physical Sun and not to its mathematical center, a new point of view emerges. Physically, Sun and planets are both matter; there is probably no basic difference in the materials from which these objects are built. Fundamentally there need be no difference in kind between Sun and planets, although there are differences in degree, i.e., in size, in bulk and other descriptive, superficial properties.

We have been one-sided in our approach due to the huge discrepancy in the sizes of the objects under consideration, the Sun being obviously so predominant. The Sun is held responsible for the attraction which keeps the planets in their orbits; it is reasonable to inquire whether the planets are centers of attraction also, perhaps on a smaller scale. We recall that both components of double stars fall toward their inertial point; we suggest now that this also happens in the solar system.

That the falling acceleration implies a mutual attraction leads to the final step in the analysis of the third law of Kepler. There are slight deviations from this law, which could not be recognized by Kepler, but which were established by later, more accurate observations. The essence of these deviations may be illustrated as follows. The orbital speed and hence the falling acceleration toward the Sun of a huge planet like Jupiter, for example, prove on the average to be slightly larger than would be expected from Kepler's third law. The small deviation in the harmonic law in the case of a planet like Jupiter can be attributed to the fact that not only is Jupiter attracted toward the Sun, but the Sun undergoes a small acceleration in the direction of Jupiter. The acceleration is therefore slightly increased and the two bodies fall toward each other at a slightly greater rate than would obtain if one of them, in this case the Sun, were not affected by the other. Obviously there must also be minute mutual accelerations between the different planets; these, however, are very small indeed and for the present need not detain us.

Concept of mass

The inverse-square law of cosmic attraction thus needs further elaboration. The increase in the attraction between two bodies is formally recognized in the assumption that the mutual acceleration is proportional to the sum of certain physical properties of these two bodies. The material property now introduced is called mass; it is assumed to remain constant both in space and in time. The notion of mass will be considered in more detail in the next chapter; tentatively it may be visualized as weight. The inertial point of two bodies may now be called the center of mass; its location between the two objects is such that the ratio of the masses appears as the inverse of the aforementioned constant distance ratio of the two components referred to their inertial point. The mass ratios of the Sun-planet binaries are obviously very high; the center of mass is close to the center of the Sun. It will be shown in Chapter 13 that the lowest ratio of masses is 1047 for the Sun-Jupiter pair; the ratio of the Sun-Earth system amounts to 334,000.

The mutual attraction between two objects exists, therefore, in the form of a mutual acceleration which is the combined effect, i.e., the sum of the accelerations, of the two individual objects. One may visualize this as a "sliding-toward" one another along the space line joining the objects, the space line

Center of Mass.

being pivoted on the center of mass. Referred to their inertial point or center of mass, the rates of falling of two bodies are inversely proportional to their masses.

Newton's law of gravitation

Hence the complete form of the law of cosmic falling, operating between two sufficiently close stars (or Sun and planet), may be stated as follows:

> The mutual acceleration between two objects is inversely proportional to the square of their separation and directly proportional to the sum of their masses.

In formula, $q = G(M + m)/r^2$. Here the acceleration q, the masses M and m and the separation r are expressed in appropriate units, for example the units of the so-called c.g.s. system in which the unit of distance is one centimeter, the unit of time one second and the unit of mass one gram. The latter unit will be defined in the next chapter. The factor of proportionality G is called the constant of gravitation. Its value, i.e., the rate of mutual acceleration, will also be discussed in the next chapter.

This law was first stated by Newton, who postulated it as a universal law of gravitation so conspicuously illustrated in pairs of stars close together due to the inverse-square relation. The general statement is assumed to hold for pointlike particles without any extension. In reality, any object possessing mass possesses size also. The complication thus introduced can always be overcome by appropriate mathematical procedure. So far as the astronomical use of the law is concerned, matters are generally simplified by the huge distances separating the objects. This means that with a high degree of approximation the celestial objects—stars, planets, etc.—may be considered as dimensionless points, in comparison with the separations between the different bodies.

In the next chapter we shall study the equivalence of Newton's law with the phenomenon of conventional falling or gravity, so well known in common experience. This will also permit us to obtain better insight into the notion of mass.

12 NEWTON'S LAW OF GRAVITATION

Gravity

We shall now extend our study of motion from celestial objects to terrestrial bodies. Historically the beginning of the latter studies preceded the development of cosmic mechanics. The motions of stars and planets in the great open astronomical spaces and times find their nearest terrestrial analogy in the motions of falling or thrown objects; it is said that Newton realized the similarity of the two phenomena when he contemplated a falling apple.

The characteristic property of the "free" path of a falling or thrown object is its veering-downward, i.e., toward the Earth. Except in the case of fluffy objects, atmospheric resistance is of no great concern and may be ignored in our considerations. No matter whether the object is simply released or deliberately thrown into space, in every case its path may be described as part of a huge curved orbit, only a minute fraction of which can materialize before the object hits the Earth "below." Limited to this brief path of freedom, the motion is analogous to what we observed as the veering, falling motion of the components of a double star, the orbital motion of the Earth around the Sun, and of the Moon around the Earth.

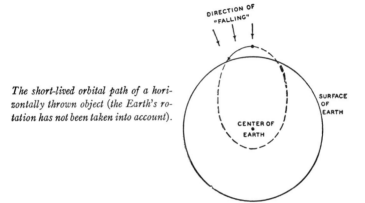

The short-lived orbital path of a horizontally thrown object (the Earth's rotation has not been taken into account).

A thrown free object may be considered as the smaller, very minute companion of a binary in which the Earth is the primary component. There is a great difference, however, between cosmic binaries and the "apple"-Earth binary. The extended size of the Earth and the minuteness of the initial throw of the apple prevent a continuance and eventual completion of the orbit of this "binary" system. A slight extension could be artificially brought about by initiating the path from a high elevation, or projecting it into a deep canyon. It is better, however, to exercise one's imagination by shrinking the Earth to a small core; then the orbital paths of falling objects can be extended and completed.

Are gravity and gravitation the same?

Let us see whether the terrestrial falling motion may be considered another illustration of the cosmic law of gravitational

motion established from the stars and planets and represented
by the formula $q = G(M + m)/r^2$ derived in the last chapter.

The minute fraction of the orbit that materializes can indeed
be considered a geometrical part of an ellipse, with the Earth's
center at one focus; so far, therefore, the similarity with cosmic
binaries is satisfied. The analogy would be complete if we could
establish that the falling acceleration is proportional to the
inverse square of the distance between the apple and the Earth,
and commensurable with the sum of their masses. Now we note
the discrepancy of the components in the present problem;
while the falling object, the "apple," may be small, the Earth
is very large. Moreover, what do we mean in this case by the
distance of the apple to the Earth? Mathematical analysis
shows that for a body of essentially spherical symmetry such as
the Earth the overall effect of attraction, as embodied in the
inverse-square law, would function as if the bulk of the whole
Earth were shrunk into its center.

*Any object falls toward the Earth as if
the mass of the entire Earth were concentrated in the Earth's center.*

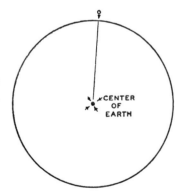

This immediately leads to an important conclusion. Since
the Earth is approximately a sphere, and a very large one, the
distance to the center of the Earth of any falling body anywhere

on Earth is about the same, slightly less than 6400 kilometers. Hence, the rate of the falling motion depends only on the sum of the masses of the Earth and the falling object. Galileo first demonstrated that the rate of falling motion of all bodies is the same. If falling, therefore, is a manifestation of the universal law of gravitation, it follows that the sum of the masses of any falling body and the Earth is virtually the same in all cases.

Notion of mass

We inquire further into the nature of the mass of objects. If the conventional falling motion between Newton's apple and the Earth is really of the same nature as the cosmic gravitational acceleration between stars and planets, then should it not operate between any two terrestrial bodies also? Obviously such mutual attraction cannot well be studied by simply releasing two objects in space; in a short time both would fall "on" the Earth and the experiment would be abruptly ended. It is impossible to dispose of the Earth, but we may eliminate the Earth's attraction by suspending the two objects, by thin strings, for example. If the two objects are thus placed in the same horizontal plane their natural free motion in the vertical falling direction is prevented; however, any mutual "falling-toward" each other in the horizontal direction can proceed and may be studied.

Experiments of this sort are of a difficult and delicate nature; they have nevertheless been made and have demonstrated the existence of gravitation between terrestrial objects, though the amount is very minute. Moreover, the experiments have furnished the rate of gravitational attraction; about the latter more will be said later. At this stage we note merely that, as in the case of gravitation between stars, or between stars and planets, the inverse-square character of the law of gravitation has been confirmed in the laboratory. The gravitational attraction is found to vary with the size and composition of the experimental binary components. This can be formulated in the following remarkable way: The intensity of gravitational attraction varies with what we conventionally refer to as the combined weight of two objects.

Equivalence of gravitation and gravity, of mass and weight

There are differences in degree, but not in kind, therefore, between the mutual gravitational "falling" of stars, and the terrestrial falling of objects so conspicuously toward the Earth and also to a minute degree toward each other. We conclude that all objects exhibit the law of universal motion on different scales depending on the space, time and mass relations involved. The terrestrial experiments mentioned above now aid us in visualizing the notion of mass introduced in the preceding chapter. The combined weight of the above-mentioned experimental binaries appears to represent the combined mass contained in Newton's law of gravitation. Thus weight proves to be a measure of mass.

The mass of an object falling toward the Earth is revealed as weight, i.e., its push or pull effect on man's muscle or man-made apparatus. An example of the latter is the spring balance, by which the weight of an object is measured through the extension of the spring. Weight and mass, though related, should not be confused. Mass is the fundamental notion suggested by the interaction of bodies in nature; weight is simply the tangible, local revelation of mass in the Earth's gravitational field. Any local changes in the latter are therefore reflected in the weight of an object as measured by a spring balance. The weight of an object on another planet would be entirely different from its weight on the Earth, since weight depends on the local gravitational acceleration. Mass does not vary with location, nor does any equality of masses, ascertained, for example, by a scale balance. If two masses of material are balanced on a pair of scales because they are of equal "weight," then they will be found to balance anywhere in the universe.

The mass of an object is assumed, however, to be an intrinsic property, determined by the actual number of elemental particles. We recall that all matter may be considered to be built up of protons, neutrons and electrons. The mass of all matter is provided essentially by protons and neutrons, which have practically the same mass of 1.66×10^{-24} grams. The electrons have the extremely small mass of 9×10^{-28} grams. The mass of any object is virtually determined by the total number of protons and neutrons in the architecture of the object.

Unit of mass

The conventional physical unit of mass is the gram; it is defined as the quantity of matter contained in a "cube" of water one centimeter on the side. (An additional specifying condition is a temperature of 4° centigrade above the freezing point.) The mass, or "quantity of matter" (really: quantity of protons, neutrons and electrons) in any other object can now be expressed in grams by appropriate measurements. A practical method of comparing the masses of different terrestrial objects is that of comparing their weights; these vary as the mass, since they are simply the tangible revelation of the so-called force of the mutual gravitation of Earth and object.

Constant of gravitation

How the quantitative rate of gravitation has been obtained in the aforementioned delicate laboratory experiments may be illustrated as follows: Suppose we place two metal spheres with a combined mass of one gram so that their centers are one centimeter apart. If the two spheres are equally large and made of, say, gold, each has to be about 0.37 centimeters in diameter. The spheres are now suspended to protect them appropriately against the Earth's attraction, and their centers are one centimeter apart; as mentioned before, the gravitational action between the spheres acts *as if* the respective masses or quantities of matter were shrunk into their respective centers. Measurements should now reveal a gravitational acceleration between the two spheres amounting to 6.67×10^{-8} cm/sec^2; i.e., the velocity of approach increases by this amount every second. This small quantity defines the constant of gravitation in the formula $q = G(M + m)/r^2$. It is a fundamental constant of nature, expressing the scale or rate at which gravitation operates in the universe; its value is assumed to be universally valid. We repeat: the mutual acceleration between two particles of combined mass one, placed one centimeter apart, amounts to 6.67×10^{-8} cm/sec^2; for any other combined mass and separation of the two particles, the corresponding value of the mutual acceleration is found by the substitution of the appropriate values of $M + m$ and of r in the formula.

Why all terrestrial objects fall equally fast

Now we understand why all terrestrial bodies fall with equal rapidity. The law of gravitation implies that the mutual falling effect of any pair of objects is proportional to the sum of their masses. In the previous chapter, which introduced the notion of mass, we noted the high value of the mass of the Sun compared with that of the planets. Since the latter are so much smaller than the Sun, it would seem that mass has something to do with size. That it is not a matter of size only is obvious from the fact that different objects have different specific densities. This means simply that the spacing or packing of the fundamental building stones is different for different materials. As we shall see in Chapters 17 and 20, a wide range in packing is possible. Nevertheless, as a conventional rule there is a general relation between size and mass, in the sense that very large objects have a higher mass, or weight, than very small ones. Thus aided by the visualization of mass through its subjective effect of weight, we are strongly inclined to assume that the mass of any falling body on Earth is negligible compared with the Earth's mass. Hence, for all practical purposes the terrestrial falling motion as embodied in Newton's law of gravitation would be simply proportional to the mass of the Earth, and therefore the same for all falling bodies. This is what we actually observe; very delicate experiments have shown that in a particular locality the falling accelerations of different objects are really the same within one part in 20,000,000.

Variation of gravity with latitude

There is a slight variation in the falling rate at different geographic latitudes. Due to the flattening of the Earth, objects near the poles are one part in 297 closer to the center of the Earth than objects near the equator. This is reflected in the inverse-square law of attraction; calculations yield a gradual decrease in the rate of falling in regions closer to the Earth's equator. The rotation of the Earth results in a further diminution which is easily explained. Through their cohesive properties the Earth's parts are kept in their diurnal circular orbits of rotation, though the Earth has obviously "given" slightly, judging from its flattened shape. The Earth's rotation results in a slight centrifugal "flying-away" or "lifting-up" effect for an object not rigidly connected with the Earth; this takes place quite apart from any gravitational falling. Or we may say: the

Earth below, by its turning-away "absorbs" part of any vertical falling motion, just as a dropping elevator momentarily absorbs part of one's weight. The resultant "lifting" acceleration effect is nil at the poles and reaches a maximum value at the equator.

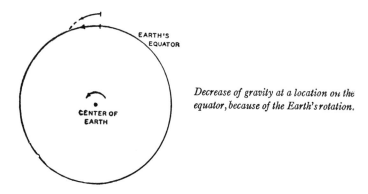

Decrease of gravity at a location on the equator, because of the Earth's rotation.

Together with the diminution of the intensity of falling due to the Earth's oblateness, it is found that the rate of falling at the equator is about half a per cent less than at the poles. The acceleration due to gravity amounts to 983 cm/sec^2 at the poles, and 978 cm/sec^2 at the equator.

Review

So far, then, there is complete confirmation of the hypothesis that gravity and gravitation are the same. First we noted the obvious analogy of accelerated motion; secondly, the constancy of the acceleration of gravity at any one location was explained by the overwhelming mass of the Earth, so that for all purposes of measurement the combined masses of Earth and any falling object is the same in all cases. Next, the variation in distance from the center of the Earth explained the slightly different falling acceleration at different latitudes, as the inverse-square law would suggest, while the rotation of the Earth was found to result in an additional lifting acceleration increasing in size toward the equatorial regions.

Thus the analogy between gravity and gravitation has been tested by small falling bodies near the surface of the Earth. The inverse-square dilution of gravitation with distance is only faintly illustrated, however, by the slight flattening of the Earth. A more drastic test should be made to observe any appreciable decrease in falling acceleration high above the Earth. Terrestrial experiments might conceivably be arranged for such a purpose. Nature, however, has provided us with an ideal testing object, namely the Moon, which, as highest falling "apple" and nearest cosmic object (except for elusive objects such as transitory meteors, meteorites, cosmic rays and the like), is the missing link.

The falling Moon

We therefore turn our attention to the Moon. The Moon revolves around the Earth in a period of 27.32 days; the distance r from the center of the Earth to the center of the Moon amounts to 384,400 kilometers on the average. (Since the Moon's orbit is slightly eccentric, this distance ranges from 406,000 to 363,000 kilometers; this minor complication does not, however, affect our subsequent reasoning.)

Let us assume that the Moon's orbit about the Earth is circular; from the above data, the orbital velocity of the Moon is found to average 1.023 kilometers per second. As in the analogous cases of binary stars and of planetary orbits, the Moon is "falling around" the Earth; a continued acceleration of the Moon is required to deflect its path. From the relation given in the last chapter, the amount of this acceleration q is found to be $q = V^2/r$ or 0.272 cm/sec^2.

Newton asked himself whether this acceleration was of the same nature as the falling acceleration of the apple near the surface of the Earth. The distance from the Moon to the center of the Earth is, on the average, a little over sixty times the radius of the Earth. It should now be remembered that the acceleration of gravity at the Earth's surface is about 980 cm/sec² or close to 3600 times the "falling" acceleration 0.272 cm/sec² of the Moon in its orbit. It is, therefore, as if the Moon's orbital path were kept curving by an acceleration of the same nature as gravity, but reduced according to the inverse square of the distance to the center of the Earth.

This is exactly what Newton's law of universal gravitation leads us to expect. The Moon provides us with a connecting link, confirming the identity of gravitation on the one hand, as revealed in the stars and planets, and gravity, on the other hand, as revealed by Moon and apple. Both are "falling," the apple near the surface of the Earth and the "Big Apple" called Moon high above the Earth. As a matter of fact, the very mass of the Moon results in some falling also of the Earth toward the Moon, a matter which will be considered again in the next chapter.

Tides and precession

Further evidence for the universal presence of gravitation is found in the occurrence of the tides (Chapter 3) and in the precession. The tidal effects are due to the slight differences between the gravitational attraction of Moon and Sun on the liquid surface surrounding the Earth and on the solid part of the Earth represented by its center. Particles on the side of the Earth nearest Sun or Moon are subject to a slight additional attraction, particles on the opposite side to a lesser attraction, than the center of the Earth; hence the tidal crests on these two opposite sides. At locations between these high tides the particles are drawn in to the surface of the Earth, thus causing low tides.

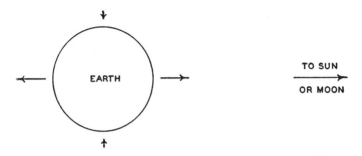

Tidal action.

The precession is a slow change in the direction of the axis of the rotating Earth. It is caused by the fact that the equatorial bulge of the Earth is generally not in the same plane with Moon and Sun. Both Moon and Sun tend to tilt the Earth's equator into the plane of the ecliptic. Due to the Earth's rotation, however, the existing inclination is not altered, but instead the Earth's axis is forced into a slow conical motion. A small-scale analogy is the slow change in direction of the axis of rotation of a spinning top under the influence of gravity. Thus, the Earth's axis changes its direction very slowly—at the rate of one revolution in about 25,800 years—and as time goes by different stars qualify as "pole stars" (Chapter 6).

Both tides and precession are proportional to the mass of the Sun and the Moon but vary with the inverse cube of their distance. The nearness of the Moon outweighs the large mass of the Sun; the influence of the Moon in the phenomena of tides and precession is about 2.2 times that of the Sun.

Universality of gravitation

The law of gravitation finds additional confirmation in that it enables us to compute accurately the paths of stars, planets, moons, etc., for years ahead of time, a fact beautifully demonstrated, for example, by the precise predictions of the times of eclipses in the Earth-Moon-Sun system. A further triumph of the law of gravitation is the discovery of unseen stars and planets from their observed gravitational effect on visible objects (Chapter 14). We can go even further. Other planets have moons, often families of moons, and in every case the behavior of these satellite systems in their orbital paths fits in beautifully with the general concept of gravitation.

We have seen that the law of cosmic motion is locally revealed as gravity or conventional falling motion. Any falling object and the Earth form a sort of binary star. These myriads of "binaries," and the stellar binaries and the solar system, too, are all relatively compact units. The orbital motions in these units are easily detected, the different orbital grooves representing different relations between mass, space and time. At the same time, individual units—single stars, binary stars, etc. —are spaced far apart; the inverse-square law results in a weakening of the mutual gravitation between these various objects. The attraction between any two of the different units is beyond the realm of direct observation.

We remember that the size of the solar system, as measured by the diameter of the orbit of Pluto, is some 11 light hours, but that the nearest star is 4.3 lightyears away. It is reasonable to assume that the great structure of the myriads of stars is governed by the law of gravitation; we shall see in Chapter 29 that it is even possible to estimate the mass of the stellar system with the aid of the law of gravitation. The orbital behavior of

Sun-planet and Earth-apple binaries is, however, barely affected by any gravitational attraction of the stellar system as a whole. This is due principally to the inverse-square character of gravitation which results in conspicuous acceleration only in objects comparatively close together. Hence, on the one hand, we generally cannot detect any deviations in the path of a single star or of the inertial point of a binary system. On the other hand, the effects of gravitation found within the compact binary-star units, within the solar system and in terrestrial falling motions led to the all-embracing picture of universal gravitation embodied in the one simple law of Newton.

Einstein's law of gravitation

Newton's law of universal gravitation describes very accurately the changes in the locations of celestial bodies. The law may not provide a real explanation of the causes of gravitational motion, but "real explanations" are beyond the domain of physical science. The astronomer's ability to predict Sun eclipses or to deduce the existence of unseen stars and planets leaves no doubt whatsoever that Newton's law is a real property of the universe. In Newton's description the notions of space, time and mass are kept independent, while positions and motions are measured by the method and properties of conventional Euclidean geometry.

Newton's law of universal gravitation has found a renewed and still more nearly correct statement in the law of motion of Albert Einstein (1879–   ). Einstein's description discards the Euclidean background but emphasizes that the distribution of mass in space and time is the "real" framework of the universe. This framework determines the choice of a fitting geometrical background that is never quite Euclidean. Einstein's technical approach, which is beyond the scope of this book, implies the equivalence of gravitational and any other acceler-ated motion. This view further generalizes the law of inertia to the free motion of any object as long as a proper geometric choice is made for the background to which the motion is re-ferred. Newton's classical law of inertia simply follows for the special case of negligible gravitational effects. We may thus speak of Einstein's law of gravitation, motion or inertia, which are all identical concepts when viewed in the proper geometrical perspective.

Although Einstein's law is a further improvement, Newton's description is generally adequate in astronomy and will be used in this book.

13 | THE MASSES OF EARTH, SUN, MOON, PLANETS AND STARS

THE universal law of gravitation $q = G(M + m)/r^2$ provides the tool for measuring the masses of celestial objects. In every case this is done by studying the gravitational influence between two objects. The mass of a cosmic object can be determined only if the object is relatively close to another object, so that their mutual gravitational acceleration is appreciable. In astronomical language this means that the object should be one of the two components of a binary; it is an interesting design of creation that there is such a great abundance of cosmic binaries.

Mass determinations are therefore restricted to binary systems; it is generally not possible to determine the mass of an "isolated" object. Special observations are required to distinguish between the masses of the two components of a binary. As we shall see later, the masses of the components of a stellar binary are generally not strikingly different. On the other hand, in the solar system the planetary masses are minute compared with the Sun's mass. Similarly the satellites of the planets are found to have small masses compared with their primaries. This is the gradually revealed design of the impressive mechanism which we call the solar or planetary system; it proves to be a stable design.

General approach to the problem

For the purpose of determining masses we shall often make use of the fact that the mass structure in the planetary system has this unique pyramidal property. We may sometimes use the minute component of a binary as a sort of test object or indicator for establishing the mutual gravitational attraction between it and the massive primary, realizing that this effect is due mostly to the primary. Technically, the observed effect furnishes information about the combined mass of primary and companion; the minuteness of the companion may be so obvious, however, that it does not matter whether the resultant mass is ascribed to both components or to the massive one only. It is as if one were required by law to include a light feather in weighing a person. It would not be possible to make allowance for this additional weight, nor would it matter.

To obtain a quantitative measure for the mass of an object it is necessary to compare the binary of which the object is part with the imaginary one-gram binary referred to in Chapter 12. We can make use of the quantitative rate of gravitational effect as established in the laboratory. We recall that the rate of mutual gravitational acceleration in a one-gram binary whose components are centered exactly one centimeter apart amounts to 6.67×10^{-8} cm/sec^2. This particular value of gravitational acceleration defines the constant of gravitation and its value is assumed to be universally valid.

Mass of the Earth

The mass of the Earth can be derived by considering our planet as the primary component of a binary, the secondary component being any falling object. The mutual gravitational acceleration in this "binary" is about 980 cm/sec^2, while the distance between the centers of the components may be taken as 6371 kilometers, i.e., 6.371×10^8 centimeters (average distance from object at surface to center of the Earth). A comparison of this large observed rate of falling with the minute rate of gravitational acceleration between the components of the one-gram binary permits at once a determination of the mass of the Earth. This may be demonstrated as follows:

The rate of acceleration between the spherical components of the one-gram binary whose centers are one centimeter apart is 6.67×10^{-8} cm/sec^2. Suppose now that the two components were 6.371×10^8 centimeters apart, instead of one centimeter. Then, in accordance with the inverse-square character of the law of gravitation, their mutual acceleration would be reduced in the ratio $(6.371 \times 10^8)^2$; i.e., it would amount to only $6.67 \times 10^{-8}/(6.371 \times 10^8)^2$ or 1.64×10^{-25} cm/sec^2. On the other hand, the law of gravitation implies that the mutual acceleration varies proportionally with the combined mass of the two objects. Now, for the same separation, the acceleration of gravity between "apple" and Earth amounts to 980 cm/sec^2 which is $980/1.64 \times 10^{-25}$ or 5.98×10^{27} times as large as the mutual acceleration between the two widely separated components of the one-gram binary. This huge ratio, therefore, represents the mass of the Earth (plus apple), expressed in grams.

If we know the Earth's mass and its size, it is a simple matter to compute the average density of the Earth. This is done as follows: Assuming the Earth to be a sphere, its volume is found to be $\frac{4}{3} \pi r^3$; here r represents the radius, while $\pi = 3.1416$ is the (rounded off) value for the ratio of the circumference of a circle to its diameter. If $r = 6.371 \times 10^8$ centimeters the volume is found to be 1.083×10^{27} cubic centimeters; hence the density of the Earth is $5.98 \times 10^{27}/1.083 \times 10^{27}$ or 5.52 times that of water. Since the average density of the surface layer of the Earth is less than this, the deep interior of the Earth must have a very high density, probably over ten times the density of water. The inner core of the Earth is believed to consist of metallic iron, alloyed with nickel and pressed into high density through the weight of the overlying layers (Chapter 3).

Masses of other celestial bodies

A similar procedure could be followed to determine the masses of the Moon, Sun and most of the planets. In this case, however, it is customary to perform the computation in a slightly different way, based on the fact that for these cosmic objects the freedom of continued orbital motion is maintained as time goes by. In every case the principle of mass determination consists in observing the mutual gravitational attraction of two bodies. This attraction may be expressed directly in terms of acceleration, but also in a more roundabout way through the size and period of the orbit of one object around another. There is no fundamental difference between these two approaches; the choice is simply a matter of convenience, of adaptation to the particular problem that is being considered. When we considered the gravitational pull between Earth and apple, the study of the mutual falling acceleration was the logical choice. For the study of the gravitational attraction between a planet and its satellite, or between the Sun and a planet, it is more convenient to introduce the overall space-time dimensions of the orbit.

The harmonic relation

The size of the orbit and its period of revolution are related in a simple way to the mutual acceleration of the components. This is easily seen in the case of circular orbits (Chapter 11). The acceleration in a circular orbit is proportional to the square of the speed and to the inverse of the radius, i.e., $q(:) V^2/a$. Now according to the law of gravitation $q: (M + m)/a^2$. Hence, $(M + m)/a^2 : V^2/a$, from which it follows that $(M + m) : aV^2$. Or, since the speed varies with the size of the orbit and the inverse of the period of revolution, we may also write $(M + m) : a^3/P^2$.

Mathematical analysis shows that exactly the same relation holds for elliptic orbits; in that case a represents the mean distance, which is one-half the size of the major axis. The combined mass of a binary in continued orbital motion is thus found to be proportional to the cube of the mean separation between the components and to the inverse square of their period of revolution about each other.

This simple relation is referred to as the harmonic relation. It is the most convenient relation for comparing the combined masses of different binaries for which the space-and-time dimensions of the orbital motion have been determined. The word binary is again used here in the general sense as describing two cosmic objects close to each other, compared with the spacing between stars in general. In addition to the binary stars, this includes the Sun-planet pairs and the different planet-satellite combinations.

The triple system Sun-Earth-Moon

In order to determine the mass of the Sun, we may compare the Sun-planet binary with, for example, the imaginary one-gram binary, or with another cosmic binary. For illustration we shall make a comparison between the Sun-Earth and the Earth-Moon binaries. We note that these two binary systems have one component in common, namely, the Earth. The astronomer has completely solved the "two-body problem": the two objects move around each other in an elliptical orbit subject to the law of areas; this is often referred to as Keplerian motion. He has, however, found it generally impossible to solve the "three-body problem." It is even impossible to calculate the behavior of as few as three objects for an indefinite time ahead, or in the past. In triple cosmic arrangements, however, two of the objects are usually close together, compared with their distance to the third object. With respect to the Sun, for example, the Earth and Moon are so close together that from many points of view they may almost be considered as blended together into one "point."

When studying such a triple arrangement of cosmic objects it is convenient and accurate to dissect the existing spacing and state of motion into two orbital motions. There is the short-period orbital spin of the closer pair, while a longer-period orbital spin exists between the closer pair and the distant object. Small deviations are noticeable in the form of minor disturbances or perturbations (Chapter 14); the slightly different distances from the components of the closer pair to the distant object have gravitational consequences which affect all three bodies to some extent.

Masses of Sun-Earth and Earth-Moon binaries

The actual calculations for the masses of the Sun-Earth and the Earth-Moon binaries are carried out as follows. The distance to the Sun is 149,700,000 kilometers on the average, that to the

Moon 384,400 kilometers; the respective periods of revolution are 365.2564 and 27.32 days. The distance ratio is 389.4, the period ratio 13.37. Hence, the harmonic relation between the combined mass and the space-and-time dimensions of the orbits requires that the combined mass of Sun and Earth is

$$(389.4)^3/(13.37)^2$$

or 330,000 times that of the Earth and Moon combined. In order to compare the Sun's mass with the mass of the Earth it is first necessary to find the mass of the Moon. A precise measure of the Moon's falling acceleration toward the Earth provides us with the combined mass of Earth and Moon; by subtracting the Earth's known mass we can determine the Moon's mass.

Mass of Moon

A more accurate measurement, however, is obtained as follows: When we speak of the Earth's orbit around the Sun, we usually have in mind the orbit of the center of mass of Earth and Moon. It describes a smooth orbit around the Sun, while Earth and Moon describe orbits around this center of mass; Earth and Moon are at all times on opposite sides of their center of mass, and at distances whose ratio is as the inverse ratio of their masses. This periodic motion of our Earth has its effect on the observed direction of the Sun as seen on the background of stars, since the Earth is sometimes ahead of, at other times behind the smoothly moving center of mass. From observations of this type it has been found that the center of the Earth describes a small orbit, with a period of 27.32 days, of course, around the center of mass of Earth and Moon. This mass center is now found to be located on the line joining Earth and Moon, about ¾ of the Earth's radius away from the Earth's center. To be more exact, a value of 81.3 is found for the ratio of the masses of Earth and Moon. In this way the Moon's mass is calculated to be $1/81.3 \times 5.98 \times 10^{27}$ or 7.3×10^{25} grams.

Mass of Sun

Now we are ready to derive the value for the Sun's mass. The combined mass of Earth (1) and Moon (1/81.3) is $1 + 1/81.3$ or $82.3/81.3$ times that of the Earth. Hence, the mass of the Sun is found to be $82.3/81.3 \times 330,000$ or $334,000$ times that of the Earth, or very close to 2×10^{33} grams.

Masses of planets

Similar calculations can be made for those planets which have satellites. The satellites are the companion objects which together with their planets provide the binary structure that is the necessary condition for any successful mass determination. Take, for example, the planet Jupiter and its closest bright moon Io, whose period of revolution around Jupiter is 1.769 days and whose average distance to the center of Jupiter is 422,000 kilometers. Note that this distance is not very different from the separation of Earth and Moon, but that the period of revolution is very much shorter than that of our Moon. A comparison of these rates of revolution implies that the Jupiter-Io system has a large mass as compared with that of the Earth-Moon binary. Compared to the latter system, the orbit of the Jupiter-Io binary is 422,000/384,400 or 1.0978 times as large, while the ratio of its period to that of the Earth-Moon system is only 0.06475. According to the harmonic relation, the mass of the Jupiter-Io binary is therefore $(1.0978)^3/(0.06745)^2$ or 315.6 times the mass of the Earth-Moon binary and 319 times the mass of the Earth alone. Hence, the combined mass of Jupiter and Io is 319/334,000 or 1/1047 times that of the Sun. The combined mass of Jupiter and any other of its satellites is found to be the same; we infer that the masses of the satellites are negligible compared with that of Jupiter and that the above-derived ratio of 1/1047 may be accepted as the mass of Jupiter in terms of the Sun's mass.

Similar computations can be made for the other planets, and it is found that their masses are in every case smaller than that of Jupiter. For the planets Mercury, Venus and Pluto no moons have been discovered; their masses may be determined from their gravitational effect on other planets. The values found thus far are not as accurate as those obtained for the planets provided with moons.

Masses of satellites and comets

It is a much more difficult problem to derive the masses of the planetary satellites and other bodies like comets, since these objects are on the "featherweight" end of the binary pair. One has therefore to rely on the mutual influence of these light bodies on each other. It is thus found that the four bright satellites of Jupiter—Io, Europa, Ganymede and Callisto—the bright satellite of Saturn—Titan—and the bright satellite of Neptune— Triton—have masses comparable to that of our Moon. The masses of all other satellites and also of the comets prove to be—astronomically speaking—negligibly small.

Masses of the stars

The harmonic relation is further used for determining the masses of stars that are components of binary stars. Tens of thousands of binary stars are known, but for only relatively few are the conditions sufficiently favorable to permit a mass determination. Needed for the present purpose is a knowledge of the size a of the orbit, and of the period of revolution P. The latter quantity is generally not difficult to determine; it is usually more difficult to derive an accurate value for a. The apparent, i.e., the angular, unforeshortened amount of a can generally be estimated from the observed orbit, but its actual value in linear measure, i.e., centimeters, or astronomical units, can be ascertained only if the distance to the double star is known. Hence, the usefulness of the method is limited to those binary stars which are relatively near to us, though important statistical information has been obtained from more distant binaries. The combined masses of several dozen binaries are known with a reasonable degree of accuracy; most of these stars are less than fifty lightyears away.

Mass of Sirius

For example, we take the binary Sirius, whose distance (8.6 lightyears) is well known. This binary consists of the familiar bright star Sirius A, and its relatively feeble companion star Sirius B; the discovery of this interesting companion is described in the next chapter. The period of revolution amounts to 50 years; the orbit is seen tilted at an angle of about 45°. Allowance can be made for this and calculations show that the average separation between the two components would amount to 7″.6 if the orbit were seen without foreshortening. Observations of the yearly parallactic displacement have revealed a maximum amplitude of 0″.38. This quantity represents the distance Sun-Earth, or the astronomical unit, as it would appear at the location of Sirius, seen from the solar system. In other words, the unforeshortened, astronomical unit (A.U.) appears as 0″.38 at Sirius. Since the average, unforeshortened separation between Sirius A and Sirius B amounts to 7″.6, this quantity is equivalent to 7.6/0.38 or 20 A.U. in linear measure. If we proceed as before, i.e., compare the harmonic relation for the Sirius binary and the Sun-Earth binary, we see that the combined mass of the Sirius system must therefore be $20^3/50^2$ or 3.2 times the mass of the Sun. The Earth's mass may be ignored in this comparison, since it is entirely negligible in computations of this sort.

Mass ratio of binary stars

In order to distinguish between the masses of the two stellar components, we recall (Chapter 10) that the two components describe similar paths, of opposite phase, around their center of mass. We recall, furthermore, that the center of mass is located through its uniform rectilinear motion and that the relative masses of the components are revealed as the inverse ratio of their distances from the center of mass. In order to carry out this procedure in practice, it is necessary to study the motion of the separate components projected on a background of "fixed" stars, of which a wide choice is always available. A study of the path of Sirius against such a background has indicated that the center of mass is always closer to the bright component, in such a ratio that its mass must be twice the mass of the companion. Since the combined mass is 3.2 times that of the Sun, the component masses are found to be 2.1 and 1.1 times the Sun's mass. The Sun's mass equals 2×10^{33} grams; hence, values for the masses of Sirius and its companion can now be expressed in grams. However, for many purposes the Sun's mass is the more convenient unit of mass.

The masses of a few dozen bmaries have been derived on the basis of the principles and methods just outlined. The practical determination of masses presents a delicate problem. Some of these determinations will be further discussed in Chapter 17. For the time being we note the relatively small range in stellar masses; their values are of the same order of size as the Sun's mass, while generally the masses of the two components do not differ by more than a factor of three. The stars are comparable to the Sun as far as the basic physical property of mass is concerned; we recall another physical property of the stars, namely, their luminosities, which are also comparable to that of the Sun (Chapter 8).

Once more: mass and weight

We shall continue to make use of the concept of mass. If one likes, the values of the masses derived for cosmic bodies may be "visualized" as "weight." One may attempt to visualize somewhere in the universe a pair of scales subject to whatever resultant gravitational effect of the stellar world determines gravity at that location. Looking at it this way, one would see that the Sirius system in one scale would require 3.2 "suns" on the other scale to effect a balancing. Whatever the intensity of the weights as determined by the local gravity, the comparison or balancing of masses would not be affected by it, since mass is a basic property of all objects.

Kepler's third law restated

We conclude this chapter by drawing attention to the significance of the harmonic relation for the orbits of the planets. The solar or planetary system may be considered to consist of a number of binaries, the Sun being the common primary component of the different planetary companions. This is a result of the predominant mass of the Sun compared to which planetary masses are very small indeed, the largest being that of Jupiter, which is 1/1047 times that of the Sun. In other words, if M is the Sun's mass and m the planet's mass, $M + m$ is virtually constant. Hence, the harmonic relation for the different planetary orbits may be written as approximately $a^3/P^2 =$ constant, which is the content of Kepler's harmonic law. The harmonic relation, however, shows clearly that minor inconsistencies in Kepler's third law must exist, because of the not quite negligible planetary masses. The harmonic relation $a^3/P^2 : (M + m)$ represents, therefore, the more nearly correct statement of Kepler's third or harmonic law.

The mutual gravitational influence between the different planets further complicates the state of motion in the solar system. Were it not for the overwhelming mass of the Sun, the state of motion of the solar system would not have the simplicity as embodied, with such a high degree of approximation, in Kepler's laws.

14 UNSEEN STARS AND PLANETS

In the past few chapters we have reviewed the historical background of the universal law of gravitation. We recognized the identity of gravitation and gravity, and used the law of gravitation for measuring the masses of cosmic objects. We emphasize the reliability of this law which appears to operate everywhere and at all times, i.e., continuously, at a definite rate represented by the constant of gravitation. This reliability permits us to calculate the future (or past) paths of celestial objects, if their locations and motions at a certain time are known. For example, the relative spacing of Sun, Moon and Earth at any time in the not too distant future may be predicted with a high degree of accuracy.

From time to time Earth, Sun and Moon are aligned sufficiently closely to cause an eclipse, either partial or total. A total Sun eclipse is observed from a location on the Earth's surface within the total shadow cast by the Moon. A total Moon eclipse occurs when the Moon passes through the total shadow of the

Earth. Solar and lunar eclipses are about equally frequent for the Earth as a whole. From any particular point of observation, however, solar eclipses are rare, since the observer has to be in the right location at the right time to be in the limited shadow

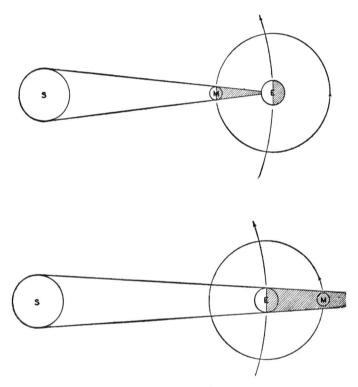

Eclipses of Sun (above) and Moon (below).

area. The beginning and end of Sun eclipses can be accurately timed, and it is a proof for the perfection of the cosmic mechanism that years ahead of their occurrence Sun eclipses can be predicted within a second of time. Similarly, the future paths of the planets in the solar system and of the components in double stars can be foretold when sufficient data are available to establish the present space-and-time relations in their orbits. The future positions of single stars and of the inertial point of binaries can be predicted with equal dependability; in these cases the gravitational effect of the rest of the stellar world is negligible and only the uniform rectilinear motion remains to be considered.

Perturbations

The Sun is the predominant factor in determining planetary motions. If the gravitational effect of other planets could be ignored, each planet-Sun binary would present the ideal example of the two-body problem. The planet would move around the Sun in an elliptical orbit subject to the law of areas; a case of perfect Keplerian motion would exist (Chapter 12). However, there are minute gravitational attractions between each planet and all other planets. Since the net effect of these attractions is a small, but never quite negligible acceleration, the elliptical orbits of the planets are slightly distorted. These disturbing effects are called perturbations, which the law of gravitation permits us to compute in terms of the relative spacing and masses of the planets. It is one more proof of the reliability of the law of gravitation that the future paths of the planets can thus be predicted more precisely than when the perturbations are neglected.

An interesting possibility now suggests itself. In the solar system we make allowance for the perturbation of the planets, insofar as the latter are known to us. Suppose now that other planets exist, but are too feeble to be seen. If such an unseen planet had sufficient mass, it would cause measurable perturbations in the paths of the known planets. Similarly, the presence of an unseen star or planet close to a visible star would be revealed in the course of time by the gravitational perturbations of the unseen object. We may even go so far as to imagine what would happen if our Sun were invisible but still had the same mass. The Sun would dominate the planetary motions gravitationally, just as it does now. Kepler's laws of planetary motion would have pointed to the existence of the Sun, even if we could not have observed it directly.

We will make a brief survey of the discovery of unseen stars and planets by the gravitational method, i.e., from the perturbations caused in visible objects within close range of the unseen objects. Both an unseen planet in the solar system and two unseen stars in the stellar world were discovered shortly before the middle of the nineteenth century.

The bright, naked-eye planets had set the limits of the solar system at the orbit of Saturn. In 1781 a more distant planet was discovered visually by William Herschel. This object is barely visible to the naked eye; in small telescopes it looks like a star. It was not recognized as a planet until Herschel happened to note its change of position from night to night on the background of stars. Herschel recognized that the new object—later named Uranus—described an orbit under the gravitational influence of the Sun and thus could be classified as a planet.

After some fifty years of observation it was found that the path of Uranus was not in complete harmony with the path which would be expected after allowance was made for the known perturbations due principally to Jupiter and Saturn. In 1845 the discrepancy between theory and observation amounted to more than two minutes of arc, truly an intolerable amount for astronomers.

Discovery of the companions of Sirius and Procyon

The name that enters the picture is again that of Bessel (Chapter 8), one of the ablest and most progressive astronomers of the first part of the nineteenth century. As early as 1824 Bessel noticed irregularities in the motion of Uranus; he was convinced that the perturbed behavior must be ascribed to the attraction of a planet, as yet unknown and unseen, beyond the orbit of Uranus. Bessel did not complete this investigation; but he did carry to conclusion a similar problem, leading to the first discovery of unseen stars by gravitational means. He studied the positions and proper motions of two of the brightest stars, Sirius and Procyon. Sirius is the brightest star in the sky; it is 8.6 lightyears away and, excluding the Sun, is the sixth nearest star. Procyon, also a star of the first magnitude, is 11 lightyears away; at present there are only ten stars known to be nearer than this. As for many other stars, the positions of these stars on the celestial sphere had been regularly observed since about the middle of the eighteenth century. From a study of these observations Bessel suspected as early as 1834 that Sirius and Procyon deviate from uniform rectilinear motion.

Uniform rectilinear motion, i.e., the law of inertia, is the rule for a single star sufficiently far away from other stars (Chapter 9). In the case of a deviation from this behavior, the qualifying condition is obviously not satisfied and the presence of a relatively close object is hypothesized to explain the observed irregularities. Remember that the center of mass of primary star and unseen companion follows a uniform rectilinear path, while both the visible star and its unseen companion describe a periodic orbit around the center of mass. An analogy would be the two birds circling around each other while at the same time pursuing a common path (Chapter 10); if one of these birds

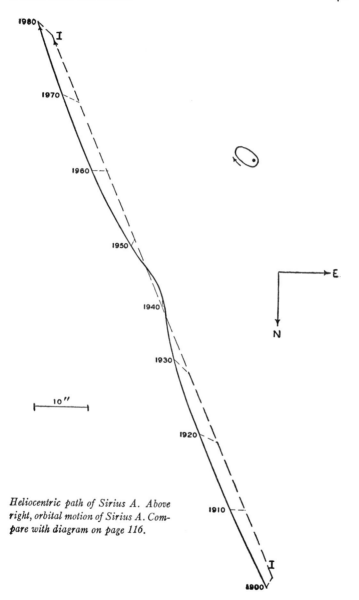

Heliocentric path of Sirius A. Above right, orbital motion of Sirius A. Compare with diagram on page 116.

were invisible, its existence might nevertheless be inferred from the behavior of the other.

Bessel noticed that the perturbations of Sirius and Procyon were periodic, i.e., went through repeated cycles, and on this basis he announced in 1844 the discovery of unseen companions both of Sirius and Procyon. That these companion objects could not be seen did not deter Bessel from his interpretation. He wrote:

> "But light is no real property of mass. The existence of numberless visible stars can prove nothing against the existence of numberless invisible ones."

The implications of his discoveries were well realized by Bessel:

> "For even if a change of motion can, up to the present time, be proved in only two cases, yet will all other cases be rendered thereby liable to suspicion, and it will be equally difficult, by observations, to free other proper motions from the suspicion of change, and to get such knowledge of the change as to admit of its amount being calculated."

Bessel's analyses were tested by others and confirmed, although his conclusions were not verified until much later. Nearly two decades later (1862) the companion of Sirius was first seen, with the 18.5-inch refractor now at the Dearborn Observatory. The very faint companion of Procyon was not seen until 1896, with the 36-inch Lick refractor. The orbital characteristics of both Sirius and Procyon are now well known. Sirius and its companion revolve around each other in 50 years; for Procyon the period of revolution is 40.6 years. The primary of Sirius is 30 times as bright as the Sun; the companion has only 1/100 times the Sun's luminosity. As noted in Chapter 13, the masses of Sirius and its companion are 2.1 and 1.1 times the

Sun's mass. The primary of Procyon is seven times as luminous. as the Sun, while the companion has only 1/2000 times the Sun's luminosity; the masses are 1.7 and 0.6 times that of the Sun. Although both companions are intrinsically of low luminosity, their large masses insure their classification as stars (Chapter 22).

Discoveries of Neptune and Pluto

The next discovery of an unseen object was that of an additional planet in our solar system, based on the aforementioned perturbations in the orbit of Uranus. The discovery of this new planet would have been a natural sequel to Bessel's discovery of the two unseen stars; but Bessel himself died in 1846. Meanwhile, however, the problem had been attacked by the mathematician John Couch Adams (1819–1892) of Cambridge, England. He computed the orbit of the unseen planet responsible for the perturbations of Uranus and submitted his results to the Greenwich Observatory; unfortunately, the telescopic check for the object was delayed. The same problem had also been investigated by the French mathematical astronomer Urbain Jean Joseph Leverrier (1811–1877). At his request, Johann Gottfried Galle (1812–1910) of the Berlin Observatory turned his telescope on September 23, 1846, in the direction calculated by Leverrier and with little delay identified the new planet, about one degree of arc from the calculated position, and easily identified by its disk of about three seconds of arc in diameter. The new planet was named Neptune.

The discovery of Neptune was another triumph for the reliability of the law of gravitation, but after some time it became clear that even allowance for the gravitational attraction by Neptune did not fully permit an accurate prediction of the future path of Uranus. The interesting possibility that there was still another unseen planet beyond Neptune presented itself. Leading among the investigators of this problem was Percival Lowell (1855–1916), who in 1906 at the Lowell Observatory in Flagstaff, Arizona, initiated a photographic search for the new planet whose existence he had inferred from calculations. An intensive systematic search was made and rewarded by the discovery of the new object on February 18, 1930. The discovery was made by Clyde William Tombaugh (1906–   ), after an inspection of some two million photographic images. The new planet was finally located through its slight displacement on two photographs taken six days apart. The new planet, named Pluto, is a very faint object, visible only in the largest telescopes.

It is not likely that any further, "trans-Plutonian" planets will be easily discovered.

Discovery of faint companion stars

There is great promise, however, of the discovery of unseen objects in the stellar world, and we shall now take up this problem. We mention first the approach to the discovery of unseen companions of stars through the application of the Doppler principle (Chapter 9).

Spectroscopic companions

In Chapter 10 we referred to the spectroscopic binaries revealed through periodic variations in the radial velocity of a star. Such stars, apparently single, show deviations from uniform rectilinear motion. In the ideal case, two superimposed spectra are present, revealing the two components. Often, however, only one spectrum is observed; nevertheless, its periodic shift demonstrates deviations from uniform rectilinear motion, and hence the presence of an unseen companion.

The spectrographic method has been particularly suitable for stars which are apparently bright, regardless of their distance. Spectrographic observations favor the discovery of relatively short-period binaries because of their large range in velocity. None of these objects has ever been observed directly as a binary; even through the telescope they remain unresolved. The spectroscopic study of these close binaries has one disadvantage; it does not show the inclination of the orbit with respect to the line of sight. Hence, the information which can be gathered for individual binaries is limited, though statistically or in connection with other types of observations important conclusions about stellar properties have been derived.

Eclipsing companions

Another special group of double stars should be mentioned briefly. Faint companion stars can often be discovered if the orbit of a binary is seen on edge or nearly so. In such cases mutual eclipses of the two components take place periodically; the resulting variation in the observed brightness reveals the binary character of a star, which visually appears single. The best-known example is the bright star Algol (Beta Persei) which is eclipsed for 10 hours every 69 hours. Hundreds of eclipsing binaries (also called eclipsing variables) are known; aided by spectroscopic observations, we have obtained important information about the masses, diameters, luminosities and densities of their component stars. Though planetary companions have not yet been discovered in this way, a planet may someday be found from the minute eclipsing effect on its star.

Visible companions

We interpolate a few words about the discovery of faint, stellar companions, which, with present observational means, are above the threshold of comparative invisibility. Such faint, visible, stellar companions, not lost in the glare of their primary stars, are discovered by careful telescopic scrutiny of comparatively nearby stars. Many faint, visible, close companions have been discovered with the large visual refractors of the Lick (36-inch aperture) and Yerkes (40-inch aperture) Observatories. Companions widely separated from their primaries are found by searching for objects which share the proper motion of the primary. Scores of such companions have been found and their number will undoubtedly increase—particularly toward very faint objects—as more powerful instruments are used. Of the proper-motion companions we mention the very faint star discovered in 1944 by George Van Biesbroeck (1880–   ) on photographs taken with the reflector (82-inch aperture) at the McDonald Observatory. This object shares the proper motion of the star named BD + 4°4048 (distance 19 lightyears), at an angular distance of 74''; it is of the eighteenth magnitude, nearly nine magnitudes fainter than the primary. The large separation of companion and primary (over 400 astronomical units) precludes the possibility that the former shines by reflected light. Here we are dealing with a bona-fide star, although we do not know its mass. Van Biesbroeck's star is the intrinsically faintest star known at present, having only 1/500,000 times the Sun's luminosity and shining only 700 times as brightly as Jupiter does in the reflected light of the Sun.

Unseen astrometric companions

We now come to the astrometric method for discovering unseen stars. The classical discoveries by Bessel of the companions of Sirius and Procyon were favored by the fact that these objects are near to us. The high positional accuracy and light-gathering power of the photographic method, used in conjunction with a long-focus refractor (Chapter 8), open new vistas. In 1937 a systematic survey of all "single" stars nearer than thirty-three lightyears and within reach of the 24-inch refractor was initiated at the Sproul Observatory; at several other observatories, including Allegheny, McCormick and Yale, similar investigations are under way. These surveys have resulted in several interesting discoveries. In almost every case the observed perturbations can be interpreted as caused by a faint, unseen companion object. From the amplitude of the perturbation and its period, information can be obtained about the mass of the companion, although the details of the analysis are complex. Most of the well-established perturbations indicate companion objects whose masses are between 0.05 and 0.5 times the Sun's mass.

Perturbations have been found also in the orbital paths of known double stars and have in each case revealed the existence of a third component attached to one of the visible companions of the binary; these objects have generally proved to be of the same nature as the companions of single stars referred to above.

The two nearest "single" stars are Barnard's star (6.1 lightyears) which was mentioned in Chapter 8 and Lalande 21185 (7.9 lightyears). In the telescope these objects appear as faint red stars; their intrinsic luminosities are 0.0005 and 0.005 times that of the Sun. From measurements on photographic plates taken at the Sproul Observatory, it has been found that the proper motions of these two stars are subject to perturbations. Their behavior is periodic and there can be little doubt that both stars are "unresolved" binaries—Barnard's star with a period of eleven months, and Lalande 21185 with a period of fourteen months. The amplitude of the perturbations indicates companion stars with masses of less than 0.1 times the Sun's mass; the average separation from their primaries is probably less than one astronomical unit, while both primary and companion are much smaller than our Sun. A well-established case of an unseen stellar companion is that of the nearby star Ross 614, which is at a distance of 12.5 lightyears. The perturbations in the proper motion of this star have a period of 16.5 years; the amplitude of the perturbation indicates a companion star with a mass of about 1/20 times the Sun's mass.

Nature of unseen companions

Considerable progress in the discovery and interpretation of unseen companion objects of nearby stars is to be expected during the next few decades. What is the nature of the very faint and unseen companions discovered so far? Since the objects are of low luminosity and of low mass, the question arises whether they are all very faint stars or whether some might possibly be planets. It will be necessary to define the distinction between stars and planets; this matter will be discussed in Chapter 22.

Obviously the search for unseen companion objects by means of perturbations of visible stars is of importance. More binaries may be found, particularly with faint companions; this will permit additional determinations of stellar masses. But light may also be shed on the possible existence of planetary companions of stars other than the Sun (Chapter 22).

PART 3

The Physical-Chemical Properties of Sun and Stars

|15| THE COMPOSITION OF LIGHT

EARLIER chapters demonstrated the differences in the luminosities (Chapter 8) and the masses (Chapter 13) of stars. Stars also differ in color. Sirius and Vega, for example, are bluish as compared with "white" sunlight; while, on the other hand, the bright stars Antares and Arcturus are orange or reddish in color. Star colors are also recognizable through the telescope, either directly with the eye or with suitable instrumental accessories.

The physical properties of luminosity, color and mass lead to further information such as diameter and density, which give us a deeper insight into the structure of the stars. We shall survey the nature of light, particularly with regard to its composition of different colors. The relation of the latter to the source of light is expressed in the laws of radiation. Next we shall study the composition of starlight, and its related properties, such as color and temperature (Chapter 16). Finally we shall make a special study of the stellar properties of the stars in our immediate neighborhood (Chapter 17).

Light is radiation

Light emitted from the Sun, from the stars or from any other visible object is transmitted to us in the form of radiation, i.e., a continuous flow along straight lines with a constant velocity (Chapter 9). No flow of light can be observed as such; light rays become visible only when they strike matter. For example, a beam of sunlight in air can be traced through dust particles struck by part of the light. The very fact that the light rays are visible suggests that part of the light has been used up to reveal to us the path of its flow; what we see is that part of the light deviating from its original direction through the reflection from the dust particles.

Light is but one type of radiation, namely, that observable by the eye. Examples of other forms of radiation are X-rays, ultraviolet and infra-red rays, heat rays, radar and radio rays: all these different types of radiation have the same velocity of transport. As we have already seen, they vary only in frequency or wave length; the differences between the various types of radiation are differences not in kind, but in degree.

Reflection and refraction of light

Light travels in straight lines as long as it does not cross any boundaries between two materials or media of different composition. In the latter case two things happen. Consider, for example, a light ray traveling through air and hitting a smooth surface such as glass. Part of the light in the ray is reflected, while the other part continues but is broken or refracted; the refracted ray continues in the original direction only when the light ray is perpendicular to the boundary surface. Both the reflected and refracted rays are in one plane with the entering ray. If the glass is coated with a thin layer of silver, for example, most of the light is reflected. If, on the other hand, the glass is very transparent, little reflection takes place; most of the light is refracted and proceeds through the glass. If the two sides of the piece of glass are plane and parallel to each other, the refracted beam of light suffers another refraction upon leaving the glass and entering air again; the final direction of the ray is parallel to the original direction which the ray had before entering the glass. This is the basis on which a plate-glass window operates, while the example of the silver coat on glass illustrates the principle of the mirror.

LEFT: *Reflection and refraction through plane-parallel glass.*
RIGHT: *Refraction and dispersion through glass prism.*

The reflected ray makes the same angle with the boundary surface as the incoming ray. We say that the angle of reflection is equal to the angle of incidence, the angle being measured with respect to the perpendicular or normal to the surface. However, the angle of refraction differs from the angle of incidence, being smaller for light entering from air into glass; we say that glass has a higher optical density than air. In the same way, it is found that the optical density of air is higher than that of a vacuum.

Dispersion of light

In the case of a narrow, sharply defined incident ray of white light, the reflected ray is equally sharp; the refracted ray, however, is no longer sharp. In fact, it is no longer a "ray," but rather a narrow, plane bundle of rays fanning out from the striking point on the boundary surface, a complete array of rays of all different colors. Thus the composite structure of white light is demonstrated. The slight difference in the angle of refraction for different colors is called dispersion; it permits a study of the composition of white light, or of any other light from any source. This dispersion is hardly noticeable in light rays passing through plate glass at an angle not far from the perpendicular direction, but it becomes noticeable in rays passing through in a direction close to the plane of the glass.

Both the refraction and dispersion of light are best exhibited if we let a light ray pass through a piece of glass having two sides which are not parallel to each other; such a piece of glass is called a prism. In this arrangement refraction takes place at both surfaces; the result is an appreciable change in the direction of the light ray after its passage through the prism. Isaac Newton, in 1666, made the first experiment of this kind. By passing a beam of sunlight through a glass prism and then letting it strike a screen, he observed the spreading out of the "white" sunlight in a continuous array of all the colors of the rainbow, arranged in order of increasing refraction from red through orange, yellow, green and blue to violet.

The spectroscope

Newton's experiment is the basis of the later instrument known as the prism spectroscope, or spectrograph when used photographically. The source of light illuminates a narrow slit; the resulting narrow strip of light is then spread out into its component colors with the aid of one or more prisms. The resulting array of colors is called the spectrum, and may be studied either visually or photographically. Color is used here in the narrow sense of the word, as indicating a specific color, limited to as narrow a range as instrumental equipment permits. Technically it is more convenient to use the notion of frequency (Chapter 9) to define a specific color in the most objective and accurate manner.

We have already referred to the rainbow, which is simply a spectrum of sunlight dispersed into its component colors by its refraction through raindrops. To study the color composition of the rainbow, a narrow sample is all that is needed; in this, as in other cases, we like to think of the spectrum of a light source as a representative cross section. The conventional prism spectroscope thus provides an array of color strips by limiting the entering light to a slit.

Continuous and line spectra; absorption spectra

Laboratory investigations made in the years 1859 to 1862 by Gustav Kirchhoff (1824–1887) and Robert Bunsen (1811–1899) showed that spectra could be classified into three principal groups, according to the source of light. The spectrum of sunlight, for example, appears, at first sight at least, as a continuous array of different colors gradually merging into one another. The light emanating from the incandescent filament of a light bulb, or from the glowing carbon particles in the flame of an oil lamp or candle, looks similar. In all these cases the color array is called a continuous spectrum.

A different situation exists for a sufficiently rarefied gas, for example, in a discharge tube or in a hot flame or arc. When thus stimulated to give off light, the rarefied vapors send out a restricted pattern of very definite colors, which is called a line spectrum. In the case of sodium gas, for example, one sharply defined yellow color is ordinarily in evidence. Hydrogen gas reveals a strikingly organized pattern of lines. In the language of music, a line spectrum would be analogous to a chord consisting of a limited number of definite tones, each of a definite intensity.

Finally there are the absorption spectra; these are continuous spectra from which a number of discrete lines are lacking. In certain cases the absorption may include extended portions of the continuous spectrum. Kirchhoff found that this important type is always caused by light from a "continuous" light source, passing through a cooler rarefied gas; from the continuous array those colors are eliminated which the gas itself would emit when properly stimulated to incandescence.

To understand the origin of line spectra, we recall the fundamental fact that all matter may be considered to be built up of one or a combination of two or more of some ninety-odd elemental materials, the chemical elements. When stimulated to radiation in the rarefied state, each element seems to yield its own characteristic line spectrum. All elements and chemical compounds have different characteristic spectra which undergo radical changes if the atoms or molecules are ionized (Chapter 18).

Kirchhoff's laws

The outcome of the experiments of Kirchhoff and Bunsen is summarized in Kirchhoff's laws.

1. The complete or continuous emission spectra have their origin in solids, liquids or very dense gases; the source of a continuous spectrum is the radiating surface of incandescent material existing in a compressed state, whether solid, liquid or dense gas.

   A continuous spectrum also results from the accumulated radiation from a sufficiently deep layer of hot ionized gases, such as the "surface" layer of the Sun (Chapter 2), even though this layer is more rarefied than our atmosphere.

2. Emission line spectra originate from glowing gases which are sufficiently rarefied.

3. Absorption spectra result from the passage of light from a "continuous" light source through a relatively cool, rarefied gas; the shadow pattern of absorption lines corresponds to the bright line colors which the gas itself is capable of emitting.

Attention is drawn to the obvious fact that a prerequisite for any light is incandescence, whether in the compressed or rarefied state. It should also be noted that radiation may be received indirectly, for example, by reflection, as in the case of sunlight reflected from the Moon, planets or sky.

Spectral analysis

Kirchhoff's laws furnish the basis for the powerful tool of spectral analysis. Since both the emission and absorption varieties of line spectra are uniquely characteristic of the chemical composition of a rarefied gas, spectral analysis proves here to be a most effective and delicate method of identifying small quantities of rarefied gases. The continuous spectra, on the other hand, do not betray the chemical composition of the light source, but disclose its surface temperature. First, the amount of radiation in all colors increases with the temperature of the source; i.e., the higher the temperature, the greater the intensity of radiation. Second, the intensity increases more rapidly in the blue part of the spectra than in the red; hence, the higher the temperature, the higher the frequency of the radiation of maximum intensity. Since the color of the light source, judged by our non-spectroscopic eye, depends on the mixture of the different color frequencies, the composite or effective color of a continuous light source is found to shift from the red to the blue as the temperature increases, a fact easily observed in very hot metals.

By studying either the amount of radiation of different colors, or the resulting effective color, one may measure the temperature of a continuous light source with the aid of the quantitative relations given at the end of this chapter.

Origin of spectra

In trying to explain the different types of spectra, we assume that radiation must in some form or other find its origin in the smallest particles of matter, the atoms of the chemical elements or the molecules of their compounds. The radiation of specific atoms or molecules is restricted to a fixed pattern of frequencies. In the rarefied gaseous state the atoms or molecules are widely separated and have plenty of space; this seems to facilitate their ability to convey color messages in the consistent, characteristic fashion revealed in a line spectrum. Since even in a very small quantity of a rarefied gas myriads of atoms are present, it is not necessary for all of them to radiate all the time. Any one atom may radiate only a small portion of the time, and at any one time may radiate only one specific color. If the analogy could be made to the language of sounds, the atoms then would express themselves in harmony with each other. Their combined voice would be a restricted pattern of color tones; the collective effect of their activity multiplied a billionfold would be a restricted array or "chord" of the characteristic frequencies.

In the solid and liquid states, however, there is a considerable degree of cohesion between the atoms or molecules, while in a very dense gas there may be little cohesion but nevertheless considerable crowding. In all compressed matter—solid, liquid or gaseous—the atoms or molecules are jammed together and have little or no space; the conditions for the characteristic line spectrum are therefore destroyed. In a hot rarefied gas the abundance of ionized atoms and "free" electrons results in a continuous spectrum, which becomes quite conspicuous if we look through a great depth of such a gas, like the hot surface layer of the Sun. In all these instances the result is a general blur of radiation or, in the language of sound, a noise comprising all tones. Statistical laws prevail and both observation and theory confirm the emergence of a complete, continuous spectrum. The latter cannot convey any information about the chemical composition of matter; but, as noted before, the spread of colors appears to be closely related to the temperature of the radiating surface.

The patterns of absorption lines caused by the passage of "continuous" light through a cooler rarefied gas, are explained as some form of resonance resulting in the absorption of certain colors. Even if this light were released again, it might go in any direction, since the radiating atom has no control over direction. As a result, the eye, or spectroscope, would notice a loss of radiation for these characteristic frequencies which have literally been led astray by the atoms or molecules of the rarefied gas between us and the continuous source of light. The atomic mechanism of radiation and absorption will be further discussed in Chapter 18.

Radiation is a form of energy

Light and other types of radiation are forms of energy. Energy may be demonstrated and measured by its ability to push or pull something. Hence radiation has the ability to do work. An example is the light pressure or radiation pressure, which can be demonstrated in the laboratory. Very light material particles, hit by a powerful beam of light, are pushed aside. Under terrestrial conditions, radiation pressure does not play a significant role. In the cosmos, however, there are several examples of the power of radiation pressure which increases with the fourth power of the temperature of the source of radiation. High temperatures are commonplace in the cosmos. At relatively close range we observe the cosmic effects of radiation pressure in the tails of comets. Comets generally have elongated orbits resulting in a considerable variation of the comets' distance from the Sun. When a comet gets very close to the Sun, the latter's radiation is sufficiently concentrated to exert a noticeable pressure on some of the small dustlike particles of the comet. They are pushed away from the main body of the comet, and the result is a tail, which simply represents particles streaming away in a direction opposite to that of the Sun and irretrievably lost to the comet. Radiation pressure also plays an important role in the architecture of the stars (Chapter 20).

The energy in the Sun's radiation is easily recognized through its conversion into heat. When sunlight of any frequency, visible or invisible, strikes another object, it is partially absorbed by that object as heat—another form of energy. In the case of sunlight dispersed throughout a spectrum, the energy of the invisible radiation beyond the extreme red and extreme violet can still be effectively demonstrated. A thermometer will register a rising temperature, thereby proving the presence of "invisible" radiation energy. The invisible energy in the violet may be used for photo-chemical purposes to create a photographic image.

Different forms of energy

The examples just mentioned all illustrate the well-known fact that energy may exist in various forms; interchange between different forms may take place at a fixed rate. For example, a stone kept in suspension contains a certain amount of potential energy; the weight of the stone is potentially able to perform work. If the stone is permitted to drop, it can accomplish this work, the amount depending on the height of the drop. The falling stone, as it gathers speed, accumulates energy of motion, or kinetic energy. If the fall of the stone is halted by a surface, the energy of motion disappears and may be converted, for example, into heat, which is simply the collective kinetic energy of myraids of atoms and molecules (Chapter 19). In any controlled experiment, from which the rest of the universe is barred, the total amount of energy remains constant, though its distribution among different forms, such as potential or kinetic energy, heat, chemical energy, etc., may vary. This fundamental physical law, the principle of conservation of energy, is basic in problems, experiments and machines dealing with energy transfer.

The Sun and the stars are great powerhouses in which energy is produced at a huge rate and is radiated away from the surface. This radiation is the only means of energy transport from the Sun and stars to the observer. In daily experience we find that heat energy is also transported either by conduction or by convection. Conduction is simply the transfer of heat through contact of one particle with another, as, for example, in a heated iron. The transfer of heat through air currents is an illustration of convection of heat. There is some conduction and convection of heat within the stars. The main agency, however, for the transportation of energy not only outside, but also inside the stars is radiation (Chapters 20 and 21).

Units of energy

The equivalence of different types of energy as we ordinarily recognize them necessitates the establishment of rates of exchange for energy. Of particular importance is the exchange of heat and of energy of a mechanical nature, such as kinetic energy. The conventional unit of heat energy is the calorie, which we have seen is the amount of heat necessary to raise the temperature of one gram of water by one degree centigrade. The conventional unit of mechanical energy is the erg, which may be defined conveniently in the form of kinetic energy. The kinetic energy of a body of mass m in grams and velocity v centimeters per second amounts to $mv^2/2$. Hence, the erg may be defined and visualized as the amount of kinetic energy of a particle having a mass of two grams and a velocity of one centimeter per second. This rate of exchange between heat and mechanical energy has been established from laboratory experiments, and is found to be 1 calorie = 4.18×10^7 ergs. This quantity is referred to as the mechanical equivalent of heat.

Laws of radiation for continuous spectra; quantum concept

In the case of continuous spectra radiation occurs in all frequencies; the relative intensity of these radiations depends on the temperature. In order to explain the distribution of radiative energy over the different frequencies and at different temperatures, Max Planck (1858–1947) introduced in 1900 the concept of a quantum of energy. Planck assumed that atoms are vibrating systems which can exist in so-called stationary states, having specific levels of energy, and that energy can be gained or lost only by transitions between these states. According to Planck, the radiation created occurs in elemental quanta, i.e., "atoms of radiation." The energy of the radiation of each quantum is assumed to be proportional to the frequency of vibration v; i.e., $E = hv$, where h is called Planck's constant, a universal constant whose numerical value is 6.55×10^{-27}. Since there is a continuum of different colors, a corresponding continuum of light quanta exists.

Both theory and observation coincide in describing the intensity of the radiation in different colors as it depends on the surface temperature; the quantitative expression of the relation is in terms of the unit surface, i.e., the square centimeter. The behavior of the radiation over all colors is described by the Planck distribution curve of radiant energy.

There are two laws, derivable from Planck's law, of particular usefulness in studying the radiation in continuous spectra. The first describes the total emission of energy per unit surface over all frequencies combined. This total radiative efficiency, called surface brightness, is proportional to the fourth power of the absolute temperature. This is the Stefan-Boltzmann law, named after the discovery in 1879 by Josef Stefan (1835–1893) and its first theoretical explanation in 1884 by Ludwig Boltzmann (1844–1906). Its formulation is as follows:

$$E = 5.75 \times 10^{-5} T^4 \ ergs/cm^2/sec$$

where T is the absolute temperature expressed in centigrades. Hence doubling the surface temperature increases the total radiation sixteenfold. The second law, the so-called displacement law of Wilhelm Wien (1864–1928), dates from 1893: the frequency ν_m of the radiation of highest intensity is proportional to the temperature of the radiating surface. The exact relation is $T = 9.65 \times 10^{-12} \nu_m$.

Planck's law of radiation and the corresponding laws of Stefan-Boltzmann and Wien hold exactly for perfect radiators, i.e., objects which are perfectly black when cool. The laws hold also, more or less, for a continuous spectrum resulting from the radiation of a sufficiently deep layer of hot ionized gases like the surface layers of Sun and stars.

By applying these laws of radiation we can determine the temperature of celestial bodies such as the Sun and stars. This will be illustrated in the next chapter.

16 | THE COMPOSITION
OF STARLIGHT

Qualitative and quantitative analysis

Methods have been developed for the qualitative and quantitative analyses of matter. The chemist can take a small sample of any material, and through proper experiments find out what elements it contains. This procedure is called qualitative analysis. A subsequent stage is the quantitative analysis—finding out the exact amount of each chemical element in the sample. The astronomer is interested in both a qualitative and a quantitative chemical analysis of cosmic objects such as Sun and stars; in addition, he is interested in physical properties such as temperature and pressure. It is obviously impossible to use conventional laboratory methods of chemical analysis; the astronomer has to rely solely on the light messages sent out by the objects which he wishes to investigate. He therefore employs the methods of spectral analysis. We noted that spectral analysis is useful for terrestrial purposes; it permits the detection of very small quantities of a chemical element and proves to be an exceedingly precise method of identification.

Stellar spectra

The laws of spectral analysis have also been applied with great success to Sun and stars. An analysis of the light from these objects reveals absorption spectra. According to Kirchhoff's law, the delicate pattern of absorption lines indicates the presence of rarefied gaseous material between us and a source which yields the continuous background of colors in the spectrum. Like the Sun, any other star appears to have a gaseous atmosphere surrounding a somewhat hotter surface layer of comparatively denser material, the photosphere. We assume, therefore, that absorption lines are caused by atoms and molecules in a star's atmosphere which diminish the intensity of radiation in certain colors. A certain small fraction of the flow of energy is either absorbed or at least diverted or scattered by these atoms or molecules. The light from the objects has also passed through our terrestrial atmosphere, causing a number of telluric absorption lines due primarily to the oxygen and nitrogen in that atmosphere. Fortunately, these lines are not abundant enough to interfere seriously with the study of cosmic spectra. We can allow for their presence since it is known which lines are due to our own atmosphere, and the matter need not concern us any further.

Spectroscopic evidence emphasizes the all-important fact that Sun and stars are very much alike. Earlier, when studying stellar luminosities (Chapter 8) and stellar masses (Chapter 13), we were led to the conclusion that, in a general way, the stars are suns and, conversely, that the Sun is a star. Now we know that Sun and stars are self-luminous, both consisting of comparatively dense incandescent material surrounded by a comparatively cooler and rarefied atmosphere.

Spectral types

Several hundred thousand stellar spectra have been photographed; according to the pattern and intensity of the absorption lines they can be classified in a sequence. The most important is the Harvard classification developed by Annie Jump Cannon (1863–1941). With the aid of a prism placed in front of a photographic camera the images of all stars down to those of about the ninth magnitude were drawn out into their respective spectral ranges, the appearance of which strongly suggested a classification of stars according to their spectra (see photographs 7, 8). Miss Cannon recognized about a dozen principal spectral types which are now labeled by the letters O, B, A, F, G, K, M, R, N, S and a few others. Over 99 per cent of all stars fell in the six groups B, A, F, G, K, M. All spectra reveal absorption lines of hydrogen, which are strongest in type A. Only in types B and O do we observe faint lines of helium. As we proceed toward types F and G and beyond, we note a conspicuous general increase in the number and intensity of metallic lines. In types K and M absorption bands due to molecular compounds make their appearance.

The Sun's spectrum is of type G and is indistinguishable from the spectra of thousands of other G-type stars studied so far. The absorption pattern of an A star like Sirius is quite different from that of a G-type star. The spectrum of Sirius contains a series of conspicuous absorption lines attributed to the presence of hydrogen atoms in the star's atmosphere. The corresponding absorption lines in the solar spectrum are relatively weak. On the other hand, the Sun contains conspicuous absorption patterns due to all sorts of metals which are obviously present in the solar atmosphere; in the spectrum of Sirius the corresponding patterns of metallic lines are extremely weak. Does the difference in spectrum imply that the atmosphere of Sirius has a different chemical composition from that of the Sun, in the sense that hydrogen is relatively more abundant for Sirius and the metals more abundant for the Sun? This is a possible, but not necessarily complete, explanation. It is not only a matter of what atoms are present in the atmosphere, but how many among those present participate in trapping certain kinds of light coming from the photosphere. Could it be that not all the atoms of any particular element are doing the same thing in different stellar atmospheres? Can it be possible that there are external conditions which determine the character and rate of the atoms' activities in this respect?

Surface temperatures

External conditions do differ from one star to another, the principal factor being temperature. Differences in surface temperature are indicated by variations in the distribution of the spectral intensities of different stars. According to the laws of radiation, the spectral region of maximum energy or intensity is shifted from the red to the violet as the surface temperature is changed from lower to higher values. Most of the radiative energy of the cooler stars is contained in the red part of the spectrum; and most of the radiation of the hotter stars is in the blue part of the spectrum. The simple quantitative law underlying this situation was described in the last chapter; the frequency ν_m of the color representing the highest energy is proportional to the surface temperature T; according to Wien's formula: $T = 9.65 \times 10^{-12} \nu_m$.

For example, consider again the bluish star Sirius and the yellowish star, our Sun. The continuous background of the spectrum of Sirius is relatively more intense in the blue than is the Sun's. The maximum intensity of radiation in Sirius occurs in the ultraviolet color of frequency 1.10×10^{15}; in the Sun it occurs in the green color of frequency 0.60×10^{15}. Hence, the surface temperature of Sirius is 10,600° K, and that of the Sun about 5750° K.

The remarkable general result is the close relation between color or surface temperature and the pattern of the absorption lines of stars. The Harvard sequence of spectral types proves to be a temperature sequence, the surface temperatures ranging from 25,000° for the bluish B stars to less than 3000° for red M stars. The corresponding atmospheric temperatures are only slightly lower; and they undoubtedly play a major role in determining the absorbing activities of the atmospheric atoms and molecules (Chapter 19).

Stellar interiors must be gaseous

The surface temperatures of certain stars—those of type O—run as high as 100,000°, while those of very red stars may be as low as 2000°. Terrestrially speaking, these temperatures are all high and reflect the state of the stellar interiors, which must in all cases be hotter than the surfaces. At these high temperatures the internal cohesion characteristic of solid and liquid structures cannot exist and we are forced to accept the fact that the interiors of Sun and stars are therefore gaseous. The average density of our Sun is 1.41 times that of water, so that the solar gases must be highly compressed indeed. There are extremely rarefied stars, however; and, on the other hand, there are also stars whose average density is much higher than the Sun's. The composition of this highly compressed matter will be discussed in Chapters 20 and 21.

Other objects

The power of spectral analysis extends, of course, to objects other than stars. We recall its significance for the study of planetary atmospheres, comets and meteors. There are the cloudlike objects in the sky classified as nebulae. Photographs of the Milky Way clearly reveal both dark obscuring nebulae and luminous diffuse nebulae (see photographs 34–40). Both types of nebulae are clouds and wisps of material, irregular in shape. Then there are the planetary nebulae, huge rarefied expanding envelopes around certain very hot stars (see photographs 32, 33). They derive their name from their frequently disklike appearance in the telescope. Both the luminous diffuse and planetary nebulae have a greenish color, whereas the extragalactic spiral nebulae (Chapter 30) are white.

Spectral analysis reveals that the green nebulae have emission-line spectra, proving that they contain rarefied gases. The white nebulae have absorption spectra which long ago suggested that these objects consist of numerous stars, a hypothesis confirmed later through direct photography with giant reflecting telescopes.

Helium, nebulium and coronium

Of the studies about the discovery and identification of a chemical element in the cosmos, we mention first the well-known element helium, which through its brightest spectral line was first discovered in the spectrum of the solar chromosphere during the eclipse of 1868. Appropriately named helium, the element was not found on the Earth until 1895. We also mention the spectra characteristic of the aforementioned green nebula and of the solar corona, the very delicate outer atmosphere of the

Sun, observed best at the time of a total eclipse of the Sun. For a long time these spectra could not be identified entirely with the spectra of any known chemical elements; they were therefore attributed to the hypothetical elements "nebulium" and "coronium." Only recently was it discovered that in these two cases well-known terrestrial elements accounted for the spectra. The character of the radiation of an element is now known to depend on such physical conditions as temperature and pressure (Chapter 19). The extreme rarefaction in the nebulae and corona results in spectral radiations different from those sent out under ordinary conditions in the laboratory. Thus it was found in 1927 that the "nebulium" lines are primarily due to ionized oxygen and nitrogen. In 1941 the lines of "coronium" were identified as radiations from highly ionized iron, nickel and similar elements. This high state of ionization in the corona results from the violent agitation of the atoms, which corresponds to a temperature of one million degrees!

Surface brightness and size

A star's size or diameter may be derived by comparing its total intrinsic luminosity with its surface brightness, i.e., radiation per square centimeter. The intrinsic luminosity can be determined if both apparent brightness and distance are known (Chapter 8). We recall from the last chapter that in the case of continuous radiation the surface brightness, including all frequencies, varies in proportion to the fourth power of the surface temperature; the latter may be determined from the observed distribution of radiant energy in the continuous background of the stellar spectra. In most astronomical studies the measured luminosities do not include the total radiation of the stars, since, like the eye, most instruments are set to receive a limited range of radiative frequencies. There is considerable practical difficulty in obtaining the total radiation comprising all frequencies. Often it is advisable to limit the study to a certain range of radiation which can be conveniently observed with the available instrumental means. Fortunately, the Earth's atmosphere is quite transparent for radiation in the visual range. Many astronomical studies are therefore based on the conventional radiation limited to the visual octave.

The size of a star is usually derived as follows: We compare the star's surface brightness with that of the Sun, whose diameter (1,391,000 kilometers) is well known from direct geometric measurements. Take again, for example, the bluish star Sirius; knowing its apparent brightness and distance (8.6 lightyears), we can deduce its luminosity, which is found to be thirty times that of the Sun in the visual octave of radiation (cf. the example in Chapter 8). Its surface temperature is about 10,600° K, in contrast with the surface temperature of the Sun, which is only 5750° K. The visual surface brightness of Sirius, i.e., its total visual radiation per square centimeter per second, is about eight times as great as that of the Sun. If Sirius had the same surface brightness as the Sun, it would therefore have thirty times the Sun's surface, or $\sqrt{30}$ times the Sun's diameter. Since, however, its visual surface brightness or radiative efficiency is eight times as great as that of the Sun, a surface of 30/8 or 3.75 that of the Sun will account for the luminosity of Sirius. Hence, we deduce that the diameter of Sirius is $\sqrt{3.75}$ or nearly twice that of the Sun.

Take as another example a cool star such as the faint red star Krüger 60 B (Chapter 17) which has a surface temperature of 3000° and a luminosity of 1/2000 that of the Sun. If the star had the same surface brightness as the Sun, its surface would be 1/2000 times that of the Sun. The surface brightness or efficiency of radiation in the visual octave at this temperature is, however, about 90 times as weak as the Sun's; hence, a surface of 90/2000 or 1/22 of the Sun's surface is required to account for the observed light and we conclude that the diameter of Krüger 60 B is $1/\sqrt{22}$, or somewhat over one-fifth that of the Sun.

Mass and density

Chapter 13 revealed how the stellar masses of the components of binary stars can be derived; since the color structure of the light from a star enables us to compute stellar diameters, we are now in a position to determine the average densities of binary components whose spectra or colors are known. In the particular case of eclipsing binary stars, the duration and depth of the eclipse furnish an ideal means for studying both the sizes and luminosities of these stars. Such measurements are among the most accurate known, and confirm those obtained by the indirect methods described above, which of course have the advantage of being applicable to any single star whose luminosity and color can be determined.

Basic properties of stars

The fundamental physical properties describing the general structure of a star are its mass, size, luminosity and surface temperature. From the mass and size we can derive the average density of the star. The luminosity of a star is known as soon as its apparent brightness and distance can be measured with sufficient accuracy. The diameter of a star can be determined by comparing the star's luminosity with its radiating efficiency or surface brightness, which depends on the surface temperature. The mass of a star can be computed only if the star is a component of a binary system. Both the period of revolution and the size of the orbit must be known, and the system must be sufficiently near so that the linear size of the orbit can be accurately measured (Chapter 13). The individual masses in a binary system may be determined by observing the components' orbital motion projected on a background of distant stars.

All these properties can generally be best derived for stars which are relatively near to us. We shall therefore make a survey of these different physical properties in a sample of stars in our immediate neighborhood; this will be good preparation for the different problems concerning stellar atmospheres (Chapter 19) and stellar interiors (Chapter 20).

17 | THE NEAREST STARS

First-magnitude stars

Before turning to the nearest stars, we shall first make another survey. From the observational point of view the very brightest stars offer obvious advantages. However, apparent brightness is not a good criterion of distance (Chapter 8). It is true that on the average the apparently brighter stars are nearer, but it is practically hopeless even to make a guess at the distance of individual stars on the basis of brightness alone.

The reason for this is the tremendous range in stellar luminosities, which is well illustrated by the small sample of the twenty brightest stars, not including the Sun (Table III). These stars are found in different parts of the sky. The distances of the nearest ones are accurately known, while for the more distant stars the values are much less certain. Several of these stars are double, or multiple, but for the present study the companion stars have been ignored. The intrinsic luminosity of each star has been computed from the apparent magnitude and the distance.

Although these stars differ little in apparent brightness, they

TABLE III. *The Twenty Brightest Stars (in order of brightness)*

NAME	MAGNITUDE	SPECTRUM	ANNUAL PROPER MOTION	PARALLAX	DISTANCE IN LIGHTYEARS	LUMINOSITY (SUN AS UNIT)
1 Sirius *	−1.6	Ao	1″.32	0″.381	8.6	30
2 Canopus	−0.9	Fo	0.02	.033	100	1,900
3 Alpha Centauri *	+0.1	G4	3.68	.761	4.3	1.3
4 Vega	0.1	Ao	0.35	.123	27	63
5 Capella *	0.2	Go	0.44	.077	42	150
6 Arcturus	0.2	Ko	2.29	.098	33	83
7 Rigel	0.3	B8	0.01	.006	540	21,000
8 Procyon *	0.5	F3	1.25	.295	11	6.9
9 Achernar	0.6	B5	0.09	.045	70	280
10 Beta Centauri	0.9	B1	0.04	.017	190	1,400
11 Altair	0.9	A5	0.66	.208	16	10
12 Betelgeuse	0.9	M2	0.03	.011	300	3,600
13 Alpha Crucis *	1.0	B1	0.05	.015	220	1,200
14 Aldebaran *	1.1	K5	0.20	.062	53	91
15 Pollux	1.2	Ko	0.62	.114	29	25
16 Spica	1.2	B2	0.05	.027	120	440
17 Antares *	1.2	M1	0.03	.013	250	1,900
18 Fomalhaut	1.3	A3	0.37	.139	23	16
19 Deneb	1.3	A2	0.00	.008	400	4,800
20 Regulus *	1.3	B8	0.24	.049	67	130

* double or multiple star

exhibit a tremendous range in their distances and hence in their luminosities. Excluding the fainter components, we find that all these stars are intrinsically brighter than the Sun. The brightest object is Rigel, one of the bright blue stars in the constellation Orion. This star, which is 540 lightyears away, proves to be about 21,000 times as luminous as the Sun. The intrinsically faintest object is the bright component of the triple star Alpha Centauri, whose luminosity is only 1.3 times that of the Sun; the combined luminosity of the three components of Alpha Centauri is 1.7 times that of the Sun. While Rigel is the most distant star in this group, Alpha Centauri is the nearest. We see that stars of the same intrinsic luminosity as Alpha Centauri but farther away might not be included in this limited sample. At the same time, an extremely luminous star like Rigel, though at a tremendous distance, is included in the brighter half of the list.

The bright stars yield data of considerable interest; nevertheless, these objects are not at all representative of the actual population of the stellar world, since they draw attention exclusively to the existence of intrinsically luminous stars.

Nearest stars

Our immediate stellar neighborhood provides a more representative sample; we shall now study all known stars within sixteen lightyears. The distance limit is arbitrary, but it is wide enough to include a sufficient number of stars to provide a workable sample of adequate scope. How have we found the stars within this particular limit of distance? We recall (Chapters 8 and 9) that a star's proper motion is by far the best criterion for its distance. For several decades astronomers have determined the distances of stars of large proper motion; and, with hardly any exceptions, such stars have proven to be rela-

TABLE IV. *Stars Nearer Than 16.5 Lightyears*

NAME	MAGNITUDE AND SPECTRUM						ANNUAL PROPER MOTION	PARALLAX	DISTANCE IN LIGHT-YEARS	LUMINOSITY (SUN AS UNIT)		
	A		B		C					A	B	C
1 Sun	..	Go	..	..	..	..	..	..	..	1	..	..
2 Alpha Centauri	0.3	G4	1.7	K1	11	M	3".68	0".761	4.3	1.3	0.36	0.00007
3 Barnard's Star	9.7	M5	*	..	..	..	10.30	.530	6.1	0.0005	..	..
4 Lalande 21185	7.6	M2	*	..	..	..	4.78	.411	7.9	0.005	..	..
5 Wolf 359	13.5	M5	..	..	..	..	4.84	.408	8.0	0.00002	..	..
6 Luyten 726-8	12.5	(M6)	13.0	(M6)	..	..	3.35	.41	8	0.00005	0.00003	..
7 Sirius	-1.6	Ao	7.1	A5	..	..	1.32	.381	8.6	30	0.01	..
8 Ross 154	11	M4	..	..	..	..	0.67	.357	9.1	0.0003	..	..
9 Ross 248	12.2	M6	..	..	..	..	1.58	.317	10.3	0.00013	..	..
10 Luyten 789-6	12.3	M5	..	..	..	..	3.27	.315	10.3	0.00012	..	..
11 Epsilon Eridani	3.8	Ko	..	..	..	..	0.97	.305	10.7	0.33	..	..
12 Procyon	0.5	F3	10.8	..	..	..	1.25	.295	11.0	6.9	0.0005	..
13 61 Cygni	5.6	K5	6.3	K6	*	..	5.22	.294	11.1	0.069	0.036	..
14 Ross 128	11.1	M5	..	..	..	..	1.40	.292	11.2	0.0004	..	..
15 Epsilon Indi	4.7	K5	..	..	..	..	4.67	.291	11.2	0.16	..	..
16 Tau Ceti	3.6	Ko	..	..	..	..	1.92	.290	11.2	0.44	..	..
17 Sigma 2398	8.9	M4	9.7	M5	..	..	2.29	.287	11.3	0.0033	0.0016	..
18 BD − 12° 4523	9.7	M4	..	..	..	..	1.24	.281	11.6	0.0017	..	..
19 Groombridge 34	8.1	M1	10.9	M6	..	..	2.91	.278	11.7	0.0076	0.0006	..
20 Lacaille 9352	7.4	M2	..	..	..	..	6.87	.271	12.0	0.014	..	..

TABLE IV. Stars Nearer Than 16.5 Lightyears (continued)

NAME	MAGNITUDE AND SPECTRUM			ANNUAL PROPER MOTION	PARALLAX	DISTANCE IN LIGHT-YEARS	LUMINOSITY (SUN AS UNIT)		
	A	B	C				A	B	C
21 BD + 5° 1668	10.1 M4	...	...	3".73	0".263	12.4	0.0013	...	...
22 Ross 614	11 M4	*	...	0.97	.260	12.5	0.0006	...	...
23 Lacaille 8760	6.6 M1	...	...	3.46	.260	12.5	0.33	...	...
24 Krüger 60	9.8 M4	11.3 M6	...	0.87	.256	12.7	0.0019	0.0005	...
25 Kapteyn's star	8.8 Mo	...	...	8.79	.256	12.7	0.0048	...	...
26 van Maanen's star	12.3 Fo	...	...	2.98	.247	13.2	0.0002	...	...
27 Groombridge 1618	6.8 K6	...	...	1.45	.231	14.1	0.036	...	...
28 Wolf 424	12.6 (M5)	12.6 (M5)	...	1.87	.230	14.2	0.0002	0.0002	...
29 CD − 46° 11540	9.4 M3	...	...	1.15	.225	14.5	0.0033	...	...
30 CC 658	11 ...	...	...	2.69	.219	14.9	0.0008	...	...
31 AOe 17415−6	9.1 M4	...	...	1.31	.216	15.1	0.0048	...	...
32 Ross 780	10.3 M5	...	...	1.12	.213	15.3	0.0017	...	...
33 CD − 44° 11909	10.0 M5	...	...	1.14	.212	15.4	0.0023	...	...
34 BD + 20° 2465	9.5 M3	*	...	.49	.210	15.5	0.0036	...	...
35 CD − 37° 15492	8.3 M3	...	...	6.09	.210	15.5	0.011	...	...
36 CD − 49° 13515	8.6 M3	...	...	.78	.209	15.6	0.0083	...	...
37 Altair	0.9 A5	...	...	.66	.208	15.7	10	...	...
38 BD + 43° 4305	10.2 M5	...	...	.84	.208	15.7	0.0019	...	...
39 o² Eridani	4.5 G5	9.2 B9	10.7 M4	4.08	.205	15.9	0.36	0.0048	0.0012
40 AC + 79° 3888	11.0 M4	...	...	.87	.199	16.4	0.0010	...	...
41 70 Ophiuchi	4.3 K1	6.0 K5	...	1.13	.197	16.5	0.48	0.10	...

* Unseen companion (Chapter 14).

tively near. Up to now fifty-four stars have been found that are nearer than sixteen lightyears; this number includes the Sun (Table IV). Of this sample of nearby stars fewer than a dozen are visible to the unaided eye. The majority are faint telescopic objects which were first recognized as being close to us because of their large proper motions. Not all fifty-four stars are isolated like the Sun. Thirty appear isolated, but eighteen are grouped two by two in nine binary systems, while six stars are grouped three by three in two triple systems. We may say that there are forty-one objects—thirty single, nine double, and two triple. In addition, irregularities in the proper motions of several of the single stars indicate the existence of unseen companions (Chapter 14). One unseen companion has also been detected in the visual binary 61 Cygni.

Spacing of stars

The spaciousness of our immediate cosmic surroundings in the world of stars is clearly demonstrated by the present survey. On the average, the forty-one objects are several lightyears apart from one another, while the sizes of the stars are generally well below one light minute; the diameter of the Sun is less than five light seconds. The spacing within the double and triple systems is extremely small compared with the wide spacing between the different single-, double- and triple-star systems. These internal spacings, expressed in light time, are generally well below one light day.

The tremendous spaces between the stars may be illustrated this way. A true-scale analogy is obtained by imagining some fifty balls—tennis balls, golf balls, marbles and smaller objects —spread through a spherical volume the size of the Earth, i.e., 12,740 kilometers in diameter. Imagine these balls moving at speeds averaging ten meters per year; this gives a true-scale idea about the vast space-and-time dimensions protecting the stars from collisions, notwithstanding their own motions which, on the average, are something like 30 kilometers per second. In this analogy the internal separation of the component stars ir binary and triple systems is generally less than 1 kilometer, a very small fraction of the average spacing between the different objects.

The incompleteness of our knowledge about intrinsically faint stars, even those in our immediate neighborhood, is illustrated as follows: Suppose we count the stars up to a distance of thirteen lightyears. The amount of space thus covered is one-half the larger sphere with the radius of sixteen lightyears. The smaller sphere contains twenty-five objects, which is well over one-half the number in the larger sphere. The incompleteness is also revealed in the observed abundance of stellar components, even if we exclude the planetary companions of the Sun and the unseen companions of other stars. The twenty-five stars nearer than thirteen lightyears represent thirty-four separate components; while the sixteen stars whose distances are between thirteen and sixteen lightyears include only twenty observed components. Obviously the observed state of duplicity or multiplicity decreases with the distance; the same is true for the number of unseen components. This decrease must be due to increased difficulty in observing the existing components.

If we double the limits of our sample, thereby covering a volume of space eight times as great, we confirm in a general way the results provided by the small, accurate sample of the very nearest stars.

Luminosities

The accurate distance values of the nearby stars permit a reliable derivation of their intrinsic luminosities; we shall compare them with the luminosity of the Sun. The results of this comparison are given in Table IV; they hold for the radiation in the visual octave. In order to organize and study this information, we arrange the fifty-four separate stars in order of their brightness; the various unseen companion stars are not included. In this luminosity array we disregard the family relations which bind certain stars together in binary and triple systems.

Only four stars of our nearby sample are more luminous than the Sun. Sirius, the sixth nearest star at a distance of eight lightyears, is intrinsically the brightest, having a visual luminosity thirty times that of the Sun. Next comes Procyon, at a distance of eleven lightyears, with a luminosity seven times that of the Sun. Following in order of brightness is Altair at sixteen lightyears, with a luminosity ten times that of the Sun. Slightly brighter than the Sun is the bright component of the triple star Alpha Centauri, the nearest stellar object at a distance of only 4.3 lightyears. All the other stars are fainter than the Sun, and represent varying degrees of luminosity. The faintest star Wolf 359 has a luminosity of only 1/50,000 times that of the Sun. Although this star is only eight lightyears away, its apparent magnitude is as faint as 13.5, and the star is difficult to observe, both visually and photographically. We recall (Chapter 14) that at a distance of nineteen lightyears, just outside our sample, a still fainter star was found by Van Biesbroeck. Van Biesbroeck's star is intrinsically ten times as faint as Wolf 359; at present it is the faintest star known.

Luminosity function

The comparative abundance of stars of different luminosities within sixteen lightyears is illustrated in Table V.

This pattern of the abundance of different luminosities represents what is called the luminosity function or luminosity curve.

TABLE V.   *Luminosity Curve of Stars Nearer*
Than 16.5 Lightyears

LUMINOSITY IN TERMS OF SUN			NUMBER OF STARS
>	1		4
.1	to	1	7
.01	"	.1	7
.001	"	.01	18
.0001	"	.001	14
.00001	"	.0001	4

We note an increase in number for each successive drop of 1/10 in luminosity down to 1/1000 times the Sun's luminosity. Below this value no further increase takes place; instead, a decrease occurs. There is, however, good reason to believe that this decrease in the abundance of very faint stars is to a large extent spurious; it is the result of incomplete information about objects which are difficult to find and study. The lower limit of luminosity in the present sample is represented, as mentioned, by the very faint star Wolf 359. We have referred to the still fainter star discovered by Van Biesbroeck. Additional faint stars toward the more indistinct side of the luminosity curve will undoubtedly still be discovered.

Main sequence

There is a remarkable relation between the luminosities and colors of the nearest stars (with a few exceptions). The fainter the star, the redder its color, so that an arrangement of the nearer stars according to decreasing luminosity proves to be a sequence, too, of increasing redness. The astronomer refers to this striking array of luminosity and color as the main sequence.

Most of the stars are red (spectral type M) and much smaller than the Sun; these are often referred to as red dwarfs. That there should be a relation between luminosity, on the one hand, and size and color, on the other hand, is not surprising, since luminosity depends on size and surface brightness. But that so

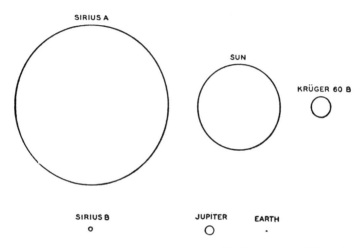

Comparative sizes of bluish (A), yellowish (G) and red (M) main-sequence stars, a white dwarf and two planets.

many stars should fall into the main sequence is remarkable indeed.

White dwarfs; the companion of Sirius

Striking exceptions to the main-sequence rule are certain stars which are small but not red. These stars have about the same "white" color as Sirius and Procyon, both of which are larger than the Sun. These exceptional stars are named white dwarfs. The best-known example is the companion of Sirius, also called Sirius B, whose luminosity is only 1/100 times that of the Sun.

Its mass slightly exceeds that of the Sun, however. The white color (spectrum A5) of this star implies a high surface temperature of about 8000° K as compared with the Sun's surface temperature of 5750° K. In the visual octave the radiation of this star is four times as intense as the Sun's. That its luminosity is small implies that it is also small in size; its diameter is only 1/20 and its volume 1/8000 times the Sun's. Hence, the density of the companion of Sirius must be on the average about 8000 times the average density (1.4) of the Sun, or about 11,000 times that of water!

The white dwarfs (of which many more are known beyond sixteen lightyears) are very small, smaller than the largest planets in the solar system. All have masses comparable to that of the Sun and other stars; hence, their densities are all extremely high. The densest white dwarf discovered so far has an estimated density 36 million times that of water. These high densities prove the existence of matter in a form unknown on this Earth. If we are astonished by these results, let us remember that any terrestrial experiments with matter are done on an extraordinarily small scale compared to that of the stars. From a cosmic viewpoint, it is not the stars which are exceptional, but rather the small-scale experiments and experiences we are accustomed to on the Earth. But it is not only a matter of size, it is also a matter of temperature and pressure, both of which may be very large inside the stars. In Chapter 20 we shall see that the exceedingly dense packing of material within some stars is not really so difficult to understand.

Gravitational red shift

Fortunately there is an independent check on the high densities found for these stars. Even in the case of the best-studied white dwarf, Sirius B, there are certain observational difficulties due to the proximity of the brilliant primary. Another observational approach to the problem makes use of the fact that light particles or photons possess mass just as "material" particles do. When a photon is radiated away from the photosphere of a star it has to overcome the gravitational pull of the star. The photon has to work; it has to use up a small part of the energy with which it started its journey. The energy E in a photon is expressed by the simple relation $E = h\nu$ (Chapter 18), where h is Planck's universal constant and ν the frequency of the radiation. The loss of a small part of this energy results in a slight decrease in the original frequency of the photon. Photons of different frequencies radiating from any one star would all be affected in the same way; the result is a slight transposition of the whole stellar spectrum toward lower frequencies or higher wave lengths, i.e., toward the red. This displacement is referred to as the gravitational red shift; by carefully comparing the frequencies or wave lengths of spectral lines in a star's spectrum with those found in laboratory experiments, the amount of the red shift may be determined. The technical procedure is very delicate, and of the same nature as the one used in measuring the Doppler shift resulting from motion in the line of sight.

The gravitational red shift is proportional to the mass of the star and inversely proportional to its size. The red shift of stars of the same size, but of different masses, increases with the mass; for stars of the same mass, but different sizes, the red shift increases with the density. The red shift is therefore most easily detected either in very heavy stars or very small stars; in the case of certain white dwarfs it may therefore be appreciable.

One of the great difficulties is knowing how much of any spectral fluctuation is due to Doppler shift and how much to gravitational red shift. Now it is fortunate that the mechanism of motion of a double star like Sirius is well known. Hence, the radial velocity of the companion of Sirius can be accurately calculated for any moment, and we can isolate the gravitational red shift in its spectrum. This was first done successfully in 1925 by Walter Sydney Adams (1876–   ) at the Mount Wilson Observatory. The observed amount of red shift yields a striking quantitative confirmation of the high density of this star.

Mass-luminosity relation; densities

Within our sample there are seven double stars whose known masses are reliable. The values for the individual components are given in Table VI.

TABLE VI.   *Masses of the Binary Components of Nearby Stars*

NAME	MEAN DISTANCE BETWEEN COMPONENTS	PERIOD OF REVOLUTION	MASSES IN TERMS OF THE SUN'S MASS	
Alpha Centauri A,B	23.3 A.U.	80 years	1.1	0.9
Sirius......... A,B	20.0	50	2.1	1.1
Procyon...... A,B	15.8	40.6	1.7	0.6
61 Cygni...... A,B	84.	720	0.6:	0.6:
Krüger 60..... A,B	9.2	44.5	0.26	0.14
o² Eridani..... B,C	34.	248:	0.4	0.2
70 Ophiuchi... A,B	23.3	87.8	0.90	0.73

We note the rather restricted range of these masses. Of particular interest is the relation between the masses and luminosities of the Sun and of the stars in Table VI (with the conspicuous exception of the faint companions of Sirius and Procyon). The stars of small mass are of low luminosity, while the intrinsically brighter stars have higher masses. The range in mass, however, is small compared with that in luminosity; the luminosities vary approximately as the third power of the mass.

The highest mass is that of the bright bluish star Sirius A (2.1 times the Sun), whose luminosity is 30 times that of the Sun; the lowest mass is that of the faint red star Krüger 60 B (1/7 times the Sun's), whose luminosity is 1/2000 times that of the Sun. The former star is the bright component of the well-known double star Sirius (Chapter 13). The latter is the fainter component of the well-known binary Krüger 60 (Chapter 16), which consists of two red-dwarf stars, whose mean separation is 9.2 astronomical units, revolving about their center of mass in 44.5 years. The masses of the components are .26 and .14 times the Sun's mass; their luminosities are .002 and .0005 times that of the Sun. While the surface temperature of Sirius A is 10,600° K, that of Krüger 60 B is only about 3000° K; it is one of the intrinsically very faint stars.

The mass-luminosity relation is confirmed through a study of more distant stars. Comparatively few stars are found to be more than 10 times as heavy and about 1000 times as luminous as the Sun. The mass-luminosity relation, except for the white dwarfs, is now one of the well-established facts of astronomy; it plays a role in all inquiries about the physical structure of stars. It is also a reliable tool for estimating the masses of stars which do not belong to binary systems; the mass of a single star may be estimated from the mass-luminosity relation as soon as the luminosity of the star has been measured. We note that the components of a binary or a triple system may have quite different physical characteristics, a puzzling matter if one attempts to explain the origin and evolution of multiple systems.

The average densities of stars may be computed from their observed masses and sizes. The densities vary tremendously, ranging from over 10,000 for certain white-dwarf stars to about 10^{-8} for certain red-giant stars. Examples of "ordinary" main-sequence stars are again Sirius A and Krüger 60 B, whose average densities are 0.5 and 18 times that of water.

Flare stars

Flare-ups of a number of nearby red-dwarf stars have occasionally been observed. None of these events can be seen with the naked eye; in all cases the observations have depended on sufficiently powerful telescopes. What happens is that for several minutes a star exhibits a manifold increase in luminosity. The phenomenon is like that occasionally observed when an area on the surface of the Sun near a sunspot becomes very much brighter for several minutes (Chapter 3). The solar eruptions are limited to a very small portion of the Sun and do not affect appreciably its total radiation. It is believed that stellar flares are of the same nature as those on the Sun, although they cover a proportionally larger area of the surface of a star. Hence the surface eruptions of these faint stars are much more cataclysmic than those of the relatively brighter and hotter Sun.

Stellar flare-ups are rare and unpredictable; up to the present there are only half a dozen known flare stars, of which Krüger 60 B is an interesting example (see photograph 28).

Beyond the nearest stars; red giants

Exploration of more distant portions of the stellar world reveals certain types of stars not found nearer to us, for example, blue stars like Rigel, Spica and others, which are bluer and intrinsically much brighter than Sirius. Another entirely different type of star is represented by objects like Betelgeuse, Antares, Aldebaran and Arcturus. These stars are not blue, but are very luminous; Arcturus and Aldebaran have an orange color and are about a hundred times as luminous as the Sun; Betelgeuse and Antares are red and are several thousand times as bright as the Sun. The red and orange colors suggest low surface temperatures, i.e., low rates of radiation. Hence these stars must be extremely large in order to have high luminosities. The diameter of Antares is about 1.5 times as large as the diameter of the Earth's orbit, while the diameter of Betelgeuse is approximately twice as large. If we centered Betelgeuse at the location of the Sun,

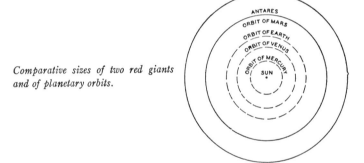

Comparative sizes of two red giants and of planetary orbits.

its surface would extend beyond the orbit of Mars! Very appropriately, stars like Betelgeuse and Antares are named red giants. We do not know much about the masses of these giant stars, but on the basis of the mass-luminosity relation, they would not be more than about fifteen times the Sun's mass. A simple computation shows that the average density of a star like Betelgeuse is extremely low, about 10^{-8} or 10^{-5} times the density of air. (The density of air is 1.3×10^{-3} grams per cubic centimeter.) For comparison we note that the density of a good vacuum obtained in the laboratory amounts to about 10^{-13} or

10^{-10} times the density of air. The density of the space between the stars represents an even purer "vacuum" with a density of about 10^{-24}! A rarefied star like Betelgeuse can exist, therefore, as a distinct object, since, after all, its density is high compared with that of interstellar space. Any apprehension about the possible dispersal of such a rarefied star is groundless; the mutual gravitation of its particles keeps the star together.

As to other stars of particular interest, we briefly mention the variable stars, i.e., those which vary in intrinsic luminosity as time goes on. For example the Cepheids, named after their prototype Delta Cephei, are stars of very high luminosity, often more than 100 times as bright as the Sun (Chapter 26). They vary in brightness in a regular, predictable fashion; this variation is probably caused by pulsations of the whole star. It is beyond the scope of this book to go into further detail about the physical behavior of these special stars. We shall later make use of these interesting stars, however, in connection with certain problems about the structure of the Milky Way system and objects beyond (Chapter 26).

Several of the red giants are variable stars of comparatively long period. The best-known example is Mira Ceti (Omicron Ceti); this star varies in a more or less regular fashion, with an average period of 330 days. At maximum Mira may be somewhat brighter than stars of the second magnitude; at minimum it may be as faint as a tenth-magnitude star.

Average density of matter in our neighborhood

The emptiness of the great open spaces between the stars may be further illustrated; the fifty-four separate stars in our present sample fill a volume with a radius of sixteen lightyears, corresponding to a volume of 17,160 cubic lightyears or 1.45×10^{58} cubic centimeters (1 lightyear $= 9.46 \times 10^{17}$ centimeters).

Hence, a space of about 320 cubic lightyears is available on the average for each star. The Sun's mass amounts to 2×10^{33} grams. Let us assume that the combined mass of these fifty-four stars is about thirty times this value. If all stars were now pulverized, and the resulting debris uniformly spread throughout the sphere of sixteen lightyears' radius, the average density would amount to 4×10^{-24} grams per cubic centimeter; in other words, one gram of matter would fill a cube whose sides were over six hundred kilometers. Compare this with the density 10^{-13} of a good vacuum, with the density 10^{-8} of a rarefied star like Betelgeuse, and with the density 10^{5} of the white-dwarf star Sirius B.

In conclusion: the principal, fundamental particles—the protons and neutrons—which form the basis of the mass of atoms have masses of 1.66×10^{-24} grams. If, therefore, the stars in our neighborhood were pulverized and permitted to fill space uniformly, they would yield about two nucleons per cubic centimeter!

18 | ATOMIC STRUCTURE AND RADIATION

Atomic physics

Atomic physics is of particular concern to the astronomer. Individual atoms are so small and so light that we cannot see them directly even with the aid of a strong microscope. The properties of atoms are revealed through their interactions with particles of the same general order of size. By letting atoms hit other atoms, or by studying the effect of photons (Chapter 9) on atoms, we can discover certain properties of the atoms involved in these experiments. It is necessary in such experiments to subject the atoms to interactions of considerable intensity. These may be provided either by atoms that move with high speed or by photons containing considerable energy, in other words, by radiation of very high frequency.

Nuclear atom; electrons, positrons

In 1911 Ernest Rutherford (1871–1937) studied the passage through matter of certain high-speed particles (helium "nuclei" or "α-particles"—Chapter 21) which are spontaneously expelled from radioactive substances. Rutherford concluded that atoms are not simple structures such as spheres, but that they are complex, each containing a very small but relatively massive nucleus surrounded by a number of "external" electrons well separated from the nucleus.

Electricity exists in charges of opposite signs, both positive and negative. The electrons are the elementary units of negative electricity, and the positrons (Chapter 21) are the units of positive electricity. The electric charges of these elemental particles amount to 4.80×10^{-10} electrostatic units. The electrostatic unit may be defined as follows: two masses of one gram each carrying an electric charge of one electrostatic unit each, placed one centimeter apart, repel or attract each other (depending on whether the signs of the electric charges are the same or different) with an initial mutual acceleration of two centimeters per second squared.

The atom is thus visualized as consisting of a small but massive nucleus surrounded by one or more electrons at some distance from the nucleus. The atom is therefore mostly empty space, and the overwhelming part of its mass is concentrated in the minute nucleus. The complete atom has no electric charge and is called neutral. Since the electrons, however, are the elemental charges of negative electricity, it is necessary to assume that the nucleus carries a charge equaling the total charge of the electrons, but of the opposite, i.e., positive sign.

For some time it had been thought that the creation of photons might have its origin in the external electrons. It was difficult, however, to explain why in the case of any particular element this radiation should be limited to a number of discrete frequencies. The structural relation between the nucleus and the external electrons was explained successfully in 1913 by

Niels Bohr (1885–   ), who introduced a novel theory of the mechanism of radiation.

The Bohr atom of hydrogen

It had been known for a long time that the visual range of the spectrum of hydrogen gas reveals a strikingly regular pattern of spectral lines (Chapter 15). When the myriads of hydrogen atoms in the rarefied state are stimulated to radiation, they form a "chorus" of a few dozen discrete color frequencies. The latter are related in simple mathematical proportions first noted in 1885 by Johann Jakob Balmer (1825–1898). No other element has as simple a spectrum as hydrogen; this could be explained by its low atomic weight, and Bohr wisely chose the hydrogen atom first to obtain a better understanding and model of the relation between atomic structure and the corresponding color composition of radiation.

Orbital structure

Bohr considered the structure of a hydrogen atom to be analogous to a planet moving about the Sun. He assumed the electron and the positive hydrogen nucleus to revolve about each other in a circular orbit. At all times there is a definite relation between the period of revolution, on the one hand, and the electrical attraction between the opposite charges, on the other. The gravitational attraction is negligibly small, while the electric properties of matter emerge very prominently. The charges of the hydrogen nucleus and the orbital electron are of the same amount but opposite signs; the masses of these particles are, however, very different. Precise measurements have indicated that the mass of the hydrogen nucleus is 1837 times that of the electron. The size of the hydrogen nucleus is very much smaller than that of the electron; the diameter of the former is of the order of 10^{-16} centimeters, that of the electron 10^{-13} centimeters.

Stationary orbits; transitions

Bohr assumed that the electron of any one hydrogen atom can move in circular orbits, and that these orbits are not of any particular size, but only of certain specific diameters. In any one of these possible orbits the electron moves in equilibrium with the electrical attraction between nucleus and electron. Breaking away from traditional knowledge, Bohr assumed that the atom does not radiate as long as the electron remains in the same "stationary" orbit. In this state of spin, the atom is inactive so far as its relation to the outside world is concerned; no radiation occurs, i.e., "nothing happens." But things do happen when the electron "changes" orbits. By appropriate stimulation—by collision with another atom, for instance—the atom becomes active. We imagine that on such an occasion the orbital electron is transferred or "lifted" instantaneously to an orbit of larger size, a so-called higher orbit. This transition to a higher orbit involves the transfer of a certain amount of energy; i.e., energy has been absorbed by the atom. The inverse process may occur; the electron may instantaneously "fall back" to a smaller or lower orbit, at which time energy is released in the form of radiation.

Quantum theory of radiation

Bohr introduced two principles. First he assumed that the radiation occurs in the form of one "particle" of radiation, or photon, and that the frequency determining the color of this photon is proportional to the amount of energy released, in accordance with Planck's law of radiation $E = h\nu$. This principle was based on Einstein's emphasis on the particle nature of radiation (1905), which in turn goes back (1900) to Max Planck's quantum theory (Chapter 15). Einstein had successfully used Planck's quantum concept to explain the photo-electric effect, i.e., the ejection of electrons from a metallic surface through the action of radiation falling on the surface. The velocity of the ejected electron depends not on the intensity but only on the color of the radiation. Einstein explained that the photo-electric effect is due to a transfer of the entire energy of one photon to one single electron in the metal. While Planck had not insisted on the maintenance of the quantum structure beyond the initial creation of radiation, Einstein emphasized the quantum structure of the radiation in transit. Thus the work of Planck and Einstein firmly established the usefulness of the concept of traveling light quanta or photons for explaining both the emission and the absorption of radiant energy.

As an illustration, the red hydrogen color known as the Hα line has a frequency $\nu = 4.57 \times 10^{14}$ vibrations per second; hence $E = 3 \times 10^{-12}$ ergs is the amount of energy contained in one quantum of this color of light. One is inclined to regard the energy represented by one photon as negligibly small. In this respect it is of interest to record that the necessary energy for a minimum visual effect lies between only 5 and 8 quanta! This determination is the result of carefully arranged laboratory experiments by Selig Hecht (1892–1947).

Mechanics of radiation and absorption

It remained for Bohr to utilize the quantum concept in developing an atomic mechanism for the emission and absorption of photons. The transition of an orbital electron from a higher to a lower orbit yields a quantum of radiation or a photon of a specified frequency corresponding to the energy loss involved, in accordance with the relation *Energy* = *hv*. The same process in reverse explains the phenomenon of absorption. Quanta can be used to lift electrons from one orbit to another; but only quanta of just the right amounts of energy are effective, namely, those which play a role in the corresponding emission phenomena. Thus the equivalence of emission and absorption lines, first noticed by Kirchhoff, finds a simple explanation in the Bohr model of transitions between restricted orbits.

Pattern of transitions

The second Bohr principle was that the energy of the different stationary electron orbits bore a simple relation to Planck's constant *h*. In the case of hydrogen, the rigid application of this principle shows that there can be only a restricted number of orbits—4, 9, 16, 25, etc., times as large as the smallest or lowest orbit of the electron. This hypothetical mechanism permits an exact quantitative explanation of the Balmer and other series of hydrogen lines. The first three spectral lines of the Balmer series result from transitions between the second and the three next higher orbits. The various orbits beyond the smallest basic orbit are said to represent different states of excitation and the atom is referred to as excited. When the electron is in the lowest orbit, the atom is nonexcited and called normal. The same nomenclature is used for atoms other than those of hydrogen.

Other atoms; orbital electrons

Other elements also have series of spectral lines. The fundamental notion of Bohr—that in its space-time-mass structure a hydrogen atom contains a positive nucleus and an electron—was successfully extended by him to other atoms. Each atom is assumed to consist of a positively charged nucleus and a number of orbital electrons. These external electrons are arranged

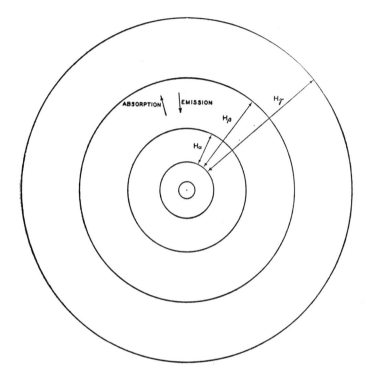

Bohr model of hydrogen atom.

in a cluster comprising several "shells" surrounding the very
small nucleus which contains most of the mass. The ordinary,
superficial, chemical and physical properties of matter depend
on the pattern of the external electrons; the internal structure
of the nucleus determines such internal subatomic or nuclear
phenomena as radioactivity, i.e., the spontaneous expulsion of
particles from the nucleus. The nature of these nuclear properties is entirely different from the peripheral physical and chemical properties; it will be studied further in Chapter 21.

Since the external electrons are subject to the attraction of the positively charged nucleus, it is of interest to inquire into the amount of this positive charge, or what amounts to the same thing, the number of orbital electrons. Important progress was made in 1913 through the systematic investigation by Henry Gwyn-Jeffreys Moseley (1887–1915) of X-ray spectra of different atoms. The so-called X-radiation, first discovered by Wilhelm Konrad von Röntgen (1845–1923), results from transitions involving the innermost electrons. Moseley discovered a striking similarity between the X-ray spectra of various elements, the only difference being that the line patterns of the more massive atoms shifted gradually to higher frequencies. Moseley found that the frequency pattern depended in a simple way on the electric charge of the nucleus.

Nuclear charge; atomic number

The X-ray spectra of atoms of different elements permit a simple measurement of their positive nuclear charge in terms of the elementary positive charge of a hydrogen nucleus. These charges are found to be integers and they are the same for one and the same chemical element and all of its isotopes. These integers are called the atomic numbers. The atomic number equals the number of orbital electrons needed to furnish a complete, electrically neutral atom (Table I, Chapter 2). The atomic number of hydrogen is 1; for helium it is 2, for lithium 3, for carbon 6, nitrogen 7, oxygen 8, iron 26, up to uranium whose atomic number is 92; the few synthetic heavy elements bring the number up to 98. The atomic number and atomic weight of hydrogen are the same (1). The atomic weight of helium (4) is twice its atomic number (2); this ratio is maintained approximately for the next dozen heavier atoms. Beyond these, the ratio of atomic weight to atomic number increases slowly up to nearly 2.6 for uranium (atomic weight 238 and atomic number 92).

Hence the number of outer electrons or—what amounts to the same thing—the nuclear charge determines the chemical element. In other words, the atomic number is *the* characteristic number, placing a chemical element in its natural position in the sequence of elements.

Structure of nucleus; protons and neutrons; isotopes

It is generally assumed that the positive charge of the nucleus of a particular element is provided by the number of hydrogen nuclei equaling the atomic number. The hydrogen nucleus emerges as one of the important building stones of atoms; the name proton has been introduced for this universal elemental unit. The remainder of the mass of the nucleus is assumed to be made up of particles without electric charge, but having nearly the same mass as protons; these neutral particles are named neutrons. Protons *and* neutrons are therefore the fundamental building stones of atomic nuclei; we note that both electricity and mass are basic concepts in atomic structure. The number of protons determines the atomic number; the number of protons plus the number of neutrons determines the atomic mass (or weight). Actually the total mass of the nucleus is found to be slightly less than the sum of the masses of the constituent particles. The significance and importance of this mass deficiency will be considered in Chapter 21.

Thus hydrogen, containing one proton only, is the only element whose atomic number and atomic mass or weight are the same. The helium nucleus contains 2 protons and 2 neutrons; the iron nucleus 26 protons and 30 neutrons, the common uranium nucleus 92 protons and 146 neutrons. The number of neutrons in one element may vary from atom to atom; this accounts for the phenomenon of isotopes. Although the masses of isotopes differ, their external electron shells determine their chemical behavior, which is therefore identical for all isotopes of the same element. For example, the two chlorine isotopes of atomic weights 35 and 37 contain 18 and 20 neutrons respectively. Both, however, contain the same number of protons (17) and electrons (17); this number determines the atomic number, and it defines both isotopes as being one and the same chemical element.

As in the case of hydrogen, the atom of any element has a restricted number of possible orbits. Transitions of the orbital electrons may occur, giving rise to the characteristic spectrum of the atoms in the rarefied gaseous state. The number of possible orbits and transitions increases rapidly with the number of orbital electrons. The theory of orbital electrons has also been extended to elliptical orbits of specified sizes and shapes.

Energy levels

The orbital atomic models have certain weaknesses, which have been partly removed by new developments in the mechanics and energy relations of these tiny space-time-mass units. In the framework of the new science of wave mechanics we do not lay claim any longer to a visual model of the different atoms. But certain general properties of the hydrogen atom and of other atoms are clear and remain "real." An atom is not one tiny solid building stone; it is a minute intricate space-time-mass structure, which may exist in any one of several restricted energy levels corresponding to different states of excitation. As before, a transition between two such levels corresponds to the emission or to the absorption of a discrete quantity of energy, possessing a certain vibrant quality technically represented by its frequency, i.e., number of vibrations per second; this quantum of radiant energy is called a photon. It is hopeless to try to visualize these photons. All we know is that they contain, or rather that they "are" energy, and, as exhibited by their collective behavior in light rays, that they have particle and wave properties, as we first noted in Chapter 9.

Atomic and molecular spectra

Any atom has a limited number of energy levels, the possible number depending on the chemical structure of the atom. All atoms of one and the same element are limited to emission or absorption transitions between identical sets of atomic-energy levels. Hence, the number of frequencies which any one atom can produce at one time or another is restricted to a number of definite pitches on the spectral keyboard. Since in our experiments countless atoms are active at the same time, a collective chord of colors is continually in evidence. We shall see in the next chapter that the relative strength of the different spectral lines depends on the intensity and the freedom of motion of the atoms, i.e., the temperature and pressure of the gas. These two physical properties have a marked influence on the appearance of any spectral pattern.

The explanation of the radiation of molecules in the gaseous state is similar to the explanation for the radiation of atoms, although the spectral patterns of molecules are more complex than those of atoms.

Ionization

So far we have discussed neutral atoms. Of particular interest is that high degree of stimulation which leads to the loss of one or more orbital electrons, in which case the atom is called ionized. Ionization has a profound effect on the patterns of transitions and radiation, which in the case of the ionized atom are quite different from those of the neutral atom. The spectral patterns of ionized atoms are shifted toward higher frequencies, as compared with the spectra of neutral atoms. Successive stages of ionization again produce widely different spectra. It is obvious that ionized hydrogen is deprived of any emission-radiation pattern, while atoms of other elements can continue to radiate as long as there is an orbital electron left with which to operate.

For the ninety-odd elements there are therefore more than ninety-odd spectral patterns. In each stage of ionization there is a different spectrum. The number of such spectral patterns is considerable in the case of the heavier elements with their complicated electron clusters. This leads to all sorts of complexities for the investigator of atomic spectra. It also points to striking and interesting similarities between certain spectra. For example, the advanced reader may understand why there is a similarity in pattern but not in color frequency or "pitch" between, say, the spectra of hydrogen, ionized helium and doubly ionized lithium.

To obtain good insight into energy levels a careful analysis of the maze of spectral lines provided by a mixture of atoms is required. Such analyses are also important because they aid us in predicting the radiation of certain frequencies whose occurrence may be rare in the laboratory, but easily possible for gases under special cosmic conditions (Chapter 16).

Size of atoms

A striking feature of atoms is their spatial emptiness. For most normal atoms the ratio of space filled with matter to the overall size of the atom is represented by a factor of something like 1 to 10^{14}.

The Bohr model of atoms implies that any atom in the gaseous state has variable dimensions, depending on the extent of the extreme electron orbits occupied at any time. Generally, the nucleus of any atom is very small, about 10^{-16} centimeters in diameter, while the outer electron orbits may be 10^9 times as large. The smallest possible diameter of a hydrogen atom is about 10^{-8} centimeters, but when the atom is stimulated and excited it may be much larger. The corresponding sizes of other atoms are of the same order.

We recall that in the compressed state, represented by ordinary solids or liquids, the atoms are spaced something like 10^{-8} centimeters apart. This is a crowded condition in which the orbital electron clusters overlap and are in no position to maintain their characteristic energy levels. This explains why the temperature agitation in the compressed state becomes a general blur of spectral patterns, statistically organized into Planck's law of radiation. The chemical structure of the compressed material no longer plays any role in determining a restricted distribution of photons over different frequencies; instead, there is a continuous array of frequencies whose relative abundance is solely determined by the temperature.

Nonrestricted energy states

So far we have discussed only the restricted energy levels corresponding to the circular or elliptical orbits of electrons. Besides these "bound" electrons there are "free" electrons, resulting from ionization in a sufficiently hot gas. The free electrons are responsible for energy transfers of any non-quantized amount between different energy states of the free electron or between a free and bound energy state of the same electron. The manifestation of these bound-free and free-free transitions is a continuous spectrum extending over all frequencies, in addition to the restricted, characteristic, line spectrum of each element. While not prominent in rarefied gases, the continuous emission spectrum becomes the outstanding feature of a sufficiently deep layer of hot ionized gas, such as the photosphere of Sun and stars. Certain stellar spectra reveal continuous absorption patterns resulting from bound-free transitions in the stellar atmosphere.

19 | THE ATMOSPHERES OF SUN AND STARS

THROUGH the discussion and information contained in the last few chapters, we are now able to make a more detailed study of the basic properties of stars. This study falls into three parts. In the present chapter we shall investigate the composition of the thin external shell of the star referred to as its atmosphere. Next comes a study of the interior below the star's surface or photosphere. Finally, we shall attempt to trace the source of energy responsible for the continued radiation of stars. This study will involve subatomic or nuclear properties and reactions.

The absorption spectrum

The observational material for the study of stellar atmospheres is provided by stellar spectra; their interpretation is aided by our knowledge of atomic structure, radiation and certain properties of matter in the rarefied state. The absorption lines in stellar spectra are caused by the somewhat cooler gaseous material in the star's atmosphere which absorbs from the "continuous" photospheric radiation exactly those colors characteristic of the same gaseous material when it emits light. This correspondence between absorption and emission is easily understood on the basis of the Bohr theory of atoms; the emission or absorption lines occur at certain frequencies corresponding to transitions between certain definite pairs of orbits—"downward" for the case of emission and "upward" for the case of absorption. The re-emission of a photon may occur in any direction, the net result being a diminution in radiative intensity, whose accumulated effect we recognize as an absorption line.

Emission spectrum; reversing layer

Although the absorption lines in stellar spectra furnish our principal knowledge of stellar atmospheres, we may ask whether this information could not be obtained in a more direct way. Generally this is not possible for stars, but it is for the Sun. At the time of a total solar eclipse, when the Sun's disk is completely covered by the Moon, we may make a detailed spectroscopic study of the reversing layer, the lower and densest parts of the solar atmosphere. The pattern and relative intensities of these emission lines are a close replica in reverse of the familiar Fraunhofer absorption pattern of dark lines through which the reversing layer ordinarily reveals itself on the background of the photosphere. Compared with the diameter of the Sun, the solar reversing layer is exceedingly thin, most of the absorbing material being under a height of 1000 kilometers.

The same situation may be assumed to hold for most stars. The spectra of certain stars, however, also show bright lines, indicating the existence of a large gaseous envelope caused principally by hydrogen or helium and extending far beyond the ordinary atmosphere.

Dependence on temperature and pressure

The pattern of stellar spectra depends almost exclusively on the temperature at the star's surface or photosphere (Chapter 16). The temperature of the atmosphere can be only slightly lower than that of the photosphere. Hence we conclude that the pattern in which the atoms or molecules in a stellar atmosphere emit and absorb radiation is primarily determined by the temperature of the atmosphere. In other words, this temperature determines which electron orbits or energy levels are available for the specific transitions which we recognize as emission or absorption lines. In addition to temperature, there are other determining factors. Before going into these matters, we shall make a brief survey of certain fundamental properties of the rarefied state, which are of importance not only for the present problem, but later on for a study of the interior of the stars.

There is good reason to believe that the density of stellar atmospheres is extremely low, of the order of 10^{-13} gm/cm^3, or about 10^{-10} times the density of the Earth's atmosphere, just about the best vacuum reached in the laboratory. The low atmospheric density of the Sun is indicated by the remarkable sharpness of the spectral lines, revealing the lack of interference between the energy levels in highly excited atoms. Another proof of the low density and correspondingly increased space is furnished by the presence of certain radiations caused by transitions involving very high energy levels (large orbits).

Density, temperature and pressure in an ideal gas;
kinetic theory

The physicist considers extremely rarefied conditions as ideal examples of the perfect or ideal gaseous state; the average space between the gas particles is large compared with their size, thus giving them plenty of room in which to move about. The particles may include atoms and molecules, but we also admit the presence of photons, and, as we shall see later, free electrons.

The properties and the character of an ideal gas are well known and clearly described in the kinetic theory based on the behavior of moving gas particles. The total mass of the particles per cubic centimeter defines the density (ρ) of a gas, which depends on the number or concentration (n) of the particles and their average mass (μ) or weight. In formula: $\rho = n\mu$. The pressure (p) of a gas is defined as the intensity with which it pushes against one square centimeter. This pressure is proportional both to the number of particles that do the pushing and to their average individual pushing power. The ability of an individual particle to do work by virtue of its motion is called the energy of motion or kinetic energy; the latter is measured as half the product of the mass of the particle and the square of its velocity.

The numerous collisions of the particles lead to an approximate equalization, or so-called equipartition, of the kinetic energy. The average value of this kinetic energy determines what we conventionally recognize and measure as temperature (T). Therefore, the equipartition of kinetic energy in a gas represents nothing but the attainment of the same temperature everywhere, and this is maintained by the continuous collisions between its particles.

Law of Avogadro

Having thus identified temperature as a measure of energy, we see that the pressure of a gas is proportional to its concentration and to its temperature. In formula: $p(:) \ nT$. Note that the chemical composition of the particles plays no role in this relation. Hence, the concentration of two different gases at the same temperature and pressure must be the same. This is the law of

Avogadro, already referred to in Chapter 2. This law has important implications. For example, if several gases are mixed together, as they are in stellar atmospheres, the equalization or equipartition of kinetic energy leads to the same temperature everywhere; hence, the contribution of each gas to the resulting pressure is simply proportional to the number of particles of that gas.

Investigations beyond the scope of this book have revealed that at a pressure of one atmosphere and at a temperature corresponding to the freezing point of water, the concentration or number of particles in any gas amounts to 2.69×10^{19} per cubic centimeter. We repeat: this number does *not* depend on the chemical structure of the particles, or on whether they are atoms or molecules.

Particle velocities

The average velocity of the particles depends on their temperature and average mass. It amounts to 1.84 kilometers per second at the temperature of 0° centigrade or 273° K for hydrogen in the molecular state (2 atoms joined together, particle weight 2). This velocity should be understood, of course, as the rate of motion. No particle could ever cover 1.84 kilometers in one stretch, but the rate of motion is such that it would cover a distance of 1.84 kilometers in a straight line if there were no collisions to interfere. As a matter of fact, at normal atmospheric pressure and temperature 273° K the average free path between collisions is only about 10^{-5} centimeters; the number of collisions per second amounts to 2×10^{10}. The corresponding particle velocity of other elements in the same gaseous state at the same temperature would be smaller than that of hydrogen. Since temperature is simply a measure of kinetic energy, the particle velocity of different gases at the same temperature is inversely proportional to the square root of the particle mass. Thus the corresponding average velocity of oxygen molecules (2 atoms joined together, particle weight 32) is $\sqrt{2/32} = \frac{1}{4}$ times that of hydrogen molecules, or 0.46 kilometers per second.

In the classical kinetic theory of gases, the internal structure of the atoms or molecules played no role; they were assumed to be simple entities such as spheres. Now we must introduce a new viewpoint, based on the electron structure around the nucleus of atoms or molecules. We shall study the loosening-up of this structure of electrons caused by the agitation of the atoms or molecules.

Effect of temperature and pressure on the pattern of transitions

Whatever its cause may be, the high temperature in stellar atmospheres implies, or rather *is* a state of high restlessness for the particles. As a result, the latter frequently collide with one another and also with the radiation escaping from the stars' interiors; this radiation contains photons of high frequency with correspondingly high energies. The result is a state of excitation to some degree for all atmospheric atoms, while several of the atoms will have lost one or more electrons and therefore exist in an ionized state. The high temperature from the beginning excludes the solid and liquid states; free atoms are the rule, while only a few molecules can resist the general trend toward disruption or dissociation. We may say that the state of high agitation leads to a general state of inflation or loosening-up for the atoms, using this expression to describe the different states of excitation and ionization. The very low atmospheric density helps to maintain the state of dissociation. This explains, for example, why there is iron in the gaseous state in stellar atmospheres, having temperatures even somewhat lower than 3000°.

Temperature and, to a lesser extent, pressure affect therefore the state of excitation and ionization, which in turn determine the possible patterns of transition between electron orbits.

Theory of thermal excitation and ionization

A first quantitative analysis of the loosening-up or dissociation of atoms and molecules in stellar atmospheres was made in 1920 by Megh Nad Saha (1893–   ). The trend toward dissociation is counteracted by the recombination of freed electrons with ionized atoms, and there is also, of course, some deflation or shrinkage of excited atoms. However, as time goes by, an appreciable portion of all atoms hover in different states of excitation, or, in other words, different energy levels, while others exist in one of several possible ionized states. At any specific temperature and pressure a corresponding state of general dissociation will be stabilized and maintained. It will be different for atoms or molecules of different elements, even though all of them are at the same temperature, i.e., are subject to the same state of agitation. The principal distinguishing factor is the atom's resistance to inflation, i.e., the energy it requires to maintain a certain state of excitation or ionization. It takes, for example, twice the energy to ionize a hydrogen atom as it takes to ionize a calcium atom, while the ionization energy necessary to remove one electron from a helium atom is again almost double the ionization energy of hydrogen. For one and the same element, any advanced state of excitation or ionization is facilitated by increased agitation, i.e., by higher temperatures, and, to a much smaller degree, by the lowering of the concentration, i.e., the pressure of the gas.

Effect of temperature and pressure on spectra

The transition between any two energy levels involves the emission or absorption of a photon of specific energy frequency. For atoms of one and the same element a restricted number of energy levels and therefore of energy transitions is possible. Now the composite pattern of energy transitions of myriads of atoms is revealed in the form of a spectrum. The strength of any one spectral line depends on the combined and sustained co-operation of a definite proportion of the total supply of atoms, viz., those which can emit or absorb a photon of a certain characteristic frequency. Depending upon their momentary transitions, other atoms of the same element will contribute to the formation of another spectral line. The pattern and relative intensities of the spectral lines of one and the same element depend, therefore, on the percentage of atoms in the different stages of excitation and ionization.

The importance of the work of Saha lies in the fact that it explained temperature as the principal factor determining the spectrum. Through his work and that of his followers, we can explain the distribution of atoms over different energy transitions.

Explanation of stellar spectra

The well-known dependence on temperature of the absorption pattern in the sequence of stellar spectra is now clarified. Take, for example, the Balmer series of hydrogen lines, so pronounced in the spectra of hotter stars like Sirius. The Bohr theory tells us that these lines correspond to transitions between the second and higher orbits in the hydrogen atom. Through thermal agitation a large proportion of hydrogen atoms in the atmosphere of Sirius must therefore be excited sufficiently for their electrons to be lifted to the second orbit. As energy pours out from the surface of the star, and passes through the star's atmosphere, photons of specific energies are trapped by different hydrogen atoms, whose orbital electrons are lifted from the second to the third, fourth, fifth or higher orbits. The composite effect of these transitions is the characteristic pattern of Balmer absorption lines. In the atmosphere of our Sun, the state of agitation is less than that in the atmosphere of Sirius; hence, fewer hydrogen atoms with electrons in the second orbit are kept in readiness, and for this reason the resulting absorption pattern of the Balmer series is weaker than in the case of Sirius. Again, in the atmospheres of still hotter stars (O and B types), the state of agitation is so high that many of the hydrogen atoms have lost their electrons altogether and are therefore completely powerless to absorb. This explains the decline in the strength of the Balmer lines of hydrogen in the spectra of the very hottest stars.

Similar examples can be given for other elements. The appearance of molecular absorption lines in the spectra of the cooler stars is explained by the lower state of agitation of these stars, which permits the existence of the molecules of certain chemical compounds. With increased temperature, the spectra of ionized atoms play an increasing role. Compared with the radiation of the neutral atoms, the spectra of the ionized elements are shifted toward higher frequencies, i.e., the blue part of the spectral keyboard.

Uniformity in the chemical composition of stellar atmospheres

The result is always the same; atoms of one and the same element exhibit considerable versatility in being able to radiate or absorb photons of different frequencies, and the behavior of these atoms is determined primarily by the temperature. Now the composite structure of the spectral patterns of different elements in the stellar atmosphere determines the spectral type of the star. This spectral type is virtually identical for thousands and thousands of stars that have the same surface temperature.

If Saha's analysis is carefully carried out in a quantitative fashion, the important conclusion is reached that the atmospheres of different stars (including the Sun) have very closely the same chemical composition; there is the same relative abundance of atoms in the atmospheres of different stars. On this assumption we can explain not only why stars of the same surface temperature reveal the same atmospheric absorption spectrum, but also why the pattern of the spectra of stars with different surface temperatures vary in a particular manner. The uniform chemical composition of the outer, atmospheric shells of Sun and stars is another striking illustration of the unity of nature.

Stars of the same spectral type, but of unlike intrinsic luminosity, differ in surface temperature and also minutely in spectral pattern. This is explained by the lower atmospheric pressures in luminous (giant) stars as compared with the atmospheric pressures of intrinsically faint (dwarf) stars. The same state of dissociation from which the spectral type is judged is reached at a lower temperature if the pressure is lowered. Since the effects of lowered pressure and lowered temperature do not exactly compensate for each other, minute differences in spectral patterns result. In giant stars certain spectral lines are slightly stronger and others slightly weaker than in dwarf stars of the same spectral type. These minute differences may be utilized to estimate the star's intrinsic luminosity.

Composition of Sun's atmosphere

We review briefly the results of an analysis of the Sun's spectrum, whose interwoven line patterns have been, to a great extent, unraveled. Thus far, sixty-six of the ninety-odd chemical elements have been found in the Sun's atmosphere. There is no good reason to assume, however, that none of the other known terrestrial elements are present in the Sun. Certain elements may occur in too small quantities to be recognized through spectral analysis. Important spectral lines of some "missing" elements are in the far violet part of the spectrum, and cannot be observed, therefore, due to obscuration in our atmosphere. We may assume that the atoms of other, heavier elements have sunk into the Sun's interior. Again, certain elements may simply not appear in the solar atmosphere, but may be abundant in the interior.

The intensities of the solar lines have given us a measure of the relative abundance of atoms of the different chemical elements. Analyses of this sort are delicate and at best approximate; nevertheless, the results are significant. The most startling finding is the overwhelming abundance of hydrogen (47 per cent by mass) and of helium (41 per cent by mass). The two lightest elements, hydrogen and helium, thus account for 88 per cent of the mass of the Sun's atmosphere! In terms of the number of particles or volume, the percentage is even higher, namely, more than 99.9 per cent! The solar atmosphere is essentially an atmosphere of hydrogen and helium, containing other, heavier chemical elements as "impurities." The heavier elements fall into two groups, according to Henry Norris Russell (1877–   ). There are the "oxygen" group, chiefly composed of carbon, oxygen, nitrogen and neon, and the "iron" group in which the principal elements are iron, silicon, magnesium and calcium—elements which also are prominent on the Earth and in meteorites. A number of molecular compounds are also found in the Sun's atmosphere. However, the great majority of particles exist in the atomic state; many of the atoms are ionized, having lost one or more electrons.

With the notable exceptions of free hydrogen and helium, all of the above elements are abundant on the Earth, mostly in the form of compounds. A common origin of Sun and Earth is thus indicated; the lack of free hydrogen and helium particles in our atmosphere may be explained as a loss due to their high average velocities, which must have enabled them to escape from the Earth's gravitational field (Chapter 32).

In view of the uniformity in composition of the atmospheres of Sun and stars, the quantitative chemical make-up of the atmospheres of the stars must be the same as that of the Sun just discussed.

20 | THE INTERIOR OF SUN AND STARS

OUR NEXT step in accumulating information about the physical nature of the stars is a study of their interiors. This knowledge has to be obtained from the general stellar properties—mass, size, luminosity and surface temperature—surveyed in Chapter 17. We recall the range in these properties for different stars, and it should be one of our tasks to provide an explanation for this range. In a sense, however, different stars present the same problem and, of course, we shall be concerned primarily with our own star, the Sun. With the aid of fundamental laws of physics and chemistry we can hope to discover certain basic properties of the interiors of Sun and stars. The difficulty of our not being able to see stellar interiors is thus overcome by what Arthur Stanley Eddington (1882–1944) called the "analytical boring machine."

Constancy of Sun and stars

Apart from certain special cases, the majority of stars reveal a remarkable constancy in their various physical properties. This is well illustrated by the Sun. The size, luminosity and rate of radiation of the Sun clearly remain the same over several decades. By combining the evidence of successive and overlapping generations, it is not difficult to establish that virtual constancy extends even over more than a century. As a matter of fact, geological evidence obtained from the study of fossils indicates that the radiation of the Sun cannot have changed very much in the past five hundred million years. So accustomed have we become to this constancy that it has ceased to strike us as remarkable. But remarkable it is that a huge object like the Sun retains its size and temperature year in and year out. Any change, too, in the mass of the Sun is unlikely; an appreciable change in mass would affect the motions of the planets in a measurable way. No such effect has been observed. Most striking of all, however, is the continued outpour of the Sun's radiation at an undiminished, constant rate; this phenomenon will be the subject of special study in Chapter 21.

Mechanical equilibrium

The unchanging size and surface temperature of the Sun suggest certain reasonable hypotheses which will aid us in our further study. We judge from the constant size that there is a constancy of the distribution of material within the Sun's surface. The density of material throughout the Sun is probably not the same everywhere; it seems reasonable to suppose that there is a concentration of material toward the center. We do not imply that every particle within the gaseous Sun remains at the same location as time goes by. We assume, however, that at any location within the Sun the concentration of material retains about the same value in the long run, though individual particles may come and go. This is called the hypothesis of mechanical equilibrium.

Thermal equilibrium

We will now consider the constant surface temperature of the Sun. The continued, unchanging outpour of radiation from the Sun's interior implies that the temperatures in that interior are still higher than those at the surface; it also points to an increase in temperature deeper and deeper below the surface of the Sun. The constancy of the flow of radiation suggests, too, that the distribution of temperature within the Sun does not vary appreciably as time goes on. We assume that the Sun's internal temperature increases toward the center, but that in any limited area it remains the same. This is called the hypothesis of thermal equilibrium. The postulation of mechanical and thermal equilibrium at any location in the interior implies a constancy of the combined effect of concentration (n) and temperature (T), i.e., the pressure $p(:)$ nT, if the interior is a perfect gas (Chapter 19).

We make the plausible assumption that the values of concentration and temperature, and hence pressure, depend only on the distance from the center. We may express this by saying that a state of spherical symmetry exists for these properties.

Stellar interiors are compressed gases

We can find out a great deal about the interior of the Sun through a careful interpretation of the two equilibrium hypotheses. Let us first inquire into the state of the material in the interior. The high internal temperatures preclude the possibility of a solid or liquid state; the high agitation leads to that state of complete loosening or dissociation of particles referred to as gaseous. We anticipated a difficulty, however, in Chapter 16. The average density of the Sun is as high as 1.41 times that of water, and the densities of many stars are still higher. Ordinarily when we speak of a gas, we have in mind a perfect or ideal gas, first described in our study of the rarefied stellar atmospheres (Chapter 19). In an ideal gas, the particles, atoms or molecules are far apart on the average compared with their size, and thus have plenty of space in which to move about. The pressure does not depend on the nature of the particles, but only on their concentration (number per cubic centimeter) and average kinetic energy—in other words, their temperature. This simple proportionality of the pressure effect to the concentration and to the temperature, $p(:) \ nT$, could not be maintained in a gas whose particles were jammed closely together.

The highly agitated star gas is perfect

Eddington found that the dense "star gas" behaves as a perfect gas. Under "normal" terrestrial conditions the structure of the elemental particles—atoms or molecules—is basically complex. Inside the Sun and the stars, however, conditions are far from "normal." Owing to the high state of agitation there, the degree of dissociation of the star gas is advanced well beyond the gaseous state known to us under ordinary conditions of temperature and pressure, or even in stellar atmospheres. Very few, if any, of the atoms are still bound together in molecules. More than that, ionized atoms must be the rule, and calculations show that an advanced state of ionization exists; many atoms have lost all orbital electrons, while all but the entourage of inner electrons of the more complicated atoms have been freed. This results in "stripped" atoms of substantially reduced size, which together with the freed electrons now form a perfect gas, even at relatively high concentrations. The stellar interior may be visualized as an exceedingly restless assembly of stripped atoms and electrons darting from one place to another and frequently colliding. In addition, there are the photons of radiation created in the interior (Chapter 21); these account for even more collisions.

Basic considerations

We are now in a better position to interpret the constancy of concentration, temperature and pressure at any point within the star. Since the agitated interior is a perfect gas, there is the simple proportionality between the pressure, on the one hand, and the concentration and temperature of the material on the other (Chapter 19). In addition, the universal law of gravitation operates between all particles. Moreover, there is the radiation making its way to the surface; and we recall that radiation, especially at high temperatures, exerts an appreciable pressure. Finally, we realize that there must be some regulating agency for controlling the flow of radiation to the outside. That there are certain obstacles to a completely free flow of radiation follows from the fact that the Sun is not a transparent object.

Gravitation versus gas pressure

If gravitation were the only active factor, Sun and stars would collapse because of the mutual attraction between all particles.

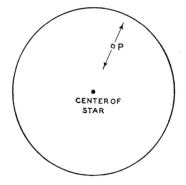

At any location P within a star the combined tendency of the particles to move outward is balanced by the gravitational pull inward.

The agitation, i.e., the temperature, of the gas furnishes the pressure necessary to support the material in the interior. Imagine for a moment what would happen if gravitation were absent. In that case, the agitation of the particles would lead to a gradual spreading-out, diffusion or evaporation such as we observe in terrestrial experiments. For illustration: if we pricked a hole in a balloon filled with hydrogen, or—to make the analogy closer—removed the balloon altogether, the gas would gradually spread out, the gravitational attraction being entirely too weak to hold it together. In the Sun and stars, however, so much material is present in a limited space that the mutual gravitational attraction is sufficiently strong to balance the diffusive tendencies. The Sun and stars do not need a balloon as an external boundary because of their internal gravitational cohesion.

Mechanical equilibrium requires high internal temperature

The mechanical equilibrium of the star represents, therefore, a balance between gravitation inward and gas pressure outward. The mutual gravitation between any two particles results in a gravitational effect directed at any point toward the center of the Sun or star. Deeper into the interior, this resultant gravitational effect, which is simply the weight of the overlying shells or layers of material, increases. To support this weight, there must be an increase in gas pressure toward the center. This increase is provided partly by a higher concentration of material, but the principal factor is the highly intensified rate of agitation of the individual particles, stripped atoms and electrons alike, all of which support the architecture of the star. In other words, the temperature of the star must increase rapidly as we approach its center.

Gas pressure aided by radiation pressure

Not all the support, however, comes from the stripped atoms and electrons. Part is provided by the outward-bound photons in the form of radiation pressure. This is especially true in hotter stars, since the radiation pressure increases with the fourth power of the temperature (Chapter 15).

Number of available particles

To calculate the equilibrium conditions between gravity, on the one hand, and gas and radiation pressure, on the other, we must know how many particles there are in the interior. We recall that the pressure exerted by a gas depends on the number of particles and their temperature (or kinetic energy), but has nothing to do with their chemical structure. If light particles (for example, hydrogen) and heavy particles (for example, iron) are mixed in the same gaseous state, then their collisions will lead to equipartition, that is, an equalization of energy, the small particles moving faster, the heavy ones moving more slowly; but as far as their pressure or pushing power is concerned, they are all equally effective, regardless of their weights. As far as gas pressure is concerned, different atoms or molecules lose their identity, and rate simply as equally effective particles.

We may seem to have an obstacle here. Take, for example, the Sun, which has a mass of 2×10^{33} grams. To how many particles does this correspond? It would seem at first that the number of particles depends on the chemical composition of the material, i.e., the average atomic weight. If the Sun were made up of hydrogen atoms, for example, it would have fifty-six times as many particles as if it were made up of iron atoms, each of which is fifty-six times as massive as a hydrogen atom.

Average particle weight of star gas

This reasoning is, as Eddington first pointed out, incorrect, however, because of the advanced state of ionization of most of the atoms in the interior. As a result, each hydrogen atom is replaced by two particles, one hydrogen nucleus or proton and one electron. A helium atom is replaced by three particles, the helium nucleus and the two freed orbital electrons. A carbon atom is represented by its nucleus and six freed electrons, i.e., seven particles in all, and so on. In general, complete ionization results in an atom's being replaced by a number of particles which is one more than its atomic number. In Chapter 18 we noted that the atomic number of the great majority of chemical elements is, on the average, slightly less than half the atomic mass. Complete ionization of most atoms, therefore, yields particles whose average weight is a little over twice that of hydrogen. Assume now that the state of ionization in the Sun's interior is complete, or, at least, very far advanced. Then with certain qualifications the chemical composition of the interior is irrelevant to the problem of deriving the total number of particles in the interior. We simply divide the total mass of the Sun by the average mass of the particles, which is about twice that of hydrogen (assuming that ionization is not quite complete).

Influence of hydrogen and helium on internal temperature

The principal qualifications concern, of course, hydrogen and helium, the two lightest elements. Complete ionization of hydrogen and helium atoms produces particles whose weights are lower, on the average, than the resulting particle weights of other ionized atoms. The particles of ionized hydrogen comprise an equal number of protons and electrons whose average weight is 0.83 × 10⁻²⁴ grams, half as much as a complete hydrogen atom. The corresponding particle weight of completely ionized helium is 1⅓ times that of a hydrogen atom. As we have found a great abundance of hydrogen and helium in the Sun's atmosphere, we should, therefore, reckon with the possibility that there is a great abundance of these same elements in the interiors of the Sun and stars.

First let us make the extreme assumption that the Sun consists of hydrogen only. In this case the total number of available particles would be the largest possible, namely,

$$2 \times 10^{33}/0.83 \times 10^{-24}$$

or about 24×10^{56}, and thus each particle would have to do the least amount of work necessary to support the architecture of the interior. By making certain reasonable assumptions about the increase of concentration toward the center, we find that a central temperature of 8,000,000°, gradually dropping to 5750° K at the surface, would be sufficient to provide the necessary internal pressure. On the other hand, if no hydrogen whatsoever nor any helium were present, the Sun would consist of only about one-quarter as many particles—6×10^{56}—as it would if it were composed entirely of hydrogen. On the average, each particle would have to work about four times as hard to support the Sun's architecture; in other words, the internal temperature everywhere would be four times as high, and the central temperature would be about thirty million degrees.

Hydrogen and helium content

Obviously one of the important problems in connection with stellar interiors is the abundance of hydrogen and helium; the internal temperature depends primarily upon this abundance.

An accurate knowledge of this temperature plays an important role in another problem—that of the energy production within Sun and stars (Chapter 21). An estimate of the hydrogen and helium contents in the interior is derived from a study of the energy production and the thermal-equilibrium condition, which implies a precisely regulated flow of radiation from the interior to the surface.

Transport of radiation

Thermal equilibrium is the maintenance of constant temperature, i.e., a constant state of agitation at any one location in the interior. Now photons are created in the interior and are transported to the surface, mostly in the form of radiation. Conduction and convection play negligible roles. The maintenance of thermal equilibrium involves the transportation of radiation toward the surface at the same rate at which the radiation is created.

We can visualize the photons as being continually absorbed and re-created in different forms. Imagine a photon of very high energy, created deep in the interior and shortly afterward absorbed by another atom. Some time later this atom emits a photon of somewhat smaller energy than the one absorbed, which in time is captured again by another atom, and so on. While going through millions of transformations the successive reincarnations of the original photon slowly find their way out into space. On the average, a photon in the Sun travels less than a centimeter between successive emissions and absorptions. The original photon of high frequency is gradually transformed into photons of lesser and lesser energy as the surface of the star is approached; and finally, the last photonic Phoenix leaps out of the photosphere.

Opacity to radiation

This transfer of radiation is obviously well regulated, since it results neither in overheating nor underheating. The controlling property of the outgoing flow of radiation is the opacity, which the physicist has found to be different for different chemical elements. For the same mass of material, heavier atoms are found to be much more opaque to radiation than lighter ones; an example is the protective quality which heavy lead atoms provide against X-rays. A star's observed energy flow depends on its size, mass, internal and surface temperature and, in addition, the opacity of its gas. Since it is related to the atomic number, the opacity to radiation provides a clue to the chemical composition of solar and stellar interiors. The interior of the Sun must be relatively transparent in order to explain its mechanical and thermal equilibrium.

Abundance of hydrogen and helium; central temperature and density of the Sun

The principal source of energy production in the Sun and stars is the conversion of mass into energy through the synthesis of hydrogen into helium discussed in the next chapter. For the moment we are concerned with the required abundance of the elements involved, particularly hydrogen, in conjunction with the other requirements of mechanical and thermal equilibrium. For the Sun and other main-sequence stars the actual conditions are obtained by considering various internal distributions of temperature and density and kind of material. The best estimates give a central temperature of 16,000,000° and a central density of 300 gm/cm³. The corresponding central pressure is some 10^{11} atmospheres. Even the high central temperature of the Sun does not bring about a complete stripping of all atoms;

the inner orbital electrons of the heavier ones remain attached, testifying to the extraordinary stability of their internal structure.

As to the chemical composition, it is found that hydrogen accounts for 70 per cent of the Sun's mass; a less certain estimate is that helium accounts for 27 per cent. The "heavy" elements account for 3 per cent, possibly more. Of the latter, the "oxygen" group (Chapter 19)—composed chiefly of carbon, oxygen, nitrogen and neon—is assumed to comprise 2.5 per cent; the "iron" group—iron, silicon, magnesium, calcium and others—about 0.5 per cent. Thus hydrogen atoms, represented by their protons and electrons, are numerically in the vast majority within the Sun as well as in the Sun's atmosphere (Chapter 19).

Other stars

The figures mentioned so far describe our own star, the Sun, but similar values are found for other stars. In Chapter 17 we noted the large range in stellar luminosities varying approximately with the third power of the stars' mass. Stars of different masses and sizes have been studied in the same way as the Sun. We shall mention only briefly a few general conclusions. As in the case of the Sun, it is found that other stars require a considerable abundance of the relatively transparent hydrogen in order to provide the proper balance between internal temperature, opacity and outgoing radiation or luminosity. It is found also that stellar luminosities depend essentially on mass and only slightly on size or chemical composition. The numerical results are found to be in agreement with the observed mass-luminosity relation.

Stars of widely different luminosities exhibit only a relatively minor range in central temperature. Take, for example, the bright blue star Sirius A (mass 2.1 times that of the Sun, luminosity 30 times that of the Sun), and, on the other hand, the faint red star Krüger 60 B (mass $1/7$ times the Sun's, luminosity 1/2000 times the Sun's). Computations show that the central temperatures of these stars differ comparatively little, the amounts being 20 million degrees for Sirius and 12 million degrees for Krüger 60 B.

White dwarfs; the degenerate state

Striking exceptions in all these considerations are the white dwarfs, the small, hot stars of low luminosity and extremely high density. Though comparable densities are unknown on Earth, our knowledge of atomic structure provides a satisfactory explanation for the existence of these high densities in stars. As a result of extreme internal gravitational pressure, insufficiently counteracted by a relatively "cool" thermal agitation, the star collapses. The result is a complete crushing of the atoms, in which nuclei and electrons are now completely severed. We recall that even in the interior of stars in general, the innermost electrons of the heavier atoms remain undisturbed. However, for the "crushed" star gas in a collapsed star, the destruction of the electron shells is complete, and under these circumstances the perfect gas laws no longer hold. The resulting state of matter is called degenerate; completely degenerate matter still contains some locked-up kinetic energy which cannot be converted into radiation.

A pressure of 150 million atmospheres is necessary for complete degeneracy or atom crushing; the pressure at the center of the massive planet Jupiter is close to this critical value. The weight of the overlying layers at the center of our Earth produces a pressure of "only" 22 million atmospheres. We conclude that all cold cosmic bodies more massive than Jupiter have partially crushed or collapsed interiors. The volume of cold "solid" bodies smaller than Jupiter increases proportionally to the mass, but the volume of "degenerate" bodies larger than Jupiter decreases with increasing mass. For example, if our Sun collapsed, it would be only one thousandth the volume of Jupiter, or about the size of the Earth.

21 | THE SOURCE OF SOLAR
AND STELLAR ENERGY

LET US consider the problem of the production of energy within Sun and stars. We are so familiar with the radiation from the Sun that we have ceased to be surprised at the magnitude of the phenomenon. The rate of radiation poured out from the Sun amounts to 4 times 10^{33} ergs every second. Compared with terrestrial sources of energy, this quantity is incomprehensibly large. The remarkable thing is that this rate of radiation appears to have been maintained for an immense interval of time; there is evidence for this from different sources. We mentioned before that the presence of certain fossils in the Earth's crust suggested that long ago the Sun must have been shining at about the same rate as now.

Age of the Earth

A good estimate of the age of the Earth is obtained from the presence of lead in a sample of uranium ore. We know that the radioactive element uranium slowly but spontaneously changes into lead; the rate of activity is such that in nearly five thousand million years one-half of the uranium will be transformed. Assuming that no lead was present in the beginning, the age of the uranium ore may therefore be found from the amount of lead in existence now. The age of the Earth has thus been set at about 3000 million years, and we may also take this number as a lower limit for the age of the Sun. Since life appears to have existed on the Earth for the last five hundred million years, it is reasonable to assume that the radiation of the Sun has not changed appreciably during that time. What is the source of the continued supply of radiation over this long interval?

Source of solar energy

Conventional sources of energy, represented by chemical reactions like burning, would be hopelessly inadequate. Assume, for example, that the Sun were made of solid carbon mixed with the proper amount of oxygen; complete combustion would provide solar radiation at its present rate for only 2500 years. Apart from the fact that this time interval is ridiculously small, the basic idea is entirely wrong. The surface temperature of the Sun is about 5750° K, and the internal temperatures are much higher. Burning is simply a chemical reaction representing the combination of a fuel with oxygen. A combination or association of atoms, however, cannot possibly occur at the high temperatures inside the Sun and stars. The state of high agitation does not permit any association of atoms into molecules; on the contrary, it results in a general state of dissociation (Chapters 19 and 20). In other words, the Sun and stars are too hot to burn.

Chemical reactions are therefore excluded; we have to look for other sources of energy within the Sun and stars. In 1854 Hermann Ludwig Ferdinand von Helmholtz (1821–1894) proposed the first useful hypothesis for the source of solar radiation, namely, a slow contraction of the Sun. The principle is simply the conversion of its potential into kinetic energy (Chapter 15).

Contraction theory

A gradual contraction of a sphere of gas involves a state in which the particles fall toward each other, and therefore toward their common center. This falling results in a loss of potential energy by virtue of the shrinking spatial arrangement of the particles. This loss of potential energy results partly in further increasing the temperature, i.e., the agitation of the particles, while the remainder appears as radiant energy. The proportion of radiant energy made available by contraction depends on the composition of the particles; in certain cases additional energy from the outside has to be provided to make contraction possible. For the interiors of Sun and stars, however, the situation is simple and favorable. The particles are isolated atoms; molecular compounds, bound to absorb an appreciable amount of energy at the expense of available radiant energy, are lacking. For a contracting sphere of atoms, the loss of potential energy is equally divided over the inside and the outside of the star; i.e., the total increase in kinetic energy of the star gas equals the radiant energy made available by the contraction. Contraction from a very large diameter to its present size would have provided enough energy to keep the Sun shining at its present rate for 30 million years. Though contraction may thus provide solar energy, it could do so only for an interval, or at a rate far below the actual requirements of the case.

Radioactivity

One might look for an explanation in radioactivity, i.e., the spontaneous disintegration of certain heavy atoms with the accompanying release of large quantities of energy. Radium, for example, expels three kinds of "radiation," identified as helium nuclei (α-particles), electrons (β-particles) and high-frequency radiation (γ-rays). Quantitatively, however, this hypothesis is also inadequate. It is unlikely that there is a great abundance of heavy radioactive atoms in Sun and stars, and even if there were, they could not possibly explain the high rate of radiation which actually exists. Nevertheless, the radioactive atoms point the way to the solution of the problem; the radioactive elements are but spontaneous examples of possible rearrangements of the internal constituents of atomic nuclei.

Chemical reactions entail rearrangements of atoms; these processes are accompanied by relatively mild energy exchanges. Only the outer orbital electrons are involved in the dissociation, association or other chemical rearrangement of atoms and molecules; the nuclei remain always undisturbed or dormant. We shall now discuss reactions in which internal changes of the nuclei take place; such nuclear changes always entail large energy exchanges. On our Earth only a few of the rare, heavy, radioactive elements spontaneously undergo such changes. For a long time, however, it has been suspected that this type of reaction is commonplace in the Sun and stars.

Nuclear reactions

The source of solar and stellar energy is sought, therefore, within the atomic nuclei. The laboratory study of the release of subatomic energy began with the artificial transmutation of atomic nuclei effected first in 1919 by Rutherford. Such nuclear reactions may take place as a combination of two different nuclei into one, or into two other nuclei. In chemical reactions atoms are rearranged so as to form different molecules; in nuclear reactions the protons and neutrons within the nucleus are rearranged into nuclei of different atoms and their isotopes. In a chemical reaction the atoms simply change places; in a nuclear reaction the even more fundamental building stones, protons and neutrons, change places. As in the case of chemical reactions, energy is set free or absorbed, but on a much larger scale.

In contrast with most chemical reactions, nuclear reactions can occur only at exceptionally high temperatures, i.e., agitation. First the armor of protective external electrons must be pierced and removed. In addition, the nuclei must have sufficient energy of motion to affect the structure of other nuclei. In terrestrial experiments, high-speed protons or helium nuclei (α-particles) are used as effective penetrating particles. Slow-moving neutrons, not deflected by electrical repulsion from the nuclei, are useful in penetrating and disrupting atomic nuclei. The effectiveness of nuclear reactions depends on the chance of collisions between nuclei and on the intensity with which these collisions take place. As in the case of chemical reactions, agitation and concentration are important factors, the principal difference being that the agitation required for nuclear reactions is of an ever so much higher order. In the laboratory nuclear reactions are now being obtained as a matter of course; as a rule, a relatively small number of nuclei is involved in such experiments.

We give an example of a nuclear reaction. A lithium and a hydrogen nucleus may combine into a beryllium nucleus and some radiation energy will be set free. The reaction may be described by an equation:

$$_3\text{Li}^7 + {}_1\text{H}^1 \rightarrow {}_4\text{B}^8 + \gamma$$

where γ is the usual symbol for radiation. The left subscript and right superscript of the atomic symbols represent the atomic numbers and masses respectively. Since nuclear reactions simply involve rearrangements of protons and neutrons, these superscripts must obey the law of addition in the equations.

It is also possible, however, that the lithium and hydrogen nuclei react differently, as follows:

$$_3\text{Li}^7 + {}_1\text{H}^1 \rightarrow {}_2\text{He}^4 + {}_2\text{He}^4 + \gamma.$$

Again proper account is taken of the reshuffling of protons and neutrons. It is a matter of theory and experiment to determine which reactions are most likely to occur in any interaction of nuclei. In the present example the second reaction is the one that actually does take place in the great majority of cases.

For the sake of completeness we mention that, as a result of nuclear reactions, particles intermediate in mass between electrons and protons may be created; these are called mesons or mesotrons.

Conditions for nuclear reactions in Sun and stars

We recall that the architecture of Sun and stars requires a high internal pressure to uphold the internal structure; this pressure is proportional to the number of particles regardless of their chemical nature, and to their average kinetic energy, i.e., their temperature. The central temperature of the Sun is found to be sixteen million degrees. We see now that the very architecture of Sun and stars provides the clue to their energy production. The state of agitation of the particles is high enough to provide the impact necessary for nuclear reactions; even so, in the laboratory we may occasionally succeed in giving particles larger velocities than any of those within Sun and stars. However, the concentration of particles inside Sun and stars is so high, and their collisions so numerous, that nuclear reactions take place in vast numbers and thus provide the answer as to how the required energy is produced.

The question is which nuclear reaction or reactions are taking place in Sun and stars. Astronomers have long realized that a process whereby a hydrogen nucleus could be transformed into a helium nucleus would furnish an excellent source of energy. We recall that hydrogen is the most common element in Sun and stars. The importance of a hydrogen-helium transformation lies in the fact that four hydrogen atoms weigh slightly more than one helium atom. Any process which would result in the synthesis of one helium nucleus out of four hydrogen nuclei would therefore be accompanied by a small loss of mass. To appreciate the significance of this small discrepancy in mass, we shall review certain basic facts concerning mass and energy.

Conservation of mass and energy

In an isolated experiment the total mass remains constant, regardless of the different chemical combinations into which the materials may enter. This law of conservation of mass in atomic and molecular interchanges is the basis of all quantitative analyses in chemical experiments. A physical law of similar importance is the law of conservation of energy (Chapter 15). Since 1915, as a result of Einstein's theory of general relativity, we have known that mass and energy are equivalent and that, under certain conditions, they are interchangeable. This concept was first obtained in a formal, theoretical manner, but experiments have confirmed it. In agreement with the theory, the rate of exchange between mass and energy is represented by the equivalence *m grams of mass* $\equiv$ *mc^2 ergs of energy* where c is the velocity of light expressed in centimeters per second.

The aforementioned fundamental laws of chemistry and

physics may therefore be synthesized into one law expressing the conservation of mass plus energy (using the above rate of exchange) in any isolated experiment. Any true loss of mass is compensated for by the creation of energy at the rate of 9×10^{20} ergs for each gram of matter.

Mass deficiency and binding energy of nuclei

The equivalence of mass and energy provides the theoretical basis for any energy release or absorption in nuclear reactions. A careful inspection reveals that the masses of nuclei (which are virtually the same as the atomic masses) are slightly less than the combined mass of the protons and neutrons in the nucleus. This mass deficiency (or mass defect) represents the energy that would be needed to pick apart the protons and neutrons bound together in the stable, near-indestructible nucleus.

The possibility of interchanges between mass and energy lies in the fact that the mass deficiency or binding energy is different for different atoms. It is highest for atoms of intermediate mass—for example, iron—which are therefore most stable, and smallest for the very light and the very heavy atoms. A nuclear reaction yielding more stable nuclei is therefore accompanied by a release of energy. In looking for possible reactions that yield energy, one should generally consider the synthesis of the very light into more stable, heavier nuclei, or the breakdown of very heavy into more stable, lighter nuclei. The latter process corresponds to the well-known phenomenon of radioactivity and also to the current studies of drawing atomic power from the heaviest elements. The former process, strikingly exemplified by a possible synthesis of hydrogen into helium, presents an explanation for the energy production in Sun and stars. A direct synthesis of four protons into one helium nucleus is excluded because the probability of a successful encounter is negligible; however, effective indirect ways exist.

The proton-proton reaction

In stars like the Sun, the conversion of hydrogen into helium is most likely provided by the simple chain of three reactions in which a hydrogen nucleus (proton) is built up into a helium atom. First, two protons combine into a deuteron (a heavy hydrogen nucleus of atomic weight 2) with the release of a positron ($_1e^0$):

$$_1H^1 + {}_1H^1 \rightarrow {}_1H^2 + {}_1e^0.$$

Next, the deuteron combines with another proton into a light helium nucleus, while radiation (γ) is emitted:

$$_1H^1 + {}_1H^2 \rightarrow {}_2He^3 + \gamma.$$

Finally, the light helium nucleus (of atomic weight 3) combines with another light helium nucleus to produce an ordinary helium nucleus (an α particle of atomic weight 4) and two protons:

$$_2He^3 + {}_2He^3 \rightarrow {}_2He^4 + 2{}_1H^1.$$

Thus, by successive steps hydrogen has been built up into helium, and at the same time energy is liberated. We may say that hydrogen is the fuel of the star, helium the ashes.

This proton-proton reaction is not very sensitive to temperature. While it is adequate for stars like the Sun and those fainter, it may not be sufficient to explain the energy production in brighter stars.

The carbon-nitrogen cycle of reactions

Another chain, or rather, cycle, of nuclear reactions, could account for most of the energy production of stars brighter than the Sun. The primary agent of this process is again hydrogen; the other prominent participants are carbon and nitrogen. What happens is the following: a carbon nucleus captures a proton and becomes a light isotope of nitrogen, while radiation (γ) is emitted:

$$_6C^{12} + {}_1H^1 \rightarrow {}_7N^{13} + \gamma.$$

The nitrogen isotope is unstable and rapidly "decays" into a heavy carbon isotope, while emitting a positive electron or positron:

$$_7N^{13} \rightarrow {}_6C^{13} + {}_1e^0.$$

This carbon nucleus is stable for a long time. After a while a second proton is captured; the result is the stable nucleus of normal nitrogen, accompanied by the emission of radiation:

$$_6C^{13} + {}_1H^1 \rightarrow {}_7N^{14} + \gamma.$$

Eventually this nitrogen nucleus captures a third proton, and is converted into a light isotope of oxygen, while some more radiation is emitted:

$$_7N^{14} + {}_1H^1 \rightarrow {}_8O^{15} + \gamma.$$

The oxygen isotope is very unstable and "decays" into a heavy isotope of nitrogen, while emitting a positron:

$$_8O^{15} \rightarrow {}_7N^{15} + {}_1e^0.$$

The nitrogen nucleus captures a fourth proton. It does not thereby become a normal oxygen nucleus, as might be expected; instead, a rearrangement inside the nuclei takes place, resulting in one normal carbon and one normal helium nucleus:

$$_7N^{15} + {}_1H^1 \rightarrow {}_6C^{12} + {}_2He^4.$$

This is where we started. We have just described a cycle of nuclear reactions, beginning and ending with the same carbon. The carbon is not used up; hence the available limited supply of this element will suffice.

Summing up the six consecutive reactions we find:

$$_6C^{12} + 4_1H^1 \rightarrow {_6C^{12}} + {_2He^4} + 2_1e^0 + \gamma$$

where γ now stands for the total amount of radiative energy released. The two positrons combine with two (negative) electrons; their mass is annihilated and appears also as radiation. The ultimate result is the gradual building-up of hydrogen into helium via the above cycle of reactions, the so-called carbon-nitrogen cycle, or carbon cycle for short. The carbon and nitrogen act as catalysts, to use the accurate chemical expression. These two elements are not lost in the cycle of reactions; their passive co-operation results in the successive capture of four protons, combining them into one helium nucleus, while at the same time energy has been created.

Rate of energy production

The activity of the carbon cycle increases very rapidly with increasing temperature, while the proton-proton reaction is not very sensitive to temperature. For the Sun the carbon cycle is not very important, accounting for less than 10 per cent of its energy production. Since the proton-proton reaction is not temperature sensitive, it is not limited to the central regions of the Sun, as the carbon cycle is, but operates over a much wider volume. Seventy per cent of the Sun's mass must be hydrogen in order for the required amount of energy to be generated. For stars several times brighter than the Sun, the proton-proton reaction is inadequate, as mentioned before, and the carbon cycle is the almost exclusive source of energy production.

In terms of the mass of a proton $(1.64 \times 10^{-24}$ grams), the mass of four hydrogen atoms is 4.0325, and that of one helium atom 4.0039, so that .0286 mass units are lost in one synthesis. In accordance with the law of conservation of mass plus energy, this loss of mass must appear as 43 microergs of energy, mostly in the form of radiation, eventually leaving the star after several thousand years of successive transformations.

Each individual nuclear reaction takes a long time; the available atoms are numerous, however, and many reactions are in operation all the time. The total liberation of energy is sufficient, for example, to explain the observed rate of radiation of the Sun for another 30 thousand million years! The complete conversion of hydrogen into helium would involve a very slight loss in mass, only 0.7 per cent for a Sun completely composed of hydrogen at the start.

Other stars

All these considerations hold for the Sun and for stars similar to the Sun, the main-sequence stars (Chapter 17). From the previous chapter we recall the comparatively small difference in the central temperatures of luminous and faint stars. The red dwarf stars have central temperatures of about 12 million degrees, the blue giants about 20 million degrees. The dependence of energy production on temperature is partly responsible for the tremendous range in luminosities exhibited by the stars.

In the cool red giants, on the one hand, and in the white-dwarf stars, on the other, physical conditions are widely different from those in the main-sequence stars. The red-giant stars are ideal gases of very low densities. Their central temperatures are five million degrees or less—for certain stars even less than one million degrees. These are low temperatures as far as the requirement for nuclear energy production is concerned. It has been suggested that the gases inside the red giants are not perfectly mixed, and that there is no hydrogen in the deep interior which consists of more massive particles such as those of helium. These particles would form a very dense nucleus in a very much rarefied star; in such a concentrated "model" the central temperature may be high enough to cause sufficient nuclear energy production.

A typical white dwarf has a density of 10^5 grams per centimeter, which is still 10^{10} less than the density of a proton! Although there is still plenty of space for the material, the interior of a white dwarf does not behave as a perfect gas. This is because material containing free electrons cannot be compressed without altering the behavior of the particles. In a normal perfect gas the particles move at random, which implies that they are more likely to have smaller velocities than larger ones. At the high concentration of material within a white dwarf, the motions of the particles, particularly the free electrons, get crowded in the sense that there is a limit to the number of particles that have small velocities. All possible velocities up to a certain limit are about equally abundant; the upper limit, and hence the average velocity, too, increases with an increased degree of crowding.

The ideal-gas law does not apply, but instead we have the law for the degenerate state: $p(:) \rho^{5/3}$ where p is the pressure and ρ the density. If we combine this law with the condition of mechanical equilibrium, we find high internal temperatures which would cause considerable energy production in case hydrogen were abundant. Since, however, the white dwarfs have low luminosities, we conclude that inside the white dwarfs there is little or no hydrogen. It looks, therefore, as if the white dwarfs were burnt-out, collapsed stars, having no more hydrogen fuel than is evident in a superficial simmering shell.

22 | STARS AND PLANETS; THE SUN AMONG STARS

IN CHAPTER FOURTEEN we discussed the discovery of unseen companion objects from observed irregularities in the motions of stars. During the past decade unseen companions to several nearby stars have been found in this way. Since these newly discovered objects are of low luminosity and mass, the question arises whether they are planets or very faint stars. In the present chapter we shall further consider what is meant by the words "stars" and "planets."

We begin with a brief review of certain properties of stars and planets. Stars are self-luminous spheres of compressed incandescent gases; their luminosities range from over 100,000 to as little as 1/500,000 times the Sun's brightness. The observed range in stellar masses proves to be quite limited; a close relation between mass and luminosity exists, the fainter stars, with the exception of the white dwarfs, being less massive. Comparatively few stars are more than ten times as massive, and about a thousand times as luminous as the Sun. The faint red component of the nearby double star Krüger 60 has the smallest known mass for a visible star, namely, $\frac{1}{5}$ the Sun's mass; this object is only 1/2000 as luminous as the Sun.

The planets of our own star—the Sun—and their satellites, though closely spherical in shape, like stars, are cool and predominantly solid bodies of small mass, shining almost exclusively by reflected light. In pondering the possible existence of planets outside the solar system, we restrict the name "planet" to a dependent of a star, i.e., an object of small mass as compared with its primary, and revolving around the latter. Such is the case for the solar planets, the mass ratio planet-Sun reaching a highest value of only 1/1047 in the case of the heaviest planet, Jupiter. The dependency of the planets in the solar system results from the Sun's dominant mass, and is impressively illustrated in Kepler's laws of planetary motion. This same kind of dependency exists for the satellite systems of different planets, also for the myriads of particles that constitute the rings of Saturn and for the numerous comets and meteors which are members of the solar family. Even the relatively heavy Moon of our own "double planet" is only 1/81.3 as heavy as the Earth. In binary stars, however, the masses differ much less, the component masses rarely having a ratio smaller than $\frac{1}{5}$.

Do stars have planets?

Our knowledge of stars and planets is strongly influenced by observational selection. The planets near our Sun were easily discovered; but planetary or very faint companions of other stars would be very elusive. Suppose that the bright component of the nearest star, Alpha Centauri, a close replica of our Sun, had a big planet like Jupiter revolving in a similar orbit with a period of nearly twelve years. An extreme separation of four seconds of arc would occur every six years. The planet would appear as an object of the twenty-third magnitude, not very different from the very faintest stars photographed at long exposures by the largest existing reflecting telescopes. The maximum separation would be very much the same as that of the bright star Procyon and its faint companion; the latter, 1/2000 as luminous as its primary, is a very difficult object to see, even in a large telescope. Now although Alpha Centauri has about the same apparent brightness as Procyon, our hypothetical planet would be about a thousand million times as faint. It would therefore be lost in the glare of its primary and could not be detected. The chances of seeing a planet ten times as large as Jupiter, and hence a hundred times as bright, are hardly better. A larger orbit might take the planet out of the glare, but it would diminish its reflected brilliance; a smaller orbit would increase the brilliance, but this again would be outweighed by the increased glare. With present observational means, therefore, we could not see a conventional planetary companion of even the nearest star; nor, conversely, could the planets in our solar system be seen from the nearest star.

The situation is not quite so hopeless, however, if we utilize the gravitational approach through the observation of perturbations. The same hypothetical Jupiter-like companion of Alpha Centauri would cause a perturbation smaller than $0''.01$, a quantity hovering on the threshold of detection. A companion appreciably more massive than Jupiter would cause a correspondingly larger perturbation, increasing the chances of discovery. As a general rule, it may be stated that it would be difficult to infer the existence of companions of even the nearest star whose masses were less than 1/100 times the Sun's mass. However, in the case of objects more massive than this, the gravitational method is promising. As a result, the possibility of finding cosmic objects with masses smaller than those of visible stars has become a reality.

Distinction between star and planet; importance of mass

We should be prepared to extend our tentative definition of a planet as a dark dependent of relatively small mass to include masses larger than Jupiter's (1/1047 times the Sun's); we may also find self-luminous stars of smaller mass than that of the faint companion of Krüger 60 ($\frac{1}{7}$ times the Sun's). So far as theory is concerned, there is no reason why such objects, intermediate in mass, could not exist. The problem was considered in 1944 by Russell, who concluded that cosmic bodies less than 1/20 times the Sun's mass should generally be unobservable by their own light even under the most favorable conditions. Such "lightweight" bodies would have a surface temperature less than 700° K, which is about the lowest temperature at which an object remains visible. As the companion of a bona-fide star, an object lighter than 1/20 times the Sun's mass would remain invisible even with additional radiation derived from heating by the neighboring primary star. Though its reflected light might be appreciable, the companion would defy any visual detection because of the comparative brilliance of its primary.

We shall accept a generalized definition of stars and planets by adopting Russell's theoretical value of 1/20 the Sun's mass as a conventional borderline. Heavier objects are per se visible stars, while objects of lower mass are the per se invisible bodies which shall be given the general designation planet. The amount of mass, therefore, determines whether a body should be classified as a "star" or as a "planet"; size is of secondary significance.

Review of unseen stellar companions

The application of the gravitational method to nearby stars has revealed in several cases the presence of faint, as yet unseen, companion objects (Chapter 14). We recall the classical discoveries by Bessel of the stellar companions of the bright stars Sirius and Procyon; these companions remained unseen for some time after their gravitational discovery, but were eventually observed directly. We also mentioned the spectroscopic binaries, and the newly initiated photographic programs for discovering astrometric companions from perturbations of nearby stars. The unseen companion objects found thus far have masses as a rule above Russell's critical limit and are therefore termed "stars." One or two of the unseen companions seem to have masses less than 1/20 times the Sun's mass. For example, the mass of the unseen third component discovered from minute perturbations in the orbital motion of the bright visual components of 61 Cygni is found to be 1/60 times the Sun's mass, which falls well within our arbitrary definition of planets. It will be of interest to obtain further data on this object and to be on the outlook for other objects of very small mass.

The Sun among stars

The Sun is a star; conversely, the stars are suns. One of the most striking differences between Sun and stars is that the stars very frequently appear in close pairs or multiple arrangements, while the Sun has no nearby companion star. On the other hand, the Sun has a large family of planets, satellites, comets, etc. We recall that the presence of planetary companions of even the nearest stars would be extremely difficult to establish. The current lack of knowledge about possible planetary companions of other stars is due primarily to observational difficulties and is no evidence against the presence of such companions (nor is it, of course, evidence in favor of their existence).

Abundance of double stars

The systematic photographic search for unseen companions started comparatively recently; the discoveries made so far, however, influence our outlook on the general property of gregariousness among stars. The large abundance of visual double stars has been known for some time. Now we note in our neighborhood the blossoming out of double into triple systems, and a prolific increase of close unseen companions for "single" stars. Consider, for example, in order of distance, the very nearest stars, the six stellar objects nearest the Sun. Excluding the Sun, the nearest star is Alpha Centauri (distance 4.3 lightyears). This object visible in the southern hemisphere is really a well-known *triple* star, in which two stars, 1.3 and 0.36 times as luminous as the Sun, revolve around each other in 80 years, with an average separation of 23.3 astronomical units. The third component is much fainter, only .00007 as bright as the Sun; it is more than ten thousand astronomical units from the close pair. Due to its nearness, the duplicity of Alpha Centauri was easily noticed; the faint, distant, third proper-motion companion was not discovered till 1915. The next two nearest "single" stars—Barnard's star and Lalande 21185—have unseen stellar companions (Chapter 14). The fourth known nearest star, Wolf 359, is very faint and no adequate study of its proper motion has yet been made. The fifth nearest star is Sirius, and it is recalled that its duplicity was also first found from perturbations in its proper motion.

Summarizing:

> Alpha Centauri (4.3 lightyears) is a triple star—we may even say, to be exact, "at least" a triple star.

Barnard's star (6.1 lightyears) is at least a double star.

Lalande 21185 (7.9 lightyears) is at least a double star.

Wolf 359 (8.0 lightyears) is a very faint star, difficult to observe. Hence this star enjoys the benefit of the doubt and still may pass for a single star. If one wishes, it is at least a single star.

Sirius (8.6 lightyears) is at least a double star.

The nearby star Luyten 726–8, whose distance is still uncertain (about 8 lightyears), is at least double.

Of the nearest six stars, therefore, excluding the Sun, one is triple, four are double, while one other is too faint to be studied at present. These six objects contain two component stars on the average. In the case of more distant stars this high average is not maintained, which is easily explained by the increased observational difficulties.

Possible exceptional status of the solar system

We have the right to wonder how exceptional single stars may prove to be. In the beginning of this century (1905) the same thought was expressed by the spectroscopic observers, William Wallace Campbell (1862–1938) and Heber Doust Curtis (1872–1942), both pioneers in the field of spectroscopic binaries:

> "In fact, the star which seems not to be attended by dark companions may be the rare exception. There is the further possibility that the stars, attended by massive [stellar] companions, rather than by small planets, are in the decided majority; suggesting, at least, that our solar system may prove to be an extreme type of system, rather than a common or average type."

Judging by the nearest stars we are tempted to conclude that stars lacking stellar companions seem to be the exception. As to planetary companions, we cannot say much at present. In one or two cases perturbations of a star's motion have been observed which could be attributed to a massive planet. But these perturbations are very small and not much above the unavoidable errors of observation. Hence one must be careful not to give any definite interpretations.

Our own star, the Sun, escapes these general conclusions. The Sun is the only star that we know to have no stellar companion, and yet at the same time to be generously endowed with planetary companions.

PART 4

The Milky Way System and Beyond

23 | THE DISTANCES OF STARS IN OUR NEIGHBORHOOD

RELIABLE individual distances have been measured by the annual parallax method (Chapter 8) for several thousand stars less than a hundred lightyears away. Beyond this limit the annual parallactic effect becomes so small that it cannot be measured accurately. Additional methods for measuring distances of stars and other objects are therefore required. There are two principal methods: the geometric and the photometric.

Geometric distances; solar motion

The geometric method of measuring distances is based on the surveyor's principle; the object is observed from two different points of view. The best-known example is, of course, the annual-parallax method. A valuable extension of the geometric method is made possible by the motion of the solar system, the solar motion. The Sun has a uniform rectilinear velocity of 20 kilometers per second, somewhat over four astronomical units per year (Chapter 27). The point toward which the solar system is moving, the apex, is not very far from the bright star Vega, while the point in the opposite direction, or antapex, is located somewhat to the south of the constellation Orion. While the Sun moves, the planets move in their orbits; the whole solar system is carried along through space without any disturbance of the mechanism of the planetary orbits.

Since all motion is relative, the above statement about the Sun's motion must be qualified by adding that it is with respect to the stars in our "neighborhood" whose motions have been studied, either in the form of proper motions, radial velocities, or both. For the present this neighborhood is rather wide, extending to distances of a thousand lightyears or more.

Parallactic and individual motion

The solar motion provides an ideal baseline for surveying the location of stars up to much larger distances than the limit of about a hundred lightyears for the annual-parallax method.

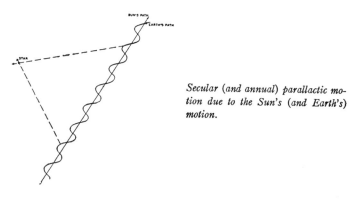

Secular (and annual) parallactic motion due to the Sun's (and Earth's) motion.

Whereas the extreme span of the baseline in the annual-parallax method amounts to only two astronomical units, solar motion provides a baseline which is cumulative or "secular"—over four astronomical units per year, forty astronomical units per decade, and so on. At first sight it would seem as if the distance of any star could be thus derived if we waited long enough to observe small shifts reflecting the solar motion. True, the baseline accumulates with time, but as the Sun moves, the stars do likewise. The observed shift (angular motion P) in the star's direction from one epoch (1) to another (2) is due not only to the Sun's motion (parallactic shift S) but also to the star's own mo-

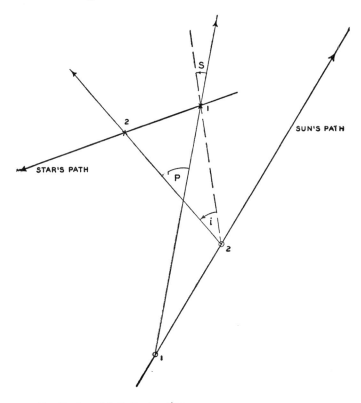

Parallactic and individual motion.

tion (individual motion i). The solar motion is therefore of little help in deriving the distances of individual stars; however, the average distances of large numbers of stars may be measured if we assume that their individual motions are random and cancel one another to some extent.

Secular parallax

The secular parallactic shifts of stars at one and the same distance, but in different directions, depend on the angular distance from the apex or antapex of solar motion. The full amount of the parallactic shift is observed at right angles to the direction of the Sun's motion. A foreshortened shift is observed in other directions; the effect is considerably reduced near the apex and antapex. For a correct evaluation of the distances of the stars, this foreshortening effect must be taken into account; by definition, secular parallax is the shift which the star would have if it were located in a direction at right angles to the Sun's path.

The method is therefore most effective in directions at right angles to the Sun's path; but close to the apex and antapex the observed effects of the secular parallactic shifts are very small, and the method loses its applicability. The average value of the secular parallax, the mean secular parallax, may now be obtained from the proper motions of a group of stars. By appropriate statistical methods, allowance is made for the spread or scatter of the distances of the individual stars in the group, and an average distance is derived.

There are other statistical methods of a geometric nature for determining the distances of stars beyond the limits of the annual-parallax method. The study of these methods, as well as further details of the secular-parallax method are beyond the scope of this book. The secular-parallax and comparable methods give us a general idea of the distances of stars up to 3000 lightyears. Some recent results will be mentioned in the next chapter.

Distance ratio

Faint stars are farther away on the average than bright stars. The increase in distance penetration with increasing magnitude is expressed by a distance ratio for groups of stars differing by one in magnitude. To estimate this ratio, we make a simplifying assumption. We recall that the apparent brightness of two stars differing by one magnitude is expressed by the light ratio of 2.512 (Chapter 6). Assume for a moment that all stars have the same intrinsic brightness as, say, the Sun. The light intensity is diluted according to the square of the distance. Hence the distance ratio is $\sqrt{2.512} = 1.58$; of two stars differing by one magnitude, the fainter one would be 1.58 times as far away.

If we compare the average distance of stars of different magnitude classes, we find that the distance ratio for a difference of one magnitude is always less than the above theoretical value 1.58. The interpretation of this fact will be given later in this chapter; first we shall discuss the photometric method of distance determination.

Photometric distances

The photometric method not only enables us to explore the more distant structure of the stellar system, but also furnishes us with virtually the only means of penetration to the tremendous distances of objects other than stars, such as globular clusters (Chapter 26) and extragalactic objects (Chapter 30). In principle, the method is very simple; the distance of the star, or other object, is derived by comparing its observed brightness, as measured by a suitable photometric device, with an assumed intrinsic brightness. For illustration take the yellow

star Alpha Centauri A, which has the same spectrum as the
Sun. Careful photometric measurements have revealed that we
receive 1/65,000,000,000 as much light from Alpha Centauri A
as from the Sun. Assume now that this star has the same absolute luminosity as the Sun. The radiation from an energy source
is spread out or diluted in inverse proportion to the square of
the distance (Chapter 8); hence Alpha Centauri A is

$$\sqrt{65,000,000,000}$$

or 272,000 times as far away as the Sun, i.e., has a distance of
272,000 astronomical units. Since one lightyear equals 63,300
astronomical units, Alpha Centauri is therefore at a distance of
272,000/63,300, or 4.3 lightyears.

For this particular nearby star the photometric method is of
course unnecessary. The power of the method, however, becomes
evident in the case of very distant objects. No matter how great
it is, an object's distance can be found, provided that an assumption may be made for the intrinsic brightness and a fair
estimate of the apparent brightness obtained. Now we recall
from Chapter 17 that there is a huge range in stellar luminosities; without any further knowledge, it is impossible to make a
fair estimate of the intrinsic luminosity of a star. The usefulness
of the photometric distance method depends to a great extent
on our ability to establish luminosity criteria which will permit
a satisfactory evaluation of intrinsic luminosity.

Luminosity criteria

The spectrum of a star is a useful luminosity criterion. There is
a well-defined relation between the luminosity and spectrum of
the majority of stars; this relation, as we saw in Chapter 17, is
referred to as the main sequence. There are exceptions, such as
the white dwarfs and red-giant stars, to this general relation.

Such difficulties may be obviated, however, if the exceptional character of the star stands revealed in certain detailed aspects of the spectrum. In the absence of spectral knowledge we may often find the color of a star a useful substitute because of the general relation between spectrum and color. The bright variable stars referred to as Cepheids have a luminosity criterion of

TABLE VII.   *Total Number of Stars Over the Whole Sky
Counted Down to Successive Magnitudes*

MAGNITUDE	NUMBER	STAR RATIO	MAGNITUDE	NUMBER	STAR RATIO
2	40		11	870,000	
		3.5			2.6
3	140		12	2,270,000	
		3.8			2.5
4	530		13	5,700,000	
		3.1			2.4
5	1,620		14	13,800,000	
		3.0			2.3
6	4,850		15	32,000,000	
		2.9			2.2
7	14,300		16	71,000,000	
		2.9			2.1
8	41,000		17	150,000,000	
		2.9			2.0
9	117,000		18	296,000,000	
		2.8			1.9
10	324,000		19	560,000,000	
		2.7			1.8
11	870,000		20	1,000,000,000	

great significance. The usefulness of these stars will be further discussed in Chapter 26.

Star counts

The photometric method has been applied to individual stars with valuable results; it has also helped us, in a statistical way, to obtain insight into the general arrangement of the thousands of distant telescopic stars beyond the grasp of the annual- or even the secular-parallax method. We remarked above that because of the tremendous range in stellar luminosities, no fair estimate could be made of the intrinsic luminosity of a star without the aid of some sort of a luminosity criterion. However, the situation is different if we cease to be concerned about the stars as individuals, but focus our attention on their properties as a group. It is in this statistical form that the photometric method has been widely applied for over a century and a half.

The procedure is usually referred to as the method of star counts; in outline it is as follows: Assume that the Sun is located in an indefinitely extended swarm of stars, and that the stars are more or less evenly distributed. There are no concentrations or rarefactions in the swarm; the star density is constant. We make again the simplifying assumption that all stars have the same intrinsic luminosity. Hence the apparent brightness of any star depends only on its distance from us. In other words, all stars of a certain magnitude m are located on a sphere of definite size with the center at the Sun; all stars one magnitude fainter, i.e., of magnitude $m + 1$ will be located on a sphere 1.58 times as large. The number 1.58 is the distance ratio of the diameters of the two spheres, including all stars down to magnitude $m + 1$ and magnitude m respectively. If we count all stars over the whole sky, from the brightest down to a certain specified limiting magnitude m, we include in our list a tally of all stars within a sphere of the definite radius corresponding to this limiting magnitude. If again we count all stars from the brightest one, but this time down to one magnitude fainter $m + 1$, we include all stars within a sphere whose radius is 1.58 times that of the former

Star counts and star ratio for uniform star density.

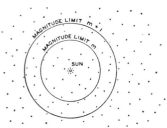

Star ratio

Since the volume or contents of a sphere varies with the cube of the radius, the volumes of the two successive spheres are in the ratio $(1.58)^3$ or 3.98. The same reasoning and results apply to any limited area of the sky, in which case the same ratios hold for the corresponding fractions of the spherical volume.

If, therefore, the star density is uniform, and if all stars are of the same intrinsic brightness, we should note an increase of 3.98, i.e., nearly 4, in star numbers whenever we extend a count of stars over an additional interval of one magnitude. The actual results of such star counts covering the whole sky are given in Table VII. We see that the ratio of star counts from one magnitude to another—the star ratio—is always found to be appreciably less than four, and diminishes as we extend our counts to fainter stars.

Significance of the observed distance and star ratios

Since the distance ratio and the star ratio are always below the theoretical values 1.58 and 3.98 respectively, our assumptions need modification. It looks as if either the hypothesis of uniform star density or the hypothesis of uniform intrinsic brightness, or both, are untenable.

First consider the luminosity hypothesis. The assumption of equal luminosity is certainly not correct; witness the results obtained for the nearer stars (Chapter 17). But we can amend this by adopting a basic distribution of luminosities among stars. Assume that the character of the stellar population—the luminosity curve—remains the same at different distances. Counts down to a certain limiting magnitude would include stars of different absolute magnitudes in spheres of different sizes; the amended hypothesis would not affect the observed values of the distance and star ratios. In any case, the principal contribution to the observational data is made by the limited fraction of comparatively more luminous stars.

The thinning-out of stars

Another explanation is possible. Obscuring material between the stars would lead to a dimming of radiation, so that the intensity of light from more distant stars might be diminished more than would be expected from the inverse-square dilution with the distance. For the time being we ignore this possibility, but shall return to it in Chapter 25.

The failure of the observed star ratios ever to reach the theoretical value 3.98 and the fact that this ratio gradually diminishes for fainter stars strongly suggest that the hypothesis of uniform star density must be modified. As we penetrate further into space, we do not count as many stars over the whole sky as would be expected from a uniform distribution of stars. There appears to be an ever-increasing deficiency of stars at greater distances as compared with the close neighborhood of the Sun. The swarm of stars seems to become less populated;

that is, the stars "thin out" at greater distances. This thinning-out would also explain the behavior of the distance ratio which is always less than 1.58 for a difference of one magnitude. As we studied fainter stars, a large fraction of nearby, intrinsically faint stars would be included, but the number of distant, intrinsically bright stars would gradually diminish. Hence further penetration toward greater distances would be slowed down.

The thinning-out of stars may be studied in different regions of space, and information derived not only for the approximate "size," but also the "shape" of the stellar system. This study will be the subject of the next chapter.

24 THE ARRANGEMENT
OF THE STARS;
THE GALACTIC SYSTEM

Galactic circle

The Milky Way, or Galaxy, faintly suggested to the naked eye, appears much more prominent in telescopic surveys of the sky (see photographs 30, 31). The comparatively narrow belt encircles the entire celestial sphere and very closely divides it into halves. The great circle, following approximately the Milky Way belt is called the galactic circle, or galactic equator. It makes an angle of about 62° with the celestial equator, crossing the latter near the constellations Aquila and Orion. The widest and brightest portion of the galactic belt is in the general direction of the constellation Sagittarius. This area will prove to have special significance. It will be useful to introduce the fundamental galactic directions 0°, 90°, 180° and 270° counted from Sagittarius. These galactic directions will be referred to as Sagittarius, Cygnus, Auriga and Argo after the constellations toward which they approximately point. They are analogous, in a sense, to the four geographic directions, north, east, south and west.

The angular distance of a star from the galactic circle is called its galactic latitude. The galactic equator represents galactic latitude 0°; the "northern" galactic pole is located in the constellation Coma Berenices, the "southern" pole in the constellation Cetus.

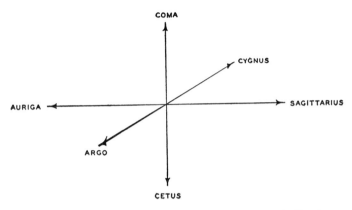

The four principal "equatorial" and the two "polar" galactic directions.

Galactic concentration; galactic plane

The fainter the stars, the higher their "galactic concentration," i.e., their concentration toward the galactic equator. The naked-eye stars appear rather evenly distributed over the sky and are only slightly more concentrated in the Milky Way region than elsewhere. The fainter, telescopic stars are conspicuously crowded, however, in the Milky Way region. Given equal areas of the sky, the number of stars brighter than the tenth magnitude is four times, the number of stars brighter than the fifteenth magnitude is ten times, and the number brighter than the twentieth magnitude is thirty times as high in the Milky Way as at the galactic poles. This implies, of course, that there is a different pattern of star ratios in different galactic latitudes, their values dropping more rapidly at the poles than at the galactic equator; there is, however, no pronounced difference north and south of the galactic equator.

These observations suggest that there are more stars at greater distances close to the equator than at high latitudes; i.e., that the system of stars extends farthest in low galactic latitudes. Remember, also, that the narrow Milky Way belt divides the celestial sphere approximately into halves. We conclude, first, that the Milky Way is a comparatively thin, flattened arrangement of stars spread symmetrically on both sides of what we shall call the galactic plane; and, second, that the Sun must be relatively close to this imaginary plane of symmetry.

Dependence of secular parallax on galactic latitude and magnitude

The secular-parallax method discussed in the previous chapter has yielded information about the arrangement of stars up to distances well over two thousand lightyears. The unforeshortened, secular parallax is found to depend conspicuously on the galactic latitude. The mean secular parallax of stars of the same apparent magnitude increases from the galactic equator to the galactic poles. Hence, stars of a particular apparent brightness at low latitudes are farther away, on the average, than are those of the same apparent brightness at high latitudes.

Some recent determinations of the distances of stars of different magnitudes in different galactic-latitude zones are given in Table VIII.* There is no pronounced difference between the corresponding values north and south of the galactic equator. In any particular latitude zone the observed distance ratio from one magnitude to the next is always below the ratio 1.58

---

* Due to the fact that there is a comparatively limited number of ninth-magnitude stars their average distance values are rather uncertain.

TABLE VIII. *Approximate Average Distance in Lightyears of Faint Stars at Different Galactic Latitudes*

| | GALACTIC | | LATITUDE | |
MAGNITUDE	0° TO 10°	11° TO 20°	21° TO 40°	41° TO 90°
9	1000	1200	1900	700
10	1300	1400	1300	800
11	2000	1900	1400	900
12	2800	2400	1800	1000

characteristic of a uniform distribution of stars of the same luminosity function. In high latitudes the distance ratio is only slightly above the value 1.0.

Concentration of stars toward the galactic plane

The significance of the above geometric determinations of the average distances of faint stars at different galactic latitudes is best understood in combination with star counts. We drew attention to the fact that the fainter the stars the greater their galactic concentration. This phenomenon implies a different progression of star ratios between successive magnitudes at high and low galactic latitudes. The star ratio in the Milky Way drops slowly as we consider fainter and fainter stars; at high latitudes it drops faster.

The great abundance of stars in the Milky Way, slowly thinning out toward greater distances, demonstrates that the system of stars is denser and has a greater extent along the galactic plane than elsewhere. The scarcity of stars in high latitudes and their more rapid thinning-out at greater distances suggest that the system of stars has relatively nearby limits on both sides of the galactic plane. This view is confirmed by the measured distances; stars of the same apparent brightness are considerably closer in high latitudes than in low latitudes.

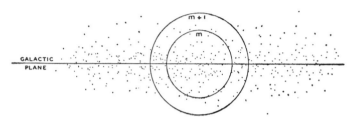

Galactic concentration of stars

The explanation is as follows: a considerable percentage of the apparently fainter stars in low latitudes are actually intrinsically bright and can therefore be seen at great distances; there are few intrinsically bright stars at great distances in high latitudes, however.

We are thus located in a stratum of stars extending along the plane of the Milky Way but of quite restricted dimensions in directions perpendicular to the galactic plane. Within this stratum the stars are concentrated toward the central plane of symmetry, the galactic plane. The extent of the stratum in the galactic plane is not sharply defined and depends to some extent on the observational power employed.

Are the stars concentrated toward the Sun?

Of particular interest is the fact that both the distance and star ratios are consistently below the theoretical values 1.58 and 3.98 respectively in all directions. This is true even of the brightest stars. Hence, a thinning-out is indicated everywhere in all directions. We have already noted the location of the Sun close to the galactic plane. Now we see also that the Sun is located very close to the densest portion of the arrangement of stars; it looks as if the Sun is not far from the center of concentration of all the stars in our neighborhood.

The galactic system

The increased galactic concentration of the fainter stars, as well as the Milky Way phenomenon itself, can now be ascribed to the flattened, disklike arrangement of stars which is the Milky Way or galactic system. The notion that the stars are confined more or less to a flattened stratum, within which the Sun is rather centrally located, was first derived from star counts by William Herschel as early as 1785. Herschel's findings were qualitative, since he did not know the distance of any star; he could estimate, however, that the "thickness" of the stellar system was less than one-fifth its average diameter in the galactic plane. Later studies confirmed Herschel's general conclusions. We shall limit ourselves to a brief outline of the structure of the stellar system as it culminated in the life work of Jacobus Cornelius Kapteyn (1851–1922). During the past decades this outline has been amended to a considerable extent.

Kapteyn's plan of selected areas

Kapteyn's work, like that of others before and after him, is to a great extent based on star counts. There are two aspects of his work which must be specifically mentioned. Kapteyn realized that it would be impossible to make a complete and accurate study of the properties of all stars down to, say, the eighteenth or nineteenth magnitude, covering the whole sky. He chose, therefore, 206 small areas evenly distributed over the sky; and assumed that a study of these samples would give a representative picture of the whole stellar system and a provisional outline of the arrangement of stars. A more detailed study of the stellar system would eventually be necessary to determine its "fine structure"; meanwhile results of significance could be obtained in a limited time.

Importance of proper motion in star counts

Another feature of Kapteyn's work was his taking into account the proper motion of the stars while probing the stellar system by the method of star counts. The size of the proper motion of a star is an excellent measure of the star's nearness (Chapter 9). Proper motions therefore furnish the astronomer with a statistical luminosity criterion; for, if we consider stars of a certain magnitude, those which have large proper motions are nearer, while those of small proper motion are farther away. Additional information about the average distances of stars of different magnitudes and different proper motions has been derived with the aid of secular parallaxes and other statistical methods. The star-count method is thus supported and has been put on a quantitative and more precise basis. Further improvement can be made by taking into account the spectra of the stars; in this way the great dispersion of the general luminosity curve is circumvented to a great extent, since the range of intrinsic luminosities within restricted spectral classes is greatly diminished.

The Kapteyn system of stars; dimensions

Kapteyn's work led to a fairly well-established picture of the density of stars at different distances and in different directions, a picture which confirmed and extended the results of earlier investigators beginning with Herschel. The Sun is close to the galactic plane and to the center of the system; the star density is highest at our location and thins out in all directions—slowly in the galactic regions, quite rapidly toward the poles. In other words, the distribution of stars is such that from either side of the galactic plane their spacing becomes rapidly more sparse. The contrasting result, therefore, is the more gradual dilution of stars as we penetrate farther and farther in directions close to the galactic plane. This diminution in star density appears to be somewhat less in the general direction of the constellation Sagittarius than in other directions; it is suggested even to the naked eye by the appearance and brilliance of the Milky Way in the Sagittarius region.

The exact boundaries of the Kapteyn system, i.e., the galactic system as conceived by Kapteyn, are very difficult to establish, especially in the galactic directions. A majority of more than

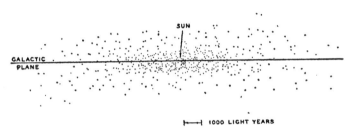

Kapteyn's outline of the galactic system (1920) as viewed from a distant point in the galactic plane.

80 per cent of all stars—both observed and inferred—are included in a stratum about 1500 lightyears thick and extending about 6000 lightyears in the galactic directions. Beyond these limits the star density decreases rapidly and it becomes difficult to assign definite limits to the arrangement.

We shall arbitrarily adopt the dimensions at which the star density is only one-tenth that in our vicinity. This degree of thinning-out is reached at a distance of about 10,000 lightyears in the galactic plane, and at about 2000 lightyears toward the galactic poles. These figures correspond, therefore, to a galactic extent of 20,000 lightyears and of 4000 lightyears perpendicular thereto. The extreme limits of the Kapteyn system extend farther still, but the figures are very uncertain.

The Sun's central location in the Kapteyn system

In all work based on star counts the Sun is found to be close to the center of all observed stars. From past experience with the geocentric and heliocentric views of the planetary system, we may well wonder whether this rather heliocentric aspect of the system of stars must not be regarded with suspicion. Are we really near the center of all stars comprising the galactic system? Have we really established the limits of the system of stars? Is there perhaps a limiting factor, caused by our very location, which gives us the illusion of being close to the center of the system of stars?

Even before the completion of Kapteyn's work there were indications that the Sun is located quite off-center in the stellar system; we recall the slower decrease in star density toward Sagittarius. In the next chapter we shall discuss a factor that played a major role in preventing us for a long time from recognizing the illusion of near-central location which eventually had to give way to an improved description of the stellar system.

25 | INTERSTELLAR MATTER AND THE DIMMING OF STARLIGHT

THE photometric distance method discussed in Chapter 23 presents one difficulty which can be particularly grave in the case of very distant objects. All studies of the distribution of the stars were based on the assumption that the intensity of light is diluted according to the inverse square of the distance from the star. It was tacitly understood that no intrinsic loss of light occurred while the light traveled from star to observer. We shall now consider the possible loss of light caused by material particles in between the stars.

Obscuring clouds; galactic or diffuse nebulae

That there may be a partial extinction of light is not at all improbable. There is direct evidence for such obstruction in the form of isolated clouds of dark material found in large numbers on photographs taken of almost any part of the Milky Way. These galactic regions are usually rich in stars and the appearance of dark clouds is revealed by their obscuring effect on the general background of stars. Also, in many cases we see clouds or wisps of luminous material. Both luminous and dark clouds are referred to as galactic or diffuse nebulae (see photographs 34–40). The luminous diffuse nebulae show an emission-line spectrum, on which a spectrum of reflected starlight is often superimposed. The material, ordinarily dark, shines by reflected light, or is stimulated to radiation if sufficiently luminous stars are in the vicinity. Certain extended nebular patches have thus been discovered; too feeble to be photographed, they could be detected through faint emission lines of hydrogen and oxygen atoms.

The presence of "invisible" diffuse nebulae has sometimes been strikingly demonstrated after the appearance of novae, also called temporary or "new" stars. These are stars which suddenly flare up, increasing their brightness from comparative obscurity up to about 25,000 times the Sun's luminosity (see photograph 29). This prodigious brightness is not maintained, and after a few years the star is usually back to its original brightness. These flare-ups must be regarded as the result of a tremendous disturbance involving the ejection of some of the star's outer material. Numerous novae are discovered each year; much less frequent are the supernovae, which exhibit the nova characteristics on a tremendous scale, yielding a maximum luminosity of 10 million or even 100 million times that of the Sun! Over the past one thousand years we have recorded three supernovae in the galactic system.

In 1901, a few months after the appearance of Nova Persei, formerly invisible clouds in the vicinity of the star were gradually illuminated. Since light travels nearly 300,000 kilometers per second, the illumination of the interstellar clouds took place at the same rate and was a striking illustration of the tremendous cosmic distances at which the velocity of light appears very much reduced.

The isolated diffuse clouds, or nebulae, are something like twenty lightyears in diameter; on the average they are spaced several hundred lightyears apart. The clouds contain small nonmetallic dust, or rather smoke particles, something like 10^{-4} centimeters in diameter.* Particles this size are not large enough to be opaque but they scatter light in all directions. The clouds also contain material in the gaseous state, preponderantly hydrogen, but also oxygen, carbon, sodium, calcium, titanium and other elements; some clouds contain molecules such as hydrocarbon (CH) and cyanogen (CN).

Interstellar matter

The isolated diffuse nebulae are the more dense manifestations of an all-pervading interstellar medium of diffuse material. While these clouds may often be seen, or their existence otherwise inferred, it is a more subtle problem to establish the presence and character of a general interstellar atmosphere of diffuse matter. The obscuring effect of the latter would be so gradual— as in the case of our own terrestrial atmosphere—that at first sight its presence might very well escape our notice.

If we may take the isolated obscuring clouds as characteristic of a possible obscuring medium in the stellar system, then this medium would also consist of small smoke particles, atoms and molecules. Atoms and molecules between the stars have been discovered from certain absorption lines in stellar spectra which obviously could not be attributed to stellar atmospheres. Interstellar hydrogen is vastly preponderant, amounting to about

---

* The designation "smoke" implies an origin due to the accretion of small particles, while "dust" suggests a "debris" origin.

three atoms per cubic centimeter, as compared with up to 50 atoms per cubic centimeter in the diffuse clouds; the first interstellar absorption lines discovered were those of ionized calcium (Ca^+). It is thought that the interstellar material accounts for at least half the mass of the stellar system.

Dimming of starlight

Light rays from distant objects are dimmed both by isolated clouds and by the interstellar atmosphere of smoke and gas. All this interstellar matter interferes with the determination of photometric distances. The interstellar atoms and molecules contribute to an obscuration which is restricted to very specific frequencies of radiation. On the other hand, the presence of the small interstellar dust or smoke particles results in a partial scattering of radiation including all frequencies to a greater or lesser extent. An analogy is furnished by sunlight passing through the Earth's atmosphere. The telluric absorption lines of oxygen and nitrogen increase in intensity as the Sun is closer to the horizon (Chapter 16); the small dust particles in the Earth's atmosphere cause a general scattering of light increasing from the red to the blue part of the spectrum. As a result, a reddening of the Sun is observed near sunrise and sunset, when the Sun's rays travel through longer and denser portions of the Earth's atmosphere. The existence of interstellar obscuration by smoke particles may therefore be tested from a reddening of distant stars.

Spurious inflation due to dimming of starlight

A general dimming of the stars is more difficult to recognize. A distant star appears dimmer because of the loss of light through interstellar particles. Hence the photometric distance of the star will be overestimated if we are not aware of this dimming, or choose to ignore it. Individual stars and also large numbers of stars studied by the method of star counts will be thought farther away than they actually are. The star counts will suggest a spurious dilution in the spacing of the stars; this thinning-out will become more and more exaggerated with increasing distance. Moreover, at still greater distances the dimming may be so strong as to remove the stars beyond the realm of observation; i.e., they are completely blacked out.

We begin to realize the effect that a dimming of starlight may have on our interpretation of the universe if its geometrical structure is based on photometrically derived distances. The effect is of an inflationary nature, the distortion in any one direction depending on the amount of dimming. The detection of such inflation is aided by the observed reddening of starlight which helps us to establish the presence and properties of any dimming material. Geometric distances are, of course, unaffected by the dimming of starlight.

Absence of dimming in high galactic latitudes

The obscuring material in the stellar system was long ignored; there was even good reason to believe that it was virtually absent. To mention an illustration: globular clusters are concentrated groupings of stars at great distances, ten thousand lightyears away and more (Chapter 26). We might expect, therefore, that the appearance of the stars in these clusters were influenced by an accumulated effect of obscuring material; no reddening was observed in the light of stars in certain distant globular clusters, at distances of as much as 100,000 lightyears, and this was considered an argument for the virtual transparency of interstellar space.

The particular clusters studied were at a high angle to the galactic plane. The conclusions on transparency should therefore be qualified as follows: there is no appreciable obscuration of light at a high angle to the galactic plane. Hence there is good reason to believe that the rapid thinning-out of stars in directions perpendicular and near perpendicular to the general plane of the Milky Way is real and not in any way due to an impairment of visibility by dimming material. The situation is entirely different, however, in the case of distant objects nearer the galactic directions, i.e., close to the galactic plane.

Galactic star clusters

A study, by Robert Julius Trumpler (1886–   ) of the galactic or open star clusters played an important role in clarifying our understanding of the dimming of light in the galactic system. There are hundreds of these open star clusters, almost all in low galactic latitudes (see photograph 41). They are intermingled with the general swarm of stars, but contribute only slightly to the total stellar population. The value of the clusters for study-ing the properties of the stellar system lies in the very fact that they *are* mixed in with the general population but at the same time are arranged in definitely recognizable formations.

In several cases an open cluster is conspicuous from its concen-trated appearance in the comparatively looser arrangement of the stars at large. An unmistakable way of recognizing the mem-bers of a cluster is from their community of motion; compare the cluster stars with a flock of birds moving in perfect formation over the landscape. The individual cluster members may be separated from the non-cluster stars in the foreground or back-ground by careful measurements of their proper motions or radial velocities; the cluster stars are separated from the "field" stars through their common motion. Unusually accurate meas-urements again indicate minute differences between the motions of the cluster members. These internal motions are due to the gravitational attraction between the stars, to the spatial extent and depth of the cluster, and sometimes to perspective effects, which in the long run are evident as an apparent convergence or divergence of the parallel space motions of the cluster stars.

The number of stars and their spacing vary from one cluster to another; neither is comparable with the high population and strong concentration found in the globular star clusters (Chapter 26). Trumpler derived the photometric distances of the open clusters by comparing the apparent brightnesses of individual cluster stars with their intrinsic brightnesses estimated from their spectral classification (Chapter 17). The most distant clusters he found were about 15,000 lightyears away; it is expected that increased telescopic power will reveal more distant clusters. The clusters are spread throughout the system of stars, generally quite close to the galactic plane. The arrangement of the clusters confirms, in a general way, our concept of the shape and extent of the galactic system.

Dimming effect in galactic clusters

After the photometric distance is known, the diameter of a cluster can be derived from its angular diameter. Though difficult to define because of their inherent vagueness of outline, the clusters may be assumed for our present purposes to be approximately spherical in shape; their diameters range from about ten to eighty lightyears. Trumpler found that the more distant galactic clusters were on the average larger than the nearer ones. This would be strange, indeed, if it were a real phenomenon. Trumpler reasoned that the increased size of the distant clusters could be ascribed to the cumulative effect of a dimming of starlight, causing an inflation in the photometrically derived distance and hence in all properties based on this distance. The inflation increases rapidly with the distance of the

cluster; for clusters of equal diameter, the more distant seem
to be larger. The result would be a spurious thinning-out in the
structure and a spurious increase in the diameter of the more
distant clusters.

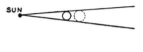

Inflationary effect of dimming of starlight on photometric interpretation of distance and size of star cluster.

Galactic obscuring layer

In 1930 Trumpler postulated the existence of a thin layer of dimming material—smoke and atoms—very concentrated toward
and extending along the central plane of the Milky Way system.
The Sun is located within the layer, close to the galactic plane;
the dimming effect is greatest for distant objects near the galactic plane (1) and least for nearby stars and also for objects seen
at a high angle (2) with the galactic plane.

The hypothesis of the galactic obscuring layer was confirmed by the observed reddening of distant stars in the Milky Way and also by the observed distribution of the globular star clusters (Chapter 26). Further information was derived from the observed distribution of the extragalactic nebulae (Chapter 30). The various investigations point to an extinction of about 60 per cent in the case of a light ray making a lateral crossing of the obscuring layer. Several hundred lightyears "thick" at

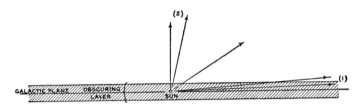

Galactic obscuring layer.

most, the obscuring layer extends over thousands of lightyears along the galactic plane and from our vantage point has its effect on the stars and other objects. The layer is densest near the galactic plane, decreasing in density and dimming power as one gets farther away both to the "north" and "south" of the galactic plane. The inner portion of the obscuring layer, close to the galactic plane, probably has a very high dimming power; this inner "sheet" is most likely not over 50 lightyears thick, and, like the rest of the layer, not uniform in structure.

Effect of obscuring layer on distant stars

Along and close to the galactic plane, the dimming effect accumulates rapidly at greater and greater distances. The actual dimming power is not accurately known; it is roughly something like 50 per cent for each thousand lightyears. Only half the light of an object at a true distance of 1000 lightyears reaches us, therefore. If this dimming is erroneously attributed to greater distance, the object is interpreted as being 1400 lightyears away. Only one-sixteenth of the light of an object at a true distance of 4000 lightyears in the galactic plane reaches us; this object is interpreted as being 16,000 lightyears away! Therefore, if we ignore or disregard the dimming effect our concept of distance will be inflated. Obviously, then, our concept of properties based upon these distances, such as the spacing of stars or the dimensions of the clusters, will be equally inflated.

Exceptionally strong dimming of starlight results from local condensations or clouds which may be several hundred lightyears in diameter and are almost completely opaque. Fortunately for our view of the cosmos, the Sun is not situated within any extremely localized condensation of dimming material.

Dimout and blackout of distant stars

We now see how the diminution in stellar density in the galactic plane may be attributed to the dimming of light by interstellar matter. If we do not recognize the dimming as such, then at great distances close to the galactic plane the stars will appear to be more thinly distributed. An example of such thinning-out was the spacing of the stars in the distant open clusters. Some of the apparently faint, distant stars, which in a transparent system might still come within the scope of the applied telescopic power, are now completely removed beyond the range of vision, thus causing additional thinning-out. Finally, the accumulated dimming effect puts a practical limit in many cases to further distance penetration, resulting in a virtual blackout of stars at greater distances.

It is clear that our central position in the observed distribution of the stars may well be due to our inability to "see" further. Our location is no more central than that of a wanderer lost in a large forest permeated with a dense fog. Wherever he finds himself, the wanderer can observe only a small fraction of the forest, which in all directions appears limited to approximately the same depth of vision. A similar situation exists for an observer elsewhere in the galactic system; he can observe only his own limited system.

Dimout and blackout of distant stars.

More than a decade before the discovery of the galactic obscuring layer it had become apparent that the Kapteyn system of stars was only part of the galactic system. The principal argument for abandoning the concept of the central location of the Sun resulted from a comprehensive study of globular star clusters. Here the photometric method of distance determination could make its power felt because of the tremendous intrinsic luminosities of these concentrated assemblies of stars which can be seen at such great distances. The globular clusters will be the subject of the next chapter.

26 THE ARRANGEMENT OF THE GLOBULAR STAR CLUSTERS

WE RECALL that the observed distribution of stars is explained by their arrangement in a comparatively thin stratum. The dimensions of the Kapteyn system were some 20,000 lightyears in the galactic plane and only some 4000 lightyears perpendicular to the galactic plane. The interstellar obscuring material concentrated toward the central plane of the stratum of stars explains the dimming and hence the apparent thinning-out of stars at great distances close to the galactic plane. Since the dimming is less in the red and infra-red than in the blue radiation used in most conventional photographic studies, we may gradually expect better distance penetration with the application of red sensitive photographic emulsions.

There is a class of objects related to the stars which is of great significance in exploring the more distant regions of the galactic system. These objects, related to the galactic system, are the globular star clusters.

Globular clusters

Nearly one hundred globular star clusters in the galactic system are known at present. They are symmetrical, dense aggregations of hundreds of thousands of stars; as contrasted with the open or galactic clusters (Chapter 25), the population of stars in globular clusters is very high. A few of these objects are bright enough to be seen with the naked eye as faint, cloudy patches. Photographs taken with powerful telescopes reveal the brilliance and beauty of the clusters; they resemble one another very much in appearance. Even in the brightest and presumably nearest clusters the stars appear to be packed together very closely. The globular clusters are exceedingly luminous and emit a tremendous amount of radiation concentrated in a relatively small portion of space; they can be seen at very great distances and are therefore of importance in leading us farther out into space. (See photograph 42.)

For an analogy we turn to the forest mentioned in the preceding chapter. We realized that although this forest of trees is pervaded by a dense fog limiting our vision in all directions it extends beyond the blackout limits imposed by the fog. Suppose that scattered throughout the forest there are one hundred very brilliant lanterns or light beacons, observable well beyond the blackout limits for the individual trees which, to improve the analogy, might be marked by burning candles. The visibility would be even more favorable in the case of those light beacons towering high above the densest portion of the fog. Let us assume that the beacons are sufficiently bright and spaced so as to outline the arrangement of the trees and the forest's expanse. From a survey of these luminous objects we may then derive the shape and extent of the forest. With these thoughts in mind we will study the most brilliant light beacons of the galactic system, namely, the globular star clusters.

Distribution over the sky

Our first acquaintance with the starry sky revealed that the stars are "everywhere," that they are not absent from any large portions of the sky. Next we noted the concentration of stars toward the Milky Way. Apart from this galactic concentration there was no striking asymmetry in the distribution of individual stars except the slightly higher density in the direction of Sagittarius as compared with other galactic directions. For the globular clusters the situation is entirely different.

The most remarkable feature is the strong concentration toward the portion of the sky around Sagittarius. As a matter of fact, one-third of all globular clusters are located in a small area of the sky outlined by the constellations Scorpio and Sagittarius, while only half a dozen are found in the hemisphere centered around Auriga!

Another striking, though not surprising property of the globular clusters is their scarcity in a narrow central region of the Milky Way. This we would expect in view of the concentration of obscuring matter toward the galactic plane. Perhaps with the aid of infra-red photography many more clusters will be found near the central plane of the Milky Way.

The asymmetrical placement of the globular clusters over the sky is intriguing, particularly since they represent distant landmarks in the galactic system. An important systematic study of globular clusters was made by Harlow Shapley (1885–   ) in the second decade of the twentieth century. Since no direct results could be expected from the geometric distance method, reliance had to be placed on the photometric method (Chapter 23). The basic luminosity criterion used by Shapley was provided by certain variable stars in the clusters.

Cepheid variable stars

The luminosity of the great majority of stars remains essentially the same indefinitely. Here and there, however, stars are found which vary rapidly in brightness, some in a regular fashion, others irregularly. One common type of regular variable star is of particular interest for its important application in photometric distance determinations. We refer to the Cepheids, named after their prototype, Delta Cephei. Cepheids are extremely

The variable star Delta Cephei is the vertex of an isosceles triangle situated between the bright stars Alpha Cassiopeia and Alpha Cygni (Deneb). With the naked eye it is easy to notice the variation in brightness of Delta Cephei as compared with the constant brightness of the two comparison stars Zeta Cephei (magnitude 3.6) and Epsilon Cephei (magnitude 4.2). Observations with the unaided eye on several consecutive nights hint at the character of variability, while a few months' observations permit the determination of both the character of the light curve of variability and its period.

luminous stars which undergo periodic variations in brightness resulting from rhythmical pulsations of the whole star. Cepheid variables have periods of light variation ranging anywhere from a fraction of a day to about a hundred days. The range in brightness of any one particular star is never more than twofold.

An important luminosity criterion:
the period-luminosity relation

Of great importance is a unique relation between the period of light variation and the luminosity of Cepheid variable stars. This was first discovered from observations of a large number of Cepheids in the Small Magellanic Cloud, one of two huge, irregular clouds of stars subordinate in size but close to the galactic system (Chapter 28). Later studies extended the findings to other Cepheids, including those in the stellar neighbor-

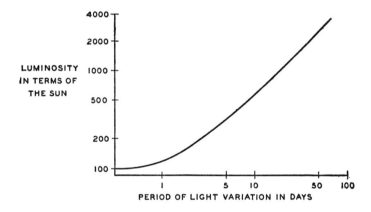

The period-luminosity relation of Cepheids.

hood. Consequently, we have a good idea about the relation between the period of light variation of a Cepheid and its average intrinsic luminosity. Cepheids whose periods are less than one day are about 100 times as luminous as the Sun. Cepheids whose periods are longer than one day have higher luminosities. The one is a measure for the other; the longer the period, the higher the luminosity. For example, the luminosity of a Cepheid with a period of fifty days is as much as 2000 times that of the Sun.

Since a higher luminosity corresponds to a larger size, the period-luminosity relation simply implies an increase in the period of pulsation with size. This is a general property of periodic, vibratory motions; compare a pendulum whose length determines the period of swing.

Because of this characteristic period-luminosity relation Cepheids are ideally suited for photometric distance determinations. As soon as the period of its light variation is established, the luminosity of a Cepheid may be accurately estimated by assuming the object to follow the period-luminosity relation.

Other luminosity criteria

Numerous Cepheids have been found in several globular clusters, thus enabling us to determine the distances of these objects. Cepheids with periods less than one day occur particularly frequently in globular clusters and for this reason are referred to as cluster-type variables. (Cluster-type variables also appear outside of clusters.)

There are numerous globular clusters in which no variable stars have yet been found; for these objects other luminosity criteria are used. The average luminosity of the brightest twenty-five stars is practically the same from cluster to cluster, namely about three hundred times that of the Sun. This proved a most useful criterion for deriving the distances of those clusters in which no variables had yet been found. Several clusters are so far away that even the brightest individual stars cannot be well resolved. Here another criterion may still be used, namely, the total, integrated luminosity of the cluster, which is approximately 300,000 times that of the Sun.

In each cluster, inside a diameter of about a hundred light-years there are some hundred thousand stars brighter than the Sun. This corresponds to a population density of more than a hundredfold that in our immediate stellar neighborhood, if we restrict ourselves to stars brighter than the Sun. Little is known about the number of fainter stars in globular clusters.

Distances and arrangement of globular clusters

The distances of the globular clusters were found to range from about ten thousand to well over a hundred thousand lightyears. The aforementioned concentration of the clusters toward the Sagittarius portion of the sky revealed itself in the space distribution of the clusters in the following manner. According to Shapley's original views the globular clusters fill an enormous volume of space very much off center with respect to our location and the stars around us. The system of clusters is elongated toward Sagittarius and its center seems to be close to the galactic plane in the general direction of Sagittarius at a distance of some 50,000 lightyears. The clusters are rather equally and symmetrically distributed on both sides of the galactic plane,

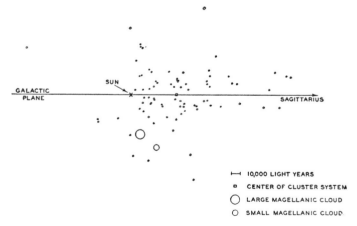

The space distribution of the globular clusters as first determined by Shapley (1919).

although there is none within 4000 lightyears on either side of that plane. In other words, the galactic plane is a plane of symmetry, not only of the stars but also of the globular clusters. This suggested that there is a connection between the spatial distribution of the globular clusters and that of the stars.

Shapley concluded that globular clusters and stars do not form separate systems but that both are part of the galactic system, which therefore extends far beyond the limits of the Kapteyn system. The outlines of the "greater" galactic system are much more nearly represented by the arrangement of the distant globular clusters than by the stars. The Sun is near the edge of the arrangement of the globular clusters, and the center of the galactic system is in the galactic direction of the constellation Sagittarius. One globular cluster, known as NGC 2419, is so distant—about a hundred thousand lightyears—that it may not even be a member of the galactic system.

Effect of dimming

Shapley's findings were the basis of a new outlook with regard to the size of the galactic system and our location in it. It proved necessary to revise our concept of the size of the system. The galactic obscuration affects the globular clusters; they, too, are subject to dimout and blackout effects. The blackout of globular clusters is evident close to the galactic plane. A general dimout is indicated by the egg-shaped structure of the huge system of globular clusters, which is elongated in the direction of Sagittarius. But it seemed curious to find an elongation toward the very center of the globular-cluster system. Moreover the concept of galactic rotation (Chapter 29) was inconsistent with any elongated arrangement and favored a more symmetrical distribution.

The elongation can be explained as a photometric inflation

effect which is most marked in distant clusters close to the galactic plane. While clusters in the higher galactic latitudes are subject to little dimming, those in low latitudes are more obscured, or possibly completely blacked out. At first the dimming was ignored and the weakening of light simply attributed to increased distance. The photometric distances of all globular clusters were therefore originally exaggerated, the increase being largest for clusters in low latitudes, which, on the average,

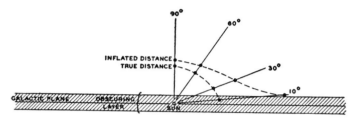

Effect of dimming on globular clusters at equal distances but at different angles from the galactic plane.

prove to be rather far away in any case. The result of all this was exactly the elongated distribution found by Shapley.

The obscuring layer revealed again

Both this elongation and the galactic "zone of avoidance" could be ascribed to the effect of dimming on the last portion of the light path close to the galactic plane. These very properties in the observed distribution of the globular-cluster system can be used to determine the amount of dimming power of the layer of obscuration. In our imagination we may "lift" the three-dimensional obscuring "veil"; this leads to a brightening-up of all clusters, which now prove to be nearer than they were thought to be, particularly in low latitudes. Hence their arrangement in space is of lesser extent than originally thought, and in fact several of the clusters in low latitudes are actually not far from the galactic plane.

We can aid our imagination by some simple calculations. On the assumption that in reality there is neither a true "zone of avoidance" nor a real elongation in the distribution of the globular clusters, the galactic obscuring layer is found to have a lateral extinction of something like 60 per cent. This finding is in good agreement with that calculated from the observed distribution of extragalactic objects (Chapters 25 and 30).

The more nearly correct arrangement of globular star clusters

If we make allowance for the dimming effects, a reduction in the photometric distances is brought about, ranging from 20 per cent near the galactic poles, to about 90 per cent for a cluster seen at an angle of five degrees with the galactic plane. The individual clusters may be "pulled in" from their inflated distances, as one pulls in a kite, and more nearly correct locations obtained. Clusters blacked out in existing surveys are of course

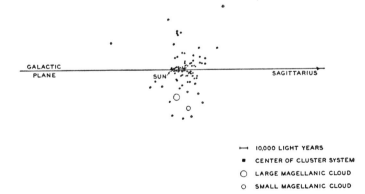

GALACTIC
PLANE

SUN

SAGITTARIUS

⊢————⊣ 10,000 LIGHT YEARS

■ CENTER OF CLUSTER SYSTEM

○ LARGE MAGELLANIC CLOUD

○ SMALL MAGELLANIC CLOUD

The space distribution of the globular clusters, corrected for the effects of dimming (1932).

not salvaged by this process of calculation; as noted before, they may eventually be located by increased telescopic power in the ranges of red or infra-red light.

The adjusted picture shows a reduction in the size of the system. The globular clusters are now seen to populate a more or less spherical portion of space; there is no avoidance of the galactic plane. There appears to be a strong concentration of clusters toward the center of their arrangement, which, of course, is still located in the direction of Sagittarius. The distance to this center is reduced from 50,000 to about 18,000 lightyears. (All these figures are still rather uncertain.)

In the past four chapters we have been concerned only with the arrangement of stars and star clusters. Next we shall study the state of motion of the stellar system as observed from our particular location. The following chapter will deal with various patterns of stellar motions observed in the galactic system.

27 PATTERNS OF STELLAR MOTIONS

Motion and gravitation

Motion is the essence of life in a universe subject to the law of gravitation. Without motion a rapid collapse of the stellar system would result from the mutual gravitation of stars. There is no general contraction of the observed part of the stellar system; at the same time the stars appear to move. A gravitational collapse of the galactic system is effectively and continuously avoided by an appropriate state of motion.

What is the nature of these motions? Are they organized into one general pattern? We have seen what general type of mechanism exists on smaller space-and-time scales. For the Moon and the Earth, for the planets and the Sun, and for the binary stars the balance between gravitational attraction and motion has been extensively analyzed (Chapters 10, 11 and 12). The orbital motions of the planets in the solar system were first studied by Kepler; we still speak of Keplerian motion when describing the orbital motion of any two cosmic objects "falling" around each other. We interject another example of the same general nature, namely, the architecture of a star which is maintained by the balance between gravitational attraction, on the one hand, and the agitation of the atoms and other particles, on the other (Chapter 20).

Viewing the abundance of Keplerian orbital motion in these relatively short, cosmic space-and-time phenomena, we wonder whether the assembly of stars moves in a comparable manner, designed to avert the gravitational collapse of the galactic system.

Comparison of solar and galactic systems

The architecture of the galactic system is obviously not as simple as that of the solar or planetary system. The number of planets in the solar system is quite limited, while the number of stars in the galactic system runs into thousands of millions. There is no evidence of a single central sun of overwhelming mass dominating the gravitational behavior of the galactic system. We note, however, one particular resemblance of the stellar system to the solar system, namely, its flattening. The orbits of the planets are more or less in the same plane and are contained in a flattened box which includes the orbit of Pluto, while the lateral extent of the box is much smaller. Even the great majority of the minor planets or asteroids remain within these spatial limitations in their circuits about the Sun.

The analogous flattening of the stellar system may be indicative, therefore, of motions comparable to those in the solar system, in the sense that the majority of stars describe vast orbits more or less in the same plane. The difference between the two systems is to a great extent one of space-time dimensions. This is partly due to the distances of the stars when contrasted with the comparatively small size of the solar system. But it is also a matter of time scale, which may be illustrated as follows.

An instantaneous glance at the distribution of the planets reveals that they are more or less in the same plane. To establish their orbital motion about the Sun, much more time is required; the analysis is complicated because we are observing from one of the very planets involved in this cosmic arrangement. We recall that it took a long time before the heliocentric view of the planetary system was clearly understood.

The motions of the stars do not show any observable sign of curvature; any possible galactic orbital motion of the stars must be on a tremendous time scale, in which a few hundred years of orbital motion may be compared with a few minutes of the orbital motions in the planetary system.

Stellar motions

We examine now the state of motion of the stellar system as revealed by stars in our neighborhood. In particular, we shall look for regularities or patterns in the mobile behavior of the stellar population. Such patterns would most likely contain a clue to a general organized motion.

We recall some of the findings presented in Chapter 9. Astrometric methods have revealed proper motions for tens of thousands of stars. The spectroscopic application of the Doppler principle has yielded radial velocities for thousands of stars, and also for the distant globular clusters and extragalactic objects. The motions in space of the nearer stars relative to the Sun can be determined if the proper motion, radial velocity and distance—all three—are known. With stars beyond one hundred lightyears, it becomes increasingly difficult to obtain this complete knowledge, and we may have to be satisfied with a knowledge either of proper motions or of radial velocities only. In any case, by various statistical devices, substantial information about stellar motions has been obtained up to distances of a thousand lightyears and more. On the average, the stars are found to move with velocities of something like 30 kilometers per second. A large range in stellar velocities has been found; there are, however, comparatively few stars with velocities over 200 kilometers per second. Apart from possible fluctuations due to close companion objects, the space velocity of any star is always uniform in direction and amount of motion. This is the law of inertia (Chapter 9). The proper motion of no star has yet been followed for more than two centuries; as mentioned before, it may well be that the observed paths are actually minute fractions of vast orbits whose curvature cannot yet be ascertained.

Velocity patterns

Our stellar neighborhood of some thousand lightyears across is small compared with the size of the galactic system. The general motions of the stars, do not depend, at first sight, on their location, and may thus be studied with greater ease if, in our imagination, the size of the stellar neighborhood is "shrunk" into a point. In other words, we ignore the exact arrangement of the stars and study the group behavior of motions in the form of a velocity pattern or velocity diagram; it is understood that this velocity diagram represents the mobile behavior of stars everywhere within the neighborhood. Only for certain aspects of stellar motions (Chapter 29) extending over a much wider neighborhood will it be desirable to take into account the arrangement of the stars.

Group motion

In 1783 William Herschel noticed that the few stellar proper motions known at that time indicated a preponderant trend toward one part of the sky. Not that the motions of these stars were parallel, but their general drift was strongly unified in direction, and is best illustrated by the one-sidedness of the distribution in the velocity diagram of these stars. This general drifting of the stars in a certain direction in space is referred to as their group motion.

There is nothing absolute about motions in nature; an absolute frame of reference does not exist (Chapter 6). For specific problems a convenient frame of "rest" may be arbitrarily adopted; for example, the train moves, the tracks are at rest; the Earth moves, the Sun is at rest, etc. The astronomer observes relations between the paths of different objects as referred to the point of observation to which he is bound by nature. Thus, after we make allowance for the Earth's annual orbital motion, all observed motions of stars and other remote celestial objects are referred to the Sun, and therefore represent a relation between the motion of the star and any motion of the Sun itself.

Solar motion

Herschel chose to recognize the group motion of the stars as the reflex effect of the motion of our observational standpoint,

"GROUP MOTION"   "SOLAR MOTION"

Velocity diagrams of group motion and solar motion.

i.e., the Sun (Chapter 23). After all, Sun and stars are objects of the same nature; hence, the very motions of stars when first observed in the early eighteenth century must have put astronomers on the alert for possible signs of motion in our own star, the Sun.

The Sun's motion, or solar motion, is defined as the reflex or opposite of the group motion; observations of the motions of a large number of stars enable us to measure the motion of the Sun, as referred to that particular group of stars. The Sun is thus found to move toward a point not very far from the bright star Vega. This is a fundamental property of the Sun when referred to stars up to something like a thousand lightyears or even more. The Doppler principle has revealed that the Sun's velocity is close to 20 kilometers per second, or a little over four astronomical units per year. This has been established by noting that in the direction of solar motion—toward the apex—the stars approach us on the average at the rate of 20 kilometers per second, while in the opposite direction—toward the antapex —the stars appear on the whole to be receding at the same rate of 20 kilometers per second.

We do, however, find different values both in the amount and direction of the solar motion if we study such objects as, for example, the distant globular star clusters or the extragalactic objects. Hence, the above findings for stellar and solar motions may be only a part of a more complex picture.

Stellar motions in our neighborhood

Within our neighborhood the observed stellar motions may be freed from the effect of the Sun's motion, i.e., the parallactic motion. A study can then be made of the individual or peculiar motions of these stars, including that of the Sun. In other words, we may change our standpoint of observation from the Sun to the stellar neighborhood as a whole and count the Sun merely as another star. The velocity diagram now loses its one-sided-

ness, since it represents a balance of the motions of the different
stars that make up the neighborhood.

Preferential motion

We might have expected that the stars move at random, equally
in all directions; in 1904, however, Kapteyn discovered that this
was not the case. Stars do move in all directions, but there seems
to be a general drift along a certain axis in the plane of the Milky
Way. Everywhere within our neighborhood, more stars are found
to move both in the galactic direction toward Sagittarius and
in the opposite direction toward Auriga than in any other direction. The two-way mobility is about 50 per cent greater in the
"preferential" galactic direction than in the direction of least

Velocity diagram of preferential motion.

mobility which is perpendicular to the galactic plane. Kapteyn
referred to this phenomenon as "stream motion"; the expression
"preferential motion" is now generally used.

　　Kapteyn's important discovery was confirmed by other investigations. The phenomenon of preferential motion exists everywhere within the neighboring stellar world. It represents, we
repeat, a preferred, two-way traffic, both in numbers and speed,
along an axis defined by roughly joining the directions Sagittarius and Auriga.

　　Two subsequent discoveries, closely related to each other, are
of significance. Both indicate a remarkable asymmetry in the
pattern of stellar motions.

High-velocity stars

At first sight there seems to be nothing striking about stellar motions in our neighborhood apart from their preferential quality; this is only true, however, if we do not include stars whose velocities are more than 60 kilometers per second. The situation changes abruptly if we investigate stars whose velocities are more than 60 kilometers per second. Such stars are comparatively rare; most of them are faint, and only gradually has a sufficiently large number been included in our surveys to permit a study of their group properties. There appears to be a section of the sky extending more than one hundred degrees along the Milky Way toward which not a single one of these high-velocity stars is moving. The center of this wide sector of avoidance is in the direction of Cygnus. We may state the finding as follows: there is a stellar speed limit of 60 kilometers per second in the

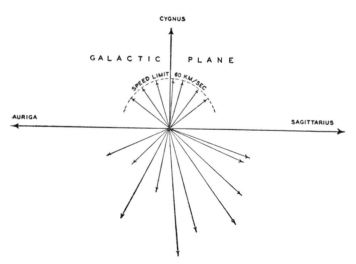

Velocity diagram of high-velocity stars.

general direction of Cygnus everywhere in our neighborhood. On the other hand, stars with much higher velocities, up to several hundred kilometers per second, are found to be moving in directions outside the sector of avoidance centered around Cygnus.

The high-velocity stars represent a very small fraction of the stellar population, but they demonstrate an important property of the general state of motion of the stellar system.

Asymmetry in stellar motions

The pattern of motion of the high-velocity stars is but one pronounced example of a general asymmetry in stellar motions at large and in the motions of other special groups of objects such

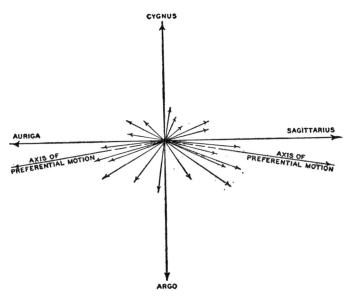

Velocity diagram illustrating asymmetry in stellar motions.

as the globular star clusters. This general asymmetry in stellar motions was studied in 1924 by Gustav Benjamin Strömberg (1882–   ). The stars at large also have slightly asymmetrical patterns of motion. Their mobility is somewhat greater in the direction of Argo than in the opposite direction of Cygnus. The velocity pattern is really such that the preferential axis of greatest mobility is slightly bent or rather broken in the direction of Argo. This implies a slightly decreased mobility toward Cygnus as contrasted with the opposite direction of Argo. While in the stars at large this asymmetrical behavior is hardly noticeable, it becomes more conspicuous as we study stars of larger velocities. Finally, the asymmetry of the rapidly moving stars with velocities over 60 kilometers per second is strikingly illustrated in the fact that none of these stars is moving in the general direction of Cygnus.

Radial velocities have been observed for several of the globular clusters. The remarkable finding is that this group of objects exhibits a general drift in the direction of Argo, amounting to as much as 200 kilometers per second. Here the phenomenon of asymmetry seems to have reached its full development.

Relativity of solar motion

The amount and direction of the group motion of any swarm of stars obviously depends on the degree of asymmetry of their individual motions. Since the motion of the Sun with respect to a swarm of stars is defined as the opposite of their motion as a group, the former is affected likewise by the degree of asymmetry. With respect to stars in a wide neighborhood, the Sun's velocity is about 20 kilometers per second toward a point not far from Vega. When referred to the high-velocity stars, the Sun's velocity comes out as high as 56 kilometers per second, while a slight difference in direction is also indicated. This higher rate of motion is the result of the general marked drift of the high-velocity stars toward Argo as compared with the general population of stars. The relative nature of solar motion becomes still more obvious if it is referred to the globular star clusters. The importance of this situation will be recognized in the next chapter.

Significance of preferential motion and asymmetry

It is notable that both the axis of preferential motion and the direction of asymmetry are located close to or in the galactic plane. Moreover, the direction of asymmetry is perpendicular to the axis of preferential motion. That the degree of mobility is smallest perpendicular to the galactic plane is important also. We are reminded of the planetary system in which the planes of the various orbits differ little. The inclinations of the different orbits are generally only slight; hence, the mobility perpendicular to the general plane is comparatively small. The familiar plane diagram of planetary motions represents, therefore, a fairly correct view of these motions.

We are familiar with the obvious relation between the organization of the orbits close to the average plane and the resulting flatness of the planetary system. We have evidence now for comparatively small mobility perpendicular to the galactic plane, and also for the flattening of the stellar system. A radical change in viewpoint must now be introduced to explain and clarify the various patterns of stellar motion as observed in our neighborhood.

28 THE GALACTOCENTRIC VIEWPOINT

SHAPLEY'S researches on the globular clusters (Chapter 26) showed for the first time that the galactic system has greater dimensions and a different center than were indicated by the Kapteyn system (Chapter 24). Our confused concepts of the boundaries of the system and of our apparently central location in it were due largely to the dimming effect of the obscuring material, which also explained the apparent thinning-out of stars in the galactic plane (Chapter 25).

The galactic center

It looks as if the off-center location of the globular clusters should be interpreted as an off-center location of our Sun. The Sun is close to the galactic plane, but is some 18,000 lightyears away from the center of the greater galactic system. The "thickness" of this extended stellar stratum is probably not very different from that found by Kapteyn, since obscuration in higher galactic latitudes plays no important role. The stellar stratum in the galactic plane, however, is assumed to extend far beyond the limits of the Kapteyn system, and, in particular, beyond the galactic center as defined by the globular clusters.

The galactic center should really be defined as the center of concentration of all material in the galactic system; it is most

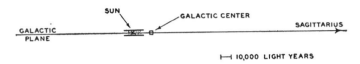

The Kapteyn system of stars in relation to the galactic center.

conveniently located from the distribution of the globular clusters, probably the most completely observed group of objects in the galactic system. Observational evidence for the central galactic concentration and its approximate location have been found in a variety of luminous objects, for example, cluster-type Cepheids and also red giants.

Galactic radio radiation

The direction of the galactic center is also indicated by radio radiation received from the galactic system. Astronomical studies of radio radiation have been made at a frequency of about one-millionth that of visible light. It was first discovered in 1931 that the principal source of radio radiation appears to be the Milky Way, a maximum of radiation coming from the galactic center. Special techniques have narrowed down the sources of radio radiation to small areas of the sky, only a few minutes of arc in diameter.

While the visual radiation received from the Sun is 400 million times that from the galaxy, the situation is entirely different in the case of radio frequencies which are transmitted by the

Earth's atmosphere (Chapter 3). At a frequency of 64,000,000 cycles per second—64 megacycles—the radiation received from the galaxy is about ten times that received from the Sun. We conclude that the Sun is a very poor radio transmitter, but that a considerable fraction of the stars are good transmitters.

Occasionally the Sun becomes a good radio transmitter for a few minutes, as a result of a solar flare (Chapter 3). Recently several faint red stars have been discovered to flare up; these flare-ups have been of the same nature as solar flares. It looks as if such violent activity is not uncommon among stars, and its combined effect might account for the galactic radio radiation.

The greater galactic system

The galactic system has thus a greater extension than we origi-nally thought, especially in the direction of Sagittarius. The majority of stars lie in a stratum about 4000 lightyears "thick." The thickness and density of the stratum increase gradually toward the galactic center. This is not unexpected, for even to the naked eye the Milky Way appears considerably wider and richer toward the galactic center than in the opposite direction. The central bulge of stars has also been demonstrated by Joel Stebbins (1878–   ) and Albert Edward Whitford (1905–   ) from photo-electric observations in infra-red light through an increase in combined stellar radiation over an area 3°5 wide and extending some 8° along the Milky Way.

We recall that, notwithstanding the dimming of starlight, a gradual increase in the crowding of stars is observed in the gen-eral direction of Sagittarius. Were it not for dimming, the stra-tum of stars would be observable up to much greater distances; we would also see a much more brilliant Milky Way, particu-larly in the direction of the galactic center, toward which not only the stars but also the obscuring material is strongly concentrated. Although this distant, central galactic concentration of stars is irregularly obscured by interstellar clouds, part of the outer region is revealed as the brilliant swarm of stars in the constellation Sagittarius.

Relation of stars and globular clusters

Should we consider the galactic system of stars as subordinate to that of the globular clusters or should we regard the clusters as satellites of the system of stars? The system of stars represents a relatively thickly populated portion of space, while the globular clusters are spread rather thinly through an enormous volume. Whether we consider the system of stars as subordinate to that of the clusters or the clusters as satellites of the stratum of stars is very much a matter of wording, or of convenience.

In addition to the stars, clusters, diffuse nebulae and interstellar material there are two conspicuous "companions" of the galactic system. These are the Large and Small Magellanic Clouds, two irregularly shaped dense aggregations of stars, globular and open clusters, diffuse nebulae, etc. (see photograph 43). The Magellanic Clouds are some 80,000 lightyears distant, and approximately 17,000 and 11,500 lightyears in diameter. The Magellanic Clouds may be considered the nearest extragalactic objects of the irregular type (Chapter 30).

Off-center location of the Sun

The off-center location of the Sun and the asymmetry of stellar motions are of great significance. The common feature of these two phenomena is their asymmetrical aspect; both contradict the notion that we are close to the center of the Milky Way system. After Shapley's work on the globular clusters, it was not difficult to accept the eccentric location of the Sun in the greater galactic system, but the asymmetrical state of motion was at first more difficult to explain. An additional factor was the preferential motion, the greater two-way mobility of stars in the galactic direction from Sagittarius to Auriga now recognized as being toward and away from the center of the greater galactic system. Note that the (galactic) direction of asymmetry is perpendicular to the (galactic) axis of preferential motion. It looks as if the asymmetry in stellar motions and the preferential axis of motion are both the result of our asymmetrical or eccentric location in a system more or less symmetrical with respect to its own center, i.e., the galactic center.

Analogy with solar system

To develop this trend of thought further we introduce an analogy. Consider a hypothetical observer located far off to one side of the solar system, say, on the distant planet Uranus, which describes a near-circular orbit around the Sun in a period of 84 years. To our observer, the bulk of the solar system is disclosed as an extended nucleus centered at the Sun. The off-center location of Uranus in the solar system would be revealed at any time by the predominantly one-sided, i.e., asymmetrical distribution of the material objects composing the solar system. The planets Mercury, Venus, Earth, Mars, and the asteroids would define a more or less central group; and this "planetary center" would point to the existence of a centrally located Sun, even if the latter were invisible.

The situation is not static, however; Uranus moves around the Sun in a near-circular orbit. Our hypothetical observer notes the motion of the extended nucleus of the Sun and "inner" planets, as projected on the background of stars. Eventually he would detect a drifting of the "planetary center" to the amount of about 7 kilometers per second. The direction of this drift would be closely perpendicular to the line of sight, and it would deviate only slightly from the general plane of the planetary system.

Dual interpretation of observed motion

To a Copernicus living on Uranus, this observed drift or group motion might suggest an alternate interpretation, viz., that Uranus drifts with respect to the Sun, at the same rate (7 kilometers per second), but in the opposite direction. After a few decades this interpretation would receive support in the observed parallactic motions of other planets (direct and retrograde motions) and of the nearer stars. The resulting change from the Uranocentric to the heliocentric viewpoint would not be dependent on observations extended long enough actually to reveal the curved orbital path of Uranus. The change of viewpoint would be suggested to our Uranian Copernicus by the

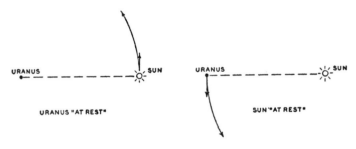

Uranocentric (left) and heliocentric (right) viewpoints.

fact that the "planetary center" moves in the general plane of the planetary system and at right angles to the Sun. This movement can be attributed to the motion of Uranus in a circular path about the Sun.

We do not want to make the mistake of elevating circular motion to its pre-Keplerian pedestal. On the other hand, we do recognize the cosmic abundance of near-circular paths, that is, elliptical orbits of comparatively low eccentricities; the planets and their satellite systems furnish abundant examples.

Group motion of the globular clusters

The analogy of Uranus and the inner portions of the solar system, the "planetary center," suggests a possible explanation for the extreme asymmetry in the group motion of the globular star clusters. Remember that the globular clusters occupy a more or less spherical section of space in which they are strongly

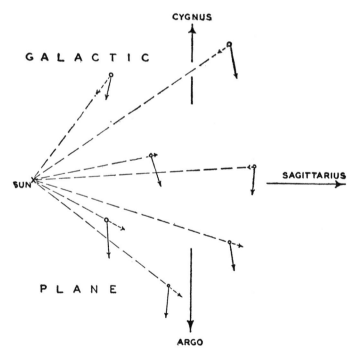

The drift of the globular-cluster system toward Argo.

concentrated toward the galactic center at Sagittarius. The Sun is located about 18,000 lightyears off the galactic center.

The proper motions of the globular clusters are too small to be observed. Their great brightness, however, permits the determination of their radial velocities, which for a large fraction of the globular clusters have been obtained from Doppler shifts in the integrated spectrum of the whole cluster. The observed radial velocities now reveal the following: Close to the galactic center the motions of the clusters do not exhibit any trend— some recede, others approach. Away from the center, toward Argo, there is a definite tendency for the clusters to recede. On the other side, toward Cygnus, there is a definite trend of approach.

These observations can be interpreted as follows: The system of globular clusters is drifting in the general direction of Argo. The direction of the drift is very close to the galactic plane, approximately perpendicular to the galactic center. We use a crude analogy: the globular clusters are partaking in a parade. The paraders perform poorly; individual members move out of line. But, as seen from our vantage point, the Sun, there *is* a parade, and it is aiming for Argo at the rate of about 200 kilometers per second.

The near-circular galactic orbit of the Sun

An alternative interpretation is possible. We may assume that the "parade" is at "rest," and that we are passing in review. The participants are restless, but the parade at large "stands still."

From this viewpoint, the Sun would drift by the system of globular clusters with a speed of 200 kilometers per second along a path close to the galactic plane. This motion would be in the opposite direction from Argo, namely, toward Cygnus, and also approximately perpendicular to the direction of the galactic center. Such an interpretation suggests that the Sun and neighboring stars move in near-circular orbits around the galactic center.

For a broader understanding of the structure and state of motion of the galactic system, the heliocentric viewpoint had to be abandoned. This first became clear from the arrangement of the globular star clusters. Further confirmation is now found in the group motion of these objects which is interpreted as a reflex of the Sun's motion in a near-circular path of tremendous space-time dimensions. The curvature of this orbit over an interval of a year, a century or even a few thousand years might well be too small to be measured by any existing means.

The galactocentric viewpoint

We abandon the concept that the Sun is centrally located in the galactic system, and replace it by the galactocentric viewpoint. The center of the galactic system is at "rest"; or more correctly,

Heliocentric (left) and galactocentric (right) viewpoints.

it is a more suitable reference point from which the structure and state of motion of the galactic system may be described. We recall the historical argument which entailed the transfer from the geocentric to the heliocentric viewpoint. A crucial test of the heliocentric theory was the annual heliocentric parallax of the stars; it was not until 1838 that the heliocentric parallax of a star was first observed. Apart from other proofs such as aberration, the first historically important argument for the heliocentric viewpoint lay in its explanation of the observed motions of the planets.

Regard the hundreds of thousands of extragalactic objects located well beyond the confines of our galactic system. If the solar system describes an extended orbit around the galactic center, should we not be able to test this by observing a "galactocentric parallactic effect" for these extragalactic objects? Should we not also expect to observe patterns of direct and retrograde motions for the stars, similar to those observed from our geocentric viewpoint for the planets in the solar system?

Galactic orbit of the Sun

Before attempting to answer these questions, we must first have some idea of the space-and-time dimensions of the galactic orbit of the Sun. The distance of 18,000 lightyears of the Sun from the center is the radius of the Sun's galactic orbit, if, for the sake of simplicity, we assume this orbit to be circular. The circumference of the circular orbit is $2\pi \times 18,000$ lightyears. It is a simple matter to calculate the period required for the solar system to complete one revolution around the galactic center. The Sun's velocity in the orbit is 200 kilometers per second, or 1/1500 times the velocity of light; hence,

$$2\pi \times 18,000 \times 1500$$

or somewhat below 200,000,000 years are required for the Sun to complete one revolution. Large as this figure seems to be, it is only a small fraction of the estimated age of the solar system, which is something like 3,000,000,000 years (Chapter 21). At face value, therefore, it appears that the Sun has already completed several revolutions around the galactic center!

Galactocentric parallax and parallactic motion

We are obviously in no position to follow an appreciable fraction of the Sun's galactic orbit; it would take numerous centuries before any curvature of this large orbit could be observed. Since it would take 100 million years to obtain maximum parallactic displacement, the problem of observing the galactocentric parallax of an external object is very much an academic question. Nevertheless we cannot refrain from remarking that the galactocentric parallactic effect of the nearest extragalactic objects would ultimately, as observed from the Sun, be more than one degree of arc. The tremendous size of the Sun's galactic orbit implies that we have a potential baseline for surveying the structure of the extragalactic world, which is of gigantic dimensions compared with the minute orbit of the Earth around the Sun.

It is going to be equally difficult to observe patterns of stellar motions similar to the direct and retrograde motions of the planets in our solar system. We shall nevertheless make use of the galactic equivalent of direct and retrograde motion which has played an important part in our elaboration of the galactocentric viewpoint. In the next chapter we shall discuss the further development of the galactocentric viewpoint as it has been derived from the assortment of stellar paths that we can observe in our neighborhood.

29 | THE ROTATION OF THE GALACTIC SYSTEM

THE FIRST successful hypothesis of a state of rotation of the galactic system similar to that of the planets around the Sun was worked out in 1925 by Bertil Lindblad (1895–   ).

Galactic orbits of stars

The gravitational behavior of the galactic system depends to a great extent on the strong concentration of the stars toward the galactic center. The Sun's velocity with respect to the globular clusters was found to be 200 kilometers per second directed toward Cygnus and 90° away from the galactic center in the direction of Sagittarius. We adopt this value as the rotational speed, which means we assume that the globular clusters are grouped symmetrically around the galactic center, so that their motions are canceled on the average.

Now we recall that stellar velocities within our stellar neigh-- borhood average only about 30 kilometers per second. Since the galactic velocity of the Sun is as large as 200 kilometers per second, it follows that the majority of stars in our neighborhood must have velocities not very different from 200 kilometers per second when referred to the galactic center. We conclude that the stellar motions as observed from the Sun simply represent relatively small differences between the much larger galactic motions in the orbital paths of the different stars. There is a

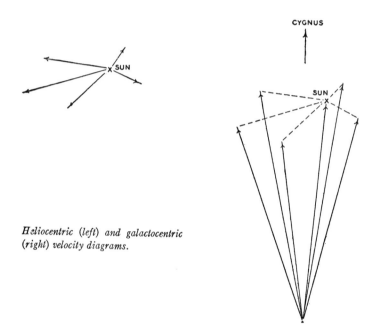

Heliocentric (left) and galactocentric (right) velocity diagrams.

strongly pronounced trend of galactic orbital motions in the direction of Cygnus. The individual velocities differ slightly in size and direction; the orbital paths are not as a rule appreciably inclined to the general plane of the Milky Way. The orbit of the Sun differs, but only slightly, from a circle.

Heliocentric view of the galactic orbits

A new perspective of the paths of the Sun and stars in the galactic system is obtained. Our present neighborhood of stars represents objects whose galactic orbits are passing close to our own orbital location at the present time. Within this neighborhood the momentary fractions of the orbital paths of different stars differ slightly. We may compare the Sun and stars with a number of airplanes flying in formation; slight differences in the velocities correspond to a small "peeling-off"; hence a gradual distortion of the formation takes place. As observed on the sky, these distortions are the proper motions of the stars. The gradual distortions of the constellations result, therefore, from the slight differences in the large galactic velocities of the stars within the neighborhood formation. One reason why the observed distortions are not at first sight more conspicuous is the small neighborhood of stars available for our studies of stellar motions.

Forward direction of stars' galactic rotation

The stars in our neighborhood are moving, therefore, in a strikingly organized way toward Cygnus. The small differences in the galactic orbital velocities are significant; they imply that not all orbits are circles. Judging by the solar system, we are not surprised. We speak of a general rotation of the solar system while fully realizing that no single orbit is circular. However, what is striking in the solar system is that the planetary orbits are predominantly near circular, i.e., have small eccentricities. It looks as if the same situation exists for the stars in the galactic system; their orbits are also generally of low eccentricity. Thus we can explain the small deviations in the motions of the stars and the Sun from the general forward rotational motion.

Flattening of the stellar system

The analogy can be carried still further. In the solar system the motions of the different planets are not only near circular, but are also more or less in the same general plane. The same appears to be true for the galactic orbits of the stars. As a result, the majority of stars remain rather close to their general plane of symmetry, the galactic plane; as time goes by the flattened character of the arrangement of stars is maintained just as in the case of the planets in our solar system. The flattening of the stellar system is thus in complete harmony with the well-organized rotations of the stellar orbits. In contrast the clusters appear to swarm about the galactic center without any organized rotation of the group as a whole. Under these circumstances they are not contained within a flattened portion of space, but their orbits fill a more or less spherical volume of space. This is in agreement with our observations of their momentary distribution; the globular clusters form a sort of super-cluster, which can be roughly fitted into a sphere.

In our imagination we may regard the galactic system from a distant point in the galactic plane. An "instantaneous" look or photograph would reveal the distribution of stars and globular clusters at the moment the light messages are received by the eye or camera. If now, instead, we took a time exposure, amounting to say a few hundred million years or so, the stars and globular clusters would form trails in the same manner that a photograph taken at night shows the trails of headlights of automobiles. These trails would trace the paths of the stars and globular clusters, and they would clearly reveal the flattened stellar system and the spherical system of globular clusters.

The momentary positions of the stars and clusters are simply the instantaneous cross sections of the long-range galactic orbits.

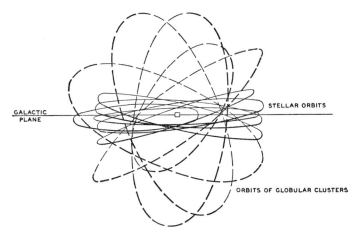

GALACTIC PLANE

STELLAR ORBITS

ORBITS OF GLOBULAR CLUSTERS

Sketch of galactic orbits of stars (full lines) and of globular clusters (dashed lines), viewed from a distant point in the galactic plane.

Explanation of preferential motion,
asymmetry and high-velocity stars

The elliptical galactic orbits of differing eccentricity point to a simple explanation for the phenomenon of preferential motion. The individual stars move forward with large velocities differing slightly in amount and direction. For illustration, assume that the orbital motions are confined to the galactic plane and that the velocities are all of the same size but differ in direction from the circular velocity OA. In this case it is easy to see that the different orbital velocities result in a spreading-out along the galactic plane of any current formation of stars. The gradual distortion of the momentary formation is therefore most

conspicuous along the direction in the galactic plane perpendicular to the forward motion.

The range in the eccentricities of the different orbital paths
of stars and Sun is thus revealed as the moving inward of certain stars and the moving outward of others as they all revolve
around the galactic center. In reality, the orbital velocities are
not equally large, and therefore the spreading-out effects also
take place in other directions; some stars move forward with

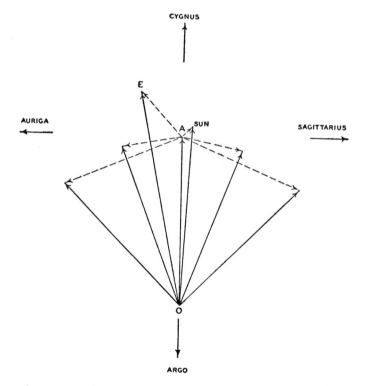

*Velocity diagram illustrating forward circular motion OA, velocity of
escape OE, preferential motion and asymmetry.*

respect to the average of the swarm, and others lag somewhat behind. Because of slight deviations in orbital inclinations, certain stars gradually move farther away from the galactic plane, while others gradually approach it.

The preferential motion of orbits of greater eccentricity would be more pronounced, but at the same time there would be less organized forward motion. Stars moving in orbits of greater eccentricity would lag behind as compared with the more effectively organized group rotation of stars moving along near-circular orbits of low inclinations. Thus the asymmetry in stellar motions is explained. Whereas we first described the degree of asymmetry in terms of differences in group motion, we can now ascribe it to differences in the unification of the forward rotational motion of different groups or types of stars or other objects such as, for example, globular clusters.

We understand also why there are no stars with velocities higher than 60 kilometers per second in the forward hemisphere centered around Cygnus. This speed limit of 60 kilometers per second, as observed within the neighboring swarm of stars, actually corresponds to a forward rotational motion of about 260 kilometers per second. This abrupt limit represents the "velocity of escape" OE; that higher velocities have not been found is explained by the fact that they would take the star beyond the gravitational influence of the galactic system. What we usually refer to as "high-velocity stars" are stars selected according to a velocity deviating appreciably from that of the local swarm of ordinary stars such as the Sun; these high-velocity stars are lagging behind in the general galactic rotation.

Subsystems

Lindblad was aware of the differences in flattening, asymmetry and preferential motion in different kinds of stars. He introduced the concept of subsystems in the galactic system, all rotating around a common axis perpendicular to the galactic plane, which axis passes through the galactic center as defined by the center of the arrangement of the globular clusters. These subsystems are all of equal extent in the "equatorial" galactic directions and are symmetrical about the common axis of rotation and with respect to the galactic plane; but they have different degrees of flattening. The average forward rotational speed of any subsystem, in particular as observed in our neighborhood, would depend on the degree of flattening, the highest speed corresponding to the flattest system. As indicated before, the rotation theory ascribes the asymmetry to differences in the velocities of rotation of the less flattened systems as compared with the more flattened systems. Certain stars such as the highly luminous and massive blue B and O stars form very flat systems which in their rotation may be slightly overtaking even the general run of "ordinary" stars; these B and O stars exemplify the maximum rotational speed that can be reached.

Galactic analogy of direct and retrograde motions

Toward the end of the last chapter we suggested a possible analogy between the direct and retrograde patterns of planetary motions and the corresponding long-range patterns of stellar motions. That we see the motions of the planets as direct and retrograde is due to our geocentric position, the patterns of these motions depending on the distances of the planets from the Earth, and on their orbital velocities.

The analogy has severe limitations, since patterns of direct and retrograde motions will be discernible only after tens of millions of years. It is as though we were asked to describe the state of motion of the planets in the solar system from a night's study of a few nearby planets. What could we do in this case?

We might, for example, study the motions of Venus and Mars when both these planets were very close to us. We would note that the inner planet Venus overtakes the Earth in its motion around the Sun, while the outer planet Mars, being farther away from the Sun, lags behind. The analogous galactic example could be found through a study of the motions of the "inner" stars, i.e., stars between us and the galactic center, and the motions of "outer" stars, i.e., those in "opposition" to the galactic center.

Oort's discovery of differential galactic rotation

This problem was worked out in 1927 by Jan Hendrik Oort (1900–   ). If we assume that the rotation of the galactic system is predominantly governed by a large central concentration of stars, just as the motions of the planets in the solar system are governed by the central Sun, the orbital velocities of the stars in the galactic system decrease with increasing distances from the center, in accordance with Kepler's third law. The ellipticities and inclinations of the orbits introduce no difficulties; we may assume that the orbits are circular as long as we deal with averages for large numbers of stars. The gradual diminution of the rotational velocity with increasing distance from the galactic center results in a slight shearing effect in the arrangement of the stars in our neighborhood; the inner stars nearer the galactic center overtake the Sun in its galactic orbit, on the average, while the outer stars lag behind. Stars in the other galactic directions would exhibit comparable effects.

Both the transverse and radial components of stellar motions reveal the shearing effect of the differential galactic rotation. The transverse or proper motions reveal the overtaking of stars nearer the galactic center (a) and the lagging behind of stars in the opposite direction—that of the "anti-center" (a'). The radial motions, in the line of sight, show a recession for "inner" stars "preceding" (b) the direction to the galactic center and for "outer" stars "following" (b') this direction. An approach is

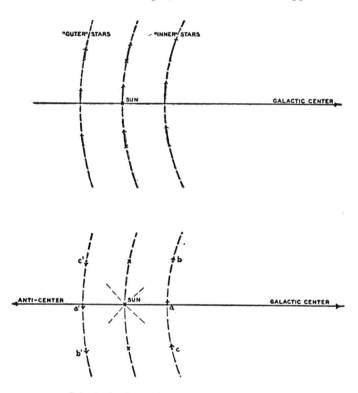

ABOVE: *Galactic circular motions.*
BELOW: *The observed differential galactic rotation.*

observed for inner stars following (c) the direction to the center and for outer stars preceding (c') this direction.

This differential galactic rotation has been observed for stars in a wide neighborhood. The rotational velocity of stars which are a thousand lightyears closer to the galactic center than we are is found to increase by 5 kilometers per second. There are, however, strong indications that the maximum rotational velocity of the stars within the solar orbit is reached at about 9/10 the distance of the Sun, i.e., about 16,000 lightyears from the galactic center. It is not unlikely that the velocity of rotation of stars within this radius diminishes toward the center. On gravitational grounds we must expect the inner part of the galactic system—the concentration of stars toward the galactic center—to rotate more or less as a solid body. This massive concentration of stars is decisive in determining the state of motion of the Sun and its neighboring stars, which is similar to the Keplerian motion of the planets in our solar system. It looks, however, as if the Sun and our neighborhood of stars were definitely beyond any such extended concentration.

The discovery of the differential galactic-rotation effect served as a corroboration of Lindblad's theory of rotation and confirmed the direction to the galactic center. The interstellar atoms also exhibit this shearing effect. There is obviously a close physical connection between the stars and the interstellar three-dimensional curtain of atoms and, presumably, other particles.

Mass of the galactic system

From the observed rotational velocity at our location in the galactic system and our distance from the center of the system, we can make an estimate of that "inner" part of the mass of the galactic system which is surrounded by the huge galactic orbit of the solar system. This may be done as follows: We recall (Chapter 13) that in a binary system the combined mass of the two components is proportional to the size a of the orbit and the square of the orbital speed V. This relation applies to a binary system consisting of planet and Moon, Sun and planet, two stars, or, as in the present case, the Sun and everything within its galactic orbit. The latter envelops thousands of millions of stars more or less symmetrically distributed around their center, which is the galactic center. The radius of the galactic solar orbit is 18,000 lightyears, or 18,000 × 63,300 times the distance between Earth and Sun. On the other hand, the galactic solar velocity is 20/3 times the orbital velocity of the Earth with respect to the Sun.

We can therefore compare the quantitative data on orbital sizes and orbital velocities for the two binaries; galactic system-Sun, and Sun-Earth respectively. According to the above relation between mass, orbital size and orbital velocity, the ratio of the mass of the galactic system (plus Sun) to the mass of the Sun (plus Earth) is given by the number

18,000 × 63,300 × 400/9.

Or, ignoring for obvious reasons the items in parentheses, we find that the galactic system has a mass of about 50,000,000,000 times that of the Sun.

This figure is not accurate, however. Both the distance of the Sun from the galactic center and the galactic circular velocity are subject to appreciable uncertainty. We have also made the simplifying assumption that all mass surrounded by the solar orbit could be shrunk into the galactic center. This implies that all such matter is distributed over a spherical portion of space, but we know that it is not. Moreover, we neglected the mass outside the solar orbit. Nevertheless, the interesting feature of a calculation like this is that it gives us an idea of the measure of a very important entity, viz., the mass of the galactic system. One can sense, somehow, or visualize the gigantic mass of this system by contemplating the large galactic velocity which the Sun must have, even at its huge distance from the galactic center, in order to counteract the gravitational attraction of the distant, massive bulk of stars and other material concentrated toward the galactic center.

Number of stars in the galactic system

We may try to go one step further. If all stars had the same mass as the Sun, the calculated mass of the galactic system would indicate the number of stars in the system. Observations have not, of course, indicated the existence of that many stars. It is estimated that there are only some 2,000,000,000 stars down to the faintest magnitude 21 that can be photographed at present. From existing counts of stars a very rough guess may be made at the total number of all stars which could be photographed if there were no technical limitations and no dimming of starlight by interstellar material. Extrapolation from counts made by Frederick Hanley Seares (1873–   ) gives an estimate of 30,000,000,000 for the total population of stars in the galactic system.

This estimate is in satisfactory agreement with the earlier figure of 50,000,000,000. Considering the various uncertainties in the measured quantities, in the average mass of stars, the presence of dark stars and multiple stars, and the large contribution of interstellar material to the mass of the galactic system, we conclude that there is some reason for satisfaction with the agreement of the two "astronomical figures" mentioned above. The order of size of the mass of the galactic system derived from gravitational considerations is in as good agreement with that estimated from direct visual and photographic evidence as could be expected.

30 | THE EXTRAGALACTIC OBJECTS

Extragalactic objects

The extragalactic nebulae derive their name from their presence outside the Milky Way region and their nebulous appearance (Chapter 16). Before the application of photography several hundred extragalactic nebulae were known. The brightest appear in the telescope as regular, faint patches of light, usually elliptical or circular in shape. One or two faintly reveal a spiral structure; most of them are brighter toward the center. The name nebulae remains of historical interest only; these objects are really stellar systems, as is evident from their "integrated" stellar absorption spectra. While the galactic, diffuse "green" nebulae mentioned before are, in part at least, gaseous, the extragalactic "white" nebulae are essentially stellar systems which appear nebulous because of their very great distances.

Photographs taken with large reflecting telescopes reveal the vast number of the extragalactic nebulae and their significance. Hundreds of thousands have been photographed; the majority —about 70 per cent—have a characteristically double spiral structure; the remainder are mostly elliptical or round in appearance. A few have an irregular structure. (See photographs 44–50.)

Some of the nearer spirals are among the most beautiful cosmic objects photographed; they show a wealth of structural detail, and a partial resolution into stars. As we shall see later, these nearer spirals give us an idea as to what our own stellar system may look like.

Distances of extragalactic objects

The tremendous distances of the extragalactic spirals were established by Edwin Powell Hubble (1889–   ) in 1929 from his study of Cepheids in the spiral arms of the Andromeda "nebula" also known as Messier 31 or simply M 31 (see photographs 46, 47). This was an extension of the method employed in the case of the globular clusters (Chapter 26). There is, however, an interesting difference. The Cepheids in globular clusters are mostly of the short-period or cluster type, averaging about a hundred times the Sun's luminosity. Fortunately, the spirals contain numerous long-period Cepheids whose luminosities, running as high as 2500 times the Sun's, bring these stars within the realm of possible observation.

The study of Cepheids in several spirals revealed one other luminosity criterion, namely, the luminosity of the very brightest stars in the spiral arms. Blue in color, they are on the average even brighter than the luminous long-period Cepheids; they are 50,000 times as bright as the Sun, and over a hundred times brighter than the brightest, reddish stars in globular clusters. The brightest stars in some 150 spiral objects have helped us penetrate farther into the extragalactic world. A final distance criterion is the total luminosity of the extragalactic objects, which averages approximately a hundred million times that of

the Sun. The luminosities range from about one-tenth to ten
times this average value, though most of the objects are within
one-half and twice the average luminosity. It is estimated that
about a hundred million extragalactic objects are within a distance of 500 million lightyears. The Andromeda system at a
distance of 800,000 lightyears is visible to the naked eye, which
fact confirms its tremendous luminosity. A few other systems
are less than a million lightyears away, while the fainter and
smaller ones are much farther away. Even the nearer of the
extragalactic objects are beyond the farthest imaginable limits
of our galactic system; the designation extragalactic is thus very
appropriate. Much of our recent knowledge of these objects
derives from the investigations of Hubble and of Walter Baade
(1893–   ) with the 100- and 200-inch reflecting telescopes of
the Mount Wilson and Palomar Observatories.

Distribution of extragalactic objects over the sky

Because of their great distances, the numerous faint extragalactic objects form a natural background on which we see
the stellar system projected. With appropriate telescopic equipment they can be photographed as small starlike images, and
their brightnesses may be measured and compared on the conventional stellar-magnitude scale. Surveys thus obtained on
long-exposure photographs covering the whole sky reveal a
striking deviation from a uniform distribution; the highest
concentration occurs in high galactic-latitude regions, where
the stars are least abundant. As we approach the Milky Way,
fewer objects are observed, while close to the galactic circle
hardly any appear. This absence of extragalactic objects in the
Milky Way is very striking, and could hardly be a real property of their distribution in space; the apparent zone of avoidance is obviously an obscuration effect.

The extragalactic world reveals the galactic obscuring layer

Assume that the extragalactic objects are evenly spread throughout the vast spaces of the universe and that all have the same intrinsic luminosity. Long-exposure photographs taken with a large telescope should then reveal an equal abundance of objects in any direction. Since, however, we are situated within a layer of obscuring material, the distance penetration is impaired. Our view of the extragalactic world is least affected toward the galactic poles; at lower galactic latitudes, the increased dimming effect cuts out more and more of the fainter, distant extragalactic objects. Finally, in the Milky Way itself the dimming is a virtual blackout effect, and no more extragalactic objects can be seen, except in a few directions of comparative transparency, sometimes called "galactic windows."

The gradual dimming-out of the extragalactic world toward the Milky Way regions is therefore perfectly explained by the galactic obscuring layer. In any particular direction the increase in the total number of nebulae is about fourfold when an additional magnitude class is included. While in our galactic system the observed star ratio (Chapter 23) never reaches the theoretical value 3.98 for uniform distribution, the "nebula ratio" in the extragalactic world is close to 3.98. The hypothesis that there is a more or less uniform distribution of extragalactic objects is thus confirmed. All the dimming obviously takes place in front of even the nearest "nebula." Extragalactic space appears to be virtually transparent.

Our impaired vision of the extragalactic world has played an important role not only in confirming the existence of the obscuring layer, but in establishing its quantitative dimming power (which turns out to be about 60 per cent for a perpendicular crossing of a light ray—Chapter 25).

Properties of extragalactic objects or galaxies

A brief survey of the principal characteristics of the extragalactic objects follows. They are more or less comparable in total luminosity; and, with the exception of a small number of irregularly shaped objects, they all exhibit a symmetrical pattern of rotation. The larger the spiral arms, the smaller the nuclei. Large spiral arms can be seen in great detail; both separate stars and obscuring material are often in evidence.

It is difficult to ascertain the dimensions of extragalactic objects because of their inherently indistinct limits. They average about 10,000 lightyears across. Objects of smaller dimensions— as small as 1500 lightyears—have been observed; while some of the nearer spirals, whose extent can be better studied are larger. Take, for example, the Andromeda system. At first sight it appears to be some 30,000 to 40,000 lightyears across. In 1932 Hubble discovered 140 nebulous images in and near the Andromeda nebula, which, judging by their fuzzy appearance, could not have been stars. Hubble provisionally identified these objects as globular clusters belonging to the Andromeda system; more recently, through improved observational techniques, the fringes of three clusters have been resolved as stars. The distribution of the clusters suggests that the diameter of the Andromeda system is twice the earlier estimated size. In 1933 Stebbins and Whitford scanned the system photo-electrically and found traces of luminosity extending twice as far as was previously supposed. Altogether it may thus be assumed that the Andromeda spiral is some 70,000 lightyears across, a value comparable to the size of the galactic system—about 60,000 lightyears across—which has been determined from the arrangement of the globular clusters.

Before the discovery of Cepheid variables in the Andromeda

system, the extragalactic nebulae were often looked upon as "island universes," with our own galactic system as a "continent." The inflationary effects of dimming material indicated that the dimensions of our galactic system had been exaggerated. The recent determinations of the dimensions of the Andromeda system have made us realize that our galactic system is not by any means exceptional in size.

Because of their analogy with our galactic system or galaxy (Chapter 31), extragalactic objects are usually denoted as galaxies.

Clusters of galaxies; the local group

There is little evidence for any organization in the distribution of the extragalactic objects or galaxies. A large number, however, are grouped into binary and multiple systems, and also into clusters (see photographs 51, 52). More than twenty-five clusters of galaxies have been discovered so far, containing hundreds, sometimes thousands of galaxies each. One of the most impressive is the cluster seen in the direction of the constellation Coma Berenices. This group has over 2000 members, filling a portion of space some 5,000,000 lightyears in diameter. It is possible that a large proportion of all galaxies are gathered together in the form of clusters.

Several hundred small "groups" of galaxies have been found. Of particular interest to us is the group of galaxies, all within one million lightyears, to which our galactic system belongs. This local group contains the Large and Small Magellanic Clouds, the well-known spirals M 31 and M 33, the two elliptical companions of M 31, and several other elliptical and irregular systems. So far a total of sixteen galaxies, including our own, are known to belong to the local group.

The red shift of galaxies

Spectra have been observed for numerous galaxies; with few exceptions they reveal an appreciable shift of the spectral lines toward the red end of the spectrum. The amount of the shift increases with the distance of the object; as a matter of fact, it is proportional to the distance.

What is the explanation of this red shift? The most likely interpretation is that it is a Doppler shift, i.e., a motion in the line of sight. The velocities of the recession of the extragalactic objects reach tremendous values; at a distance of ten million lightyears, the velocity of recession is about 900 kilometers per second; at a distance of twenty million lightyears it is twice as large, i.e., 1800 kilometers per second, and so on. Velocities up to about 61,000 kilometers per second have been recorded, corresponding, presumably, to a distance of over 600 million lightyears!

At first sight it may seem strange that the more distant objects are "running away" faster than the nearer ones. A simple interpretation is the following: We are not in a privileged position, and, as time goes by, all galaxies, including our own galactic system, are getting farther away from each other.

The extragalactic world is expanding

There is a very simple explanation for the proportionality of the velocity of recession to the momentary distances of different galaxies from us. The more distant galaxies do not have larger velocities of recession because they are farther away; they are farther away because they have larger velocities of recession. It looks as if a long time ago the galaxies, including our own, were much closer together than they are now. Each galaxy was endowed with a certain velocity, the huddle of galaxies started to spread, and of course by this time those with the largest velocities have gone farthest (Chapter 32).

If we divide the rate of expansion into the spacing which the galaxies have attained, it is possible to calculate the epoch at which they were packed closely together. Take, for example, a galaxy at a distance of ten million lightyears. The galaxy is receding from us at the rate of 900 kilometers per second. All we need do is to divide the present distance, ten million lightyears, by the corresponding rate of expansion, 900 kilometers per second. The resulting age of the closely packed universe of galaxies is somewhat over 3000 million years. This figure is similar to the age of the Earth derived from entirely different evidence. Does the coincidence mean that the Earth and perhaps the other planets were created at a time when the galaxies were much closer together than they are now? Were the stars within our galaxy also closer together than they are now, and may this have contributed to the origin of the solar system? No definite answers can be given to these challenging questions, but a few pertinent remarks will be made about them in the last chapter.

Meanwhile we realize that calculations like the one just given extend so far beyond our grasp of space and time that they must be accepted with considerable caution. We have assumed a uniform rate of expansion; actually there may have been a change in rate, either gradual or sudden. Even past or future changes from expansion to contraction are not excluded.

THE GALACTIC SYSTEM AMONG EXTRAGALACTIC OBJECTS

Review of Chapters 23 to 29

We recapitulate briefly the knowledge of the galactic system obtained so far. The globular star clusters are within a huge spherical volume of space some sixty thousand lightyears in diameter; their arrangement in space outlines the size of the galactic system and also indicates the location of its center. By and large the stars occupy a flattened part of space, extending like the globular clusters some sixty thousand lightyears in the central galactic plane, while ranging in thickness from only about 4000 lightyears near the Sun to a somewhat larger figure near the galactic center. An atmosphere of interstellar matter, consisting of smoke particles and also gaseous material, is spread through this stellar stratum. Relatively few stars are more than 30,000 lightyears from the galactic center; the Sun is in the outskirts of the system, some 18,000 lightyears from the center but close to the galactic plane.

Our location in the midst of stars, and particularly in the midst of the obscuring interstellar material, profoundly affects our view of the galactic system. The dimming of light from distant stars and clusters, if ignored, causes a spurious inflation of cosmic distances based on apparent brightness; this in turn results in a dilution in the spacing of stars and clusters. We attempted to make allowance for this obscuring material. The apparent thinning-out of stars in all the galactic directions was described, partly at least, as a dimout effect resulting in an apparent central location for the Sun. Our view of the extragalactic world is also affected by the obscuring material; the observed number of extragalactic objects drops very sharply in regions near and in the Milky Way.

The current description of the galactic system is based on the galactocentric viewpoint. The center of the system, the galactic center, is not conspicuously revealed to us by the stars at large. It is best determined as the center of the nearly one hundred globular clusters known up to now. Since these objects are extremely luminous and for the most part outside the region of strongest obscuration, the globular clusters provide us with a good measure of the approximate outline of the galactic system.

The paths of Sun and stars, as currently witnessed in our neighborhood, show certain general characteristics which are satisfactorily interpreted as a general state of rotation of the galactic system. Sun and stars describe galactic orbits of huge dimensions. The vast majority of stars rotate in a well-defined, "forward" direction. Due to their predominantly small inclinations, the majority of stellar orbits fit into a portion of space which extends principally in the plane of the galaxy, and is of comparatively limited thickness. The so-called preferential motion (the momentary inward and outward motions caused by the eccentricities of the different stellar orbits in our neighborhood) and the asymmetry and velocity of escape of stellar motions are all indications of galactic rotation.

For intervals of a few thousand years, the population in our stellar neighborhood or any other part of the galactic system remains essentially the same, save for a gradual internal shifting due to slight differences in the orbital paths. We recall particularly the slowing-down of rotation with increasing distance from the center. The resulting shearing effect, together with the different orbital inclinations and eccentricities, clearly imply the fleeting character of companionship in any particular stellar neighborhood. There are, of course, the double stars and star clusters, whose members have parallel motions and remain together for much longer intervals. In any case, the galactocentric picture developed in Chapter 29 is very much idealized, and will have to be tested and improved by long-range observations.

Distant view of the galactic system

The arrangement of the stars, globular clusters and diffuse material in our galactic system is better understood if we obtain a distant view of our galactic system. Let us in our imagination travel out to a great distance, say, one million lightyears in the direction of the constellation Argo, for example. From this vantage point the mind's eye will obtain a "side" view, a "skyline" or "elevation" of our galactic system, which will look somewhat like the diagram. Only the most luminous, blue stars in the outskirts of the system are separately visible on imaginary long-exposure photographs taken with large telescopes. The brighter long-period Cepheids are quickly recognized from their periodic variation in brightness, as are the novae.

From our distant viewpoint the globular clusters are feeble, fuzzy spots. The visible general stellar population appears as a fairly luminous, continuous stratum, somewhat wider near the center of the galactic system. The densest portion of the layer of diffuse material will probably look like a comparatively dark lane blotting out the majority of stars near the galactic plane. The boundaries of the system are indistinct and depend on the observational power used. The off-center location of the Sun is

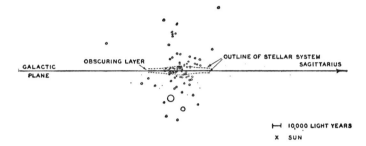

Outline of the galactic system—stars, globular clusters and obscuring layer —looking toward Cygnus from a distant point in the galactic plane.

indicated in the diagram; the Sun itself is too faint to be seen with existing instruments.

Analogy between the galactic system and resolved spiral objects

The imaginary side view of our galactic system shows considerable resemblance to the photographs of scores of spirals that are viewed edgewise; the most conspicuous point of similarity is the concentration of obscuring material toward the central plane of symmetry. But there are many other points of resemblance between the galactic system and the several extragalactic objects of the well-resolved spiral type that have been studied. These are, for example, the same order of size, and both a plane and pronounced center of concentration of stars. We mention the recent work (1944) of Baade, who succeeded in resolving the dense nucleus of the Andromeda nebula (M 31) into separate stars. This was accomplished with the aid of red-sensitive plates, and its success may be attributed partly to the predominantly red color of the brighter stars in the central nucleus of the system. A further analogy is the rotation deduced from the radial velocities in different portions of several spirals. For example, the rotational velocities of the nearby spirals M 31 and M 33 are comparable in size and behavior to those in the galactic system. The rotational velocities in these two objects increase outward, and the maximum rotational velocity is reached far out, some 18,000 lightyears from the center; at greater distances the rotational velocities diminish again. The same increase and subsequent decrease of rotational speed is found in the galactic system (Chapter 29). Other common properties are Cepheids, novae and supernovae, diffuse matter, both luminous and dark, star clouds, and the luminosity of the brightest blue stars. "Satellite" systems of globular clusters have been tentatively identified for several other nearer spirals besides the Andromeda system.

Possible spiral structure of our galactic system

Considerable observational uncertainty still exists, however, about any similarity in the most striking property—the spiral structure. The appearance of the Milky Way certainly does not preclude any spiral structure in our galactic system. That our galactic system might be a spiral was suggested in 1900 by Cornelius Easton (1864–1929). According to Easton, the center of the spiral is revealed to us as the bright portion of the Milky Way in Cygnus. The apparent branching of the Milky Way over a large area could be explained as a perspective result of two spiral arms in slightly different planes. Easton's theory cannot be accepted at the present time without modification. The center of the galactic system is not in the direction of Cygnus, but toward Sagittarius. Moreover, the apparent branching of the Milky Way can also be attributed to streaks of obscuring material. Attempts are currently being made to establish a possible spiral pattern for the galactic system; it is likely that in the near future some positive results will be obtained from a study of the distribution of blue-giant stars and diffuse material, which appear to be closely associated both in our galaxy and in the arms of extragalactic spirals. The diffuse material in the latter is recognized by its obscuration of the numerous distant, very faint galaxies in the background.

The essential difficulty is, of course, our location in the Milky Way system. We have a much better knowledge of the structural patterns of thousands of extragalactic spirals than of our own system. Each of these objects covers a very small portion of the sky, and the view is not impaired by the presence of obscuring material. In our own system, however, our view in different directions is affected unevenly by the obscuring material. Even if our galactic system were free from obscuring material it would still be difficult to ascertain its structure because of our inability to obtain a panoramic view of the system. The situation is comparable to that of an observer in an airplane flying high over a city. This observer may not be able to see any detail, but he has a much better grasp of the map of the city than any city dweller confined to a city block, since the latter's vision is obstructed by buildings, by haze and by smoke.

The galaxy among galaxies

It is of little comfort to us that an imaginary observer, in the Andromeda spiral, for example, has an equally good bird's-eye view of our galactic system as we have of the Andromeda system, but may be in comparative ignorance about the structure of his own system. In any case we are strongly disposed to introduce the hypothesis that our own galactic system and the more resolved spiral extragalactic objects are similar in nature. Shapley's definition of galaxy is useful in this respect. The word may be used for extragalactic systems because of their analogy with our system. Conversely, our own "galaxy" is considered to have the properties of the extragalactic systems. Needless to say, this is merely a useful hypothesis, possibly a temporary idealization. Continued studies will be required to shed further light on the structure and state of motion of our galactic system; the "external galaxies" will provide numerous suggestions, on a miniature scale, as to what our galactic system looks like. Thus our imagination is stimulated to different possible observational approaches to the study of our own galaxy. Meanwhile we may regard either the Andromeda system (Messier 31) or the neighboring galaxy, Messier 33, as "models" of our own galactic system. (See photographs 46–48.)

32 | ORIGINS AND OUTLOOK

THUS FAR we have attempted to outline some of the properties of the world of stars and of galaxies. We have a fair knowledge of the cosmos as we see it right now. But what about its origin and its future? These questions are easily asked, but well nigh impossible to answer. We shall nevertheless outline a few of the attempted answers; but we must be fully aware that attractive though some of the attempts are, they are extremely hypothetical.

Origin of galaxies

It is generally agreed that some 3,000,000,000 years ago the part of the universe known to us was contained in a very much smaller portion of space than it is now (Chapter 30). All matter consisted of an exceedingly concentrated "gaseous" mixture of the elemental particles: protons, neutrons and electrons, at a tremendously high temperature of thousands of millions of degrees. This original arrangement of matter exploded, and we can still observe the result of that explosion in the general expansion of the galaxies. As the universe expanded its temperature dropped to a point where the protons and electrons began to combine into the nuclei of the chemical elements. Deuterium (heavy hydrogen) nuclei ($_1H^2$) were formed from the combination of one proton and one neutron, tritium nuclei ($_1H^3$) from the combination of one proton and two neutrons. Helium nuclei ($_2He^4$) resulted from the merging of two protons and two neutrons—and so on. As these nuclei combined with additional protons or neutrons, the nuclei of the heavier elements were formed. The creation of all the elements, as they exist now in the universe, took place presumably during the first half-hour of the original expansion.

Assuming that the original gaseous universe had a chaotic, irregular outline, the primary explosion inevitably led to turbulent motions, i.e., irregular currents, changing constantly both in space and time. The turbulent currents were gradually molded into more regular forms by the law of gravitation. Locally the mutual attraction of particles must have led to concentrations of matter, and such groupings of matter generally whirled into a state of rotation. The concentrations of matter combined gradually, and in several cases the combined formation was again in a state of rotation.

A large body formed in this way retains its rotation. As the internal turbulence diminishes, the rotating object becomes flattened. The rotational speeds increase toward the center; the resulting shearing effects lead to turbulent cloud formations which by the rotation are spooled up in the form of spirals.

Spiral formations by turbulence are very common. Examples are whirlpools in a disturbed flow of water, curling flames in a wood fire, tornadoes in our atmosphere, sunspots in the Sun's atmosphere. Cream poured into a cup of coffee or tea, when disturbed, leads to spiral formations. Such spirals often have a remarkable resemblance to cosmic spirals such as the well-known "whirlpool" nebula M 51. (See photograph 49.)

The formation of spiral extragalactic objects is thus explained. In the distant future, the rotation of spirals will cease, because the energy of rotation will be dissipated, essentially by the friction of the turbulent motions. The result may be globular systems of matter.

Origin of stars

Hydrogen is the fuel for the energy production of all stars. The radiation from the very luminous stars proves that these stars must be relatively young; they could not have existed in their present state as long as the Sun, for example, and still have kept up their prodigious outpour of energy. The spectra of these luminous stars reveal a pronounced state of rotation; this may indicate that these objects were created comparatively recently. In our stellar system the very luminous blue stars are intermingled with obscuring material. The same is true in several of the nearby spiral galaxies; the spiral arms contain blue-giant stars and diffuse material.

Both in the galactic system and in other galaxies, the very luminous stars may have been formed, therefore, comparatively recently from the gas and dust formations in the spiral arms. Starting with the original gas there are collisions of atoms with atoms, or atoms with radiation. The heavier atoms stick together and form molecules which in turn form larger molecules, and finally result in small particles. Radiation exerts a pressure on these particles. While ordinarily this results in a pushing of particles in random directions, a different situation arises when a number of small particles get relatively close together; the shadows between the particles permit the radiation

to push the particles still closer together. In this way an extended dark cloud of matter could be formed in some ten million years. When the cloud is sufficiently large, the radiation
pressure becomes relatively ineffective, since it cannot penetrate
deeply into the opaque cloud; gravitation now produces further
attraction. In this way, by slow accretion under the influence
of light pressure and gravitation, atoms could be built up into
stars. In this connection we mention that small dark globular
clouds have been observed, something like one lightyear in
diameter; these "globules" may be protostars.

Origin and evolution of the planetary system

Any theory of the origin and evolution of the solar or planetary
system must explain the organized orbital motions (of both the
planets and satellites) and the rotation of the planets. At
the same time the few striking exceptions must be explained.
The motions of the comets are disorganized and obviously,
therefore, present a separate problem.

An explanation must be given also for the tremendous amount
of "spin" or angular momentum of the solar system, manifested
in the revolutions and rotations of Sun and planets. Technically,
the angular momentum, or "quantity of rotation," is proportional to the mass, the rotational velocity and the distance of
the particles or object to the center of rotation. The angular
momentum in a system of objects cannot increase or decrease
as time goes by unless there is outside interference. It cannot
develop "by itself," but must have a cause. The orbital motion
around the Sun of the massive planet Jupiter accounts for as
much as 60 per cent of the angular momentum of the whole
solar system; the slowly rotating mass of the Sun accounts for
only 2 per cent.

The above-mentioned properties of the solar system have to

be elucidated; but, more than that, the formation of the existing planets, satellites and asteroids must be explained in detail. There is no theory of the origin and evolution of the solar system that is satisfactory from all points of view. We shall, nevertheless, outline some of the numerous attempts that have been made.

The encounter theory

The "encounter theory" assumes that the planets were torn from the Sun by a passing or colliding star. One version of the theory is the planetesimal hypothesis of Thomas Chrowder Chamberlin (1843–1928) and Forest Ray Moulton (1872–). The passing star raises high tides in the Sun, matter breaks loose and starts spiraling around the Sun. Most of the matter falls back on the Sun and accounts for its rotation. The remainder of the disrupted gases condenses in small fragments, planetesimals, which gradually are gathered and swept up into a number of planets. James H. Jeans (1877–1946) and Harold Jeffreys (1891–) proposed that the passing star draws a long tidal filament from the Sun. Parts of this filament condense into huge "drops" which later become planets. Jeffreys proposes an actual collision rather than a close approach.

The encounter theory explains the angular momentum of the solar system, but also runs into serious difficulties. The dispersed material coming from the inside of the Sun would be extremely hot, perhaps something like ten million degrees centigrade. These gases would tend to explode and disperse, and it is difficult to see how "condensations" could be formed.

Others have suggested that the Sun originally had a companion star. Struck by a passing star, the companion is somehow broken down and the debris leads to the formation of planets and satellites. This theory also explains the considerable angular momentum of the solar system. Since all stars have closely the same chemical composition, there is no diffi· culty on this account in accepting the formation of the planets from a former solar companion. This theory, however, has little in its favor; its principal support comes from the Sun's hypothetical former companion's being conspicuous by its absence, in comparison with the abundance of stellar companions for other stars.

We interpolate a few remarks on the possible origin and evolution of the Earth-Moon system. The tidal friction of the oceans on our Earth results in a slow increase in both the day and month, or to be more exact, in the periods of the rotation of the Earth and the revolution of the Moon. Calculations show that several thousand million years ago the separation of the centers of Earth and Moon was only 15,000 kilometers, instead of the present value of 384,400 kilometers. The time scale of this process is in good general agreement with that of the age of the Earth. In that past era, month and day must have been nearly equal—about four hours. This leads to the idea that the Moon may have been separated from the Earth as a result of its rapid state of rotation and huge solar tides. The Pacific Ocean, in this theory, may be considered the former location of the Moon. Jeffreys proposes instead that Earth and Moon were formed practically in contact.

The nebular hypothesis

Another approach to the origin and evolution of the solar system is the theory of the contraction of a huge cloud of gases, extending to the outermost regions of the solar system. The planets would be formed as condensations in this contracting cloud. This "nebular theory," as originally proposed by Pierre Simon de Laplace (1749–1827) was unsatisfactory; among other difficulties it did not explain the large angular momentum of the solar system. However, the nebular hypothesis has recently been developed in a very promising way by Carl Friedrich von Weizsäcker (1912–   ).

Imagine that originally the Sun was a rapidly rotating body, formed from a condensation of turbulent interstellar material. The rotation slows down through the escape of material from the outside which is rotating too fast. This uncondensed material surrounding the Sun forms a large envelope or disk, rotating also. The material thrown off by the Sun consists, for the greater part, of hydrogen and helium, the two elements which are predominant in the Sun. Only a very small portion is formed by the more massive atoms, which gradually combine into solid dust particles of material common on Earth, such as iron-oxides, silicum compounds, ice crystals, and water. The planets are formed from a gradual accretion of these dust particles. A detailed analysis shows that collisions between the particles leads to a more or less geometric spacing of the planets in the sense that each successive planet is about twice as far from the Sun as the preceding one. The observed ratios are actually not too far below two (if we include the "average" asteroid). There is the same agreement between theory and observation for the satellite systems, indicating that the latter were formed in a similar way.

According to the nebular theory, the light atoms of hydrogen and helium did not combine into solid particles but evaporated, to a great extent, into interstellar space. The high gravitational attraction of the Sun preserved the abundance of these elements in the solar atmosphere. Only the major planets had enough gravitational power to keep a large abundance of hydrogen (and perhaps helium). Nitrogen is sufficiently abundant in the Sun to explain its presence on the major planets as a component of ammonia. Planets of the size of the Earth and Venus were able to retain enough nitrogen, oxygen, carbon and hydrogen; these elements are prominent in the atmosphere of these two planets as molecules of oxygen, nitrogen, carbon dioxide and water. Objects smaller than Mars, such as Mercury, the Moon, most satellites and all asteroids, could not hold any atmosphere at all.

On the basis of the theory just outlined, planetary systems may have been formed in large numbers. The search for possible planetary companions of stars other than the Sun remains, therefore, of great interest.

The cosmic experiment

We may regard the physical world of cosmic objects as a major experiment in mechanics, physics and chemistry. The very fact that the experiment is running without our efforts and beyond our control puts a peculiar responsibility on the astronomer. We must strategically choose our approach to the cosmic experiment. Our observational material is based on the light rays from the stars, which communicate stellar messages at the crawling, yet unsurpassed speed of 300,000 kilometers per second. Our standpoint of observation is tied to the planet Earth, and we are therefore handicapped both by the intense gravitation at the surface of Earth and by having to observe from the bottom of an ocean of air, our atmosphere.

The Milky Way system contains something like 50,000 million stars. Beyond, millions of similar systems are known to exist. Hundreds of thousands of stars in our Milky Way system are subject to individual scrutiny by the astronomer; each of these huge spheres of gases represents a physical experiment whose magnitude may be illustrated if we realize that our own Sun, a representative star, is 340,000 times as massive as the Earth.

The cosmic experiment consists, therefore, of myriads of stars and other celestial bodies spread through space and time, their motions governed by the universal law of gravitation and their radiation by the fundamental laws of atomic and nuclear physics. A beautiful example of cosmic motion is the mechanism of our solar system; the circuits of the planets about the Sun take place with a precision which in the long run may be far more accurate than that of any man-made clock. Stars and nebulae provide opportunities for physical and chemical studies beyond the limits of the laboratory. Because of their high temperatures and the huge number of atoms, the interiors of stars are fascinating large-scale extensions of the atomic experiments made on our Earth.

Progress in many scientific problems takes place very slowly; the historical order of discovery is not necessarily the one which we would logically prefer in presenting the final results. The scientific approach introduces a systematic, though artificial dissection of the subject matter. Such a dissection has no real significance as far as the structure of the material universe is concerned. It merely involves detailed planning and organization of separate investigations, each determined by the inherent limitations of method, instruments, the time and space allotted to man, his ability and imagination. We have intimations, obtain glimpses, carefully measure and check the various revelations, which, in combination with other evidence, gradually give us some insight into a problem that is often of overwhelming complexity.

It is the task of the astronomer to disentangle the various limitations and complications inherent in our very methods of observation and in our location. We make use of the well-established methods of scientific inquiry, and should observe, and record our observations, as correctly and accurately as possible.

When the time is ripe we attempt to interpret these observations and propose tentative models or hypotheses. These in turn lead to predictions which are tested by further observations. In other words, there must be a sound balance between theory and observation, while preconceived notions about what the universe should be like must be carefully avoided.

The generally slow rate of the cosmic experiment points to stellar lifetimes of the order of 10,000 million years. The astronomer is therefore aware of the need for conditions favorable to continued scientific endeavor, both in space and time. The limited span of life is overcome by a continued transfer of problems and knowledge to the next generation. The one-world idea is beyond question; national boundaries are ignored. During the Second World War continued co-operation in astronomy was carried on as much as possible, without regard to the divisions between friend and foe.

Astronomy and astronomers

What are the uses of astronomy? There are the obvious applications to nuclear physics, navigation, map making, determination of time, and others. These are by-products of research in astronomy for its own sake, however. The place of applied science should be recognized, but it must be clearly understood that the latter can grow only as the result of the desire for and the absolute freedom of pure science.

What makes an astronomer? He must have the capacity for being receptive to the revelations of the universe, mostly in the form of light messages. He should be guided by observational evidence. The astronomer must be patient, because of the intangible, long-range character of his subject. Mathematics, mechanics, physics and chemistry are essential tools, but above these are needed imagination, persistence, curiosity and faith.

A SELECTED BIBLIOGRAPHY

Baker, R. H., *Astronomy*. Henry Holt & Co., New York

Duncan, J. C., *Astronomy*. Harper & Brothers, New York

Eddington, A. S., *The Nature of the Physical World*. The Macmillan Co., New York

Freeman, I. M., *Modern Introductory Physics*. McGraw-Hill Book Co., New York

Hecht, Selig, *Explaining the Atom*. The Viking Press, New York

Jeans, J. H., *Physics and Philosophy*. The Macmillan Co., New York

McKready, K., *A Beginner's Star-Book*. G. P. Putnam's Sons, New York

Russell, H. N., Dugan, R. S., and Stewart, J. Q., *Astronomy*. Ginn & Co., New York

Shapley, H., *Flights from Chaos*. The McGraw-Hill Book Co., New York

Skilling, W. T., and Richardson, R. S., *Astronomy*. Henry Holt & Co., New York

Smart, W. M., *Some Famous Stars*. Longmans, Green & Co., Inc., New York

Thompson, A. J., *Making Your Own Telescope*. Sky Publishing Corp., Cambridge, Mass.

A New Popular Star Atlas. Gall and Inglis, Edinburgh

Sky and Telescope (A Monthly Magazine). Sky Publishing Corp., Cambridge, Mass.

The Harvard Books on Astronomy, written by Harvard Observatory astronomers and published by The Blakiston Co., Philadelphia; each book covers a specific subject:

Bok, B. J. and Bok, P. F., *The Milky Way*

Campbell, L., and Jacchia, L., *The Story of Variable Stars*

Dimitroff, G. Z., and Baker, J. G., *Telescopes and Accessories*

Goldberg, L., and Aller, L. H., *Atoms, Stars and Nebulae*

Menzel, H., *Our Sun*

Shapley, H., *Galaxies*

Watson, F. G., *Between the Planets*

Whipple, F. L., *Earth, Moon and Planets*

INDEX